Early American
TOWER CLOCKS

EARLY AMERICAN TOWER CLOCKS

Surviving American tower clocks
from 1726 to 1870, with profiles
of all known American makers.
Over 250 illustrations.

FREDERICK SHELLEY

Special Order Supplement #2
NATIONAL ASSOCIATION OF WATCH
AND CLOCK COLLECTORS, INC.

NAWCC, Inc. Special Order Supplement #2.
Published and printed in the United States by the
National Association of Watch & Clock Collectors, Inc.
514 Poplar Street, Columbia PA 17512-2130

Library of Congress catalog card number:
ISBN #: 0-9668869-0-9

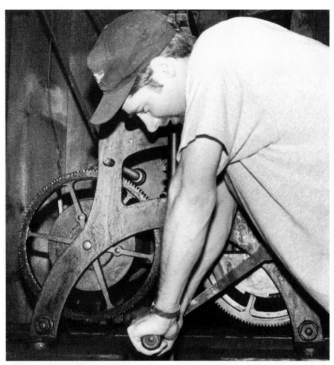

DEDICATION

To the often unknown and unsung tower clock custodians, without whom these large time machines would not have survived.

EARLY AMERICAN TOWER CLOCKS
TABLE OF CONTENTS

ACKNOWLEDGEMENTS

During years of research into this subject many people have shared their expertise, special information, photographs, and leads to the possible location of hitherto unknown early American tower clocks. The author gratefully acknowledges significant contributions made by Charles Aked, Leonard Alderman, Chris Bailey, Richard Balzer, Edwin Battison, Thomas Beckman, Jonathan Betts, Dana Blackwell, Bent Blondal, Norman Boyden, Roger Brockett, Douglas Brown, Steven Burne, Herschel Burt, Raymond Cable, Harold Cantrell, Bruce Cheney, Harold Cherry, Edward Christensen, Lorraine Clapp, Stanley Craig, Norman Cucuel, Robert Dahmer, Lee Davis, Marvin DeBoy, Steven Denny, William Dilworth, Eileen B. Doudna, Alton DuBois, Joel Dumont, Robert Edwards, Max Elser, Kathy I. Everett, George Finkenor, Bruce Forman, Cleveland Forrester, Ward Francillon, James Gibbs, Charles Haines, J.C. Halbrooks, Michael Harrold, Albert Herrmann, John Hillhouse, Robert Hopfe, Richard Husher, Donald Jackson, Elizabeth J. Johnson, Marilyn Johnson, Barbara B. Jones, Bruce Kingsbury, William Klauer, William Knode, Edward LaFond, J.R. Lamberton, Martha Lang, Lloyd Larish, Donn Haven Lathrop, Allen and Evelyn Lloyd, Walter Lynn, Nancy MacEwen, Ken Marvin, Henry Mattson, Chris McKay, John Metcalfe, David Morgan, Carroll Morse, Nancy Nonnenmocher, Jill O'Brien, David Proper, Emile Racine, Rev. Carl Reynolds, Patrick Reynolds, Charles Roeser, Robert Rood, Ian Roome, Donald Saff, William Shea, Raymond V. Shepherd Jr., Robert Silliman, Suzanne Sizer, Howard Sloan, James Starrow, Henry Stover, Snowden Taylor, Winthrop Warren, James B. West, William L. Willard, Dee Wolfe, Cas Woodbridge, Kay Youngflesh, and Joan Youngken. Special thanks to Russell Oechsle for his major contribution on Upstate New York tower clocks, and to the National Association of Watch and Clock Collectors for their encouragement and support.

EARLY AMERICAN TOWER CLOCKS
INTRODUCTION

Meeting House, Madison, Connecticut.

"A CHURCH tower without a clock and bells seems an unfurnished edifice...like a form without life, a body without a soul. A good Church clock is useful to everybody; it is the friendly monitor alike of rich and poor,— the regulator of every private time-piece,— the standard of time for the whole parish or township...by it, in a word, are all the multi-farious transactions of everyday life more or less regulated and measured, and when the church clock stops, it produces a social discomfort and anarchy throughout a whole neighborhood, to an extent scarcely credible...."

So wrote J.W. Benson in *Time and Time-Tellers*, a book published in 1875 that gave the National Association of Watch and Clock Collectors (NAWCC) its trademark of the old gent checking his watch against a sundial. How he managed on cloudy days, and his thoughts on solar versus mean time remain a mystery. In his day, he would have done better to check his watch against a town clock, the local time standard. In 1827, the people of New Haven, Connecticut, faced what Benson described as "social discomfort and anarchy" when a new Town Clock telling *mean* time was placed less than a block away from Yale's old tower clock telling *apparent* time. A torrent of letters to the editor of the town newspaper protested having two public clocks on the Town Green that at best agreed only four times a year! Eli Terry, maker of the new clock, argued in favor of mean time, already adopted in many European countries and in principal cities of the United States. He saw it as the only practical way to keep all good clocks and watches nearly alike, and appointments met with the degree of precision critical to a populous city. In 1823, Stephen Hasham sold a town clock to Troy, New York, with similar logic—that it could be seen "from more than one thousand doors and windows, and strike a handsome blow"; it would keep perfect time, making at once a complete standard for all clocks and watches, and, in addition, be a more prestigious ornament for the city than possible with the same money in any other way. People living in relative isolation, farmers and the like, continued to be guided by the passage of the sun as they had for centuries, but emerging urban centers gave notice of their coming of age, their prosperity, and future prospects with the installation of a tower clock, the common man's wristwatch of that day. Right or wrong by a few minutes, it gave reasonable assurance that all within sight of its dials or sound of its bell marched to the beat of the same drummer.

Scope

Webster's defines the tower clock simply as a clock for turrets or towers having one or more dials separate from the movement. To this we would add that it is usually separated from one or more huge bells, and is a large, strongly built machine designed to operate with precision in a hostile environment. Tower clocks are variously described as turret, public, town, church, steeple, and cupola clocks depending on their location. They can include clocks with large dials mounted on the outside walls of schools, factories, or municipal buildings. The terms *town* and *church* typically identify clock ownership with attendant responsibility for winding and maintenance. Regardless of what they are called, all tower clocks are *public*, in the sense that their dials and the sound of their bell are exposed to large numbers of people, particularly urban dwellers. Lantern, tall case, regulator, gallery, post, and bank clocks, which can be public and also serve as local time standards, fall outside the scope of this work.

Part Two of this book lists *alphabetically by name* salient detail on all known makers, dealers, and other persons associated with American tower clocks, from about 1660 to 1998. It provides a maker index and a framework for future research, discovery and update. The main focus, however, is found in **Part One** where surviving tower clocks and their makers from 1726 to

1870 are documented *chronologically* by earliest installation date. This was the golden age of American tower clock craftsmanship when a few highly skilled individuals, working in small shops or alone with apprentices, produced a limited number of tower clocks of great variety. Part One's cutoff date of 1870 is not entirely arbitrary. Just as the golden age of domestic clock craftsmanship ended about 1820 with the mass production of cheap Connecticut shelf clocks, so "factory" tower clocks made in the thousands after 1870 put most small-time entrepreneurs out of the business. The "factory" tower clocks of E. Howard & Co. and Seth Thomas & Co., were superbly engineered, but largely standardized around well-proven horological solutions borrowed mostly from the English. In addition, we know almost nothing about the people who made them, compared to the tower clock craftsmen before 1870 about whom we know a great deal. This rich biographical dimension adds to our appreciation of the work produced between 1726 and 1870. Who can see the genius of Hasham's clocks without calling to mind his irascible character, or see the elegance of a late Van Riper model and not mourn his early death, or see the fine workmanship of Simon Willard at age 80, and not be puzzled by the poverty of his last years. Ironically, market domination of "factory" tower clocks began about the same time as the first real success of watches made on "the American Plan." The low-cost pocket watch, along with the wristwatch after World War I, substantially reduced demand for mechanical tower clocks, the manufacture of which ceased altogether by the 1960s. Unfortunately, the 1870 cutoff date reduces extended coverage of several makers, mostly foreign immigrants, who otherwise belong with the skilled entrepreneurs at work in the golden era of tower clock craftsmanship. Included are Joseph Barborka, Charles Fasoldt, Nels Johnson, Mathias Schwalbach, Louis Spellier and American-born Warren Johnson. The tower clocks of these post-1870 makers, although limited in number, were very innovative, well made, and often won out over their higher financed rivals in open competition.

Early History

Most authorities agree that the mechanical clock, in the modern sense, was well established by the fourteenth century, probably first appearing a century earlier in Italy, then spreading rapidly to the southwestern European continent and England. Its emergence at about the same time as the cannon is attributed to the remarkable proliferation of skilled metal workers in that period. The clock, which comes from the Latin *clocca,* meaning bell, originated in monasteries as a mechanical wakeup alarm for the monk who called his brothers to morning prayer. Shortly thereafter, the first public clocks emerged as bell towers located in the plazas of cities or wherever large numbers of people congregated. They have ever since been considered an attribute of urban centers where life is lived by the clock. Later, bell towers were outfitted with elaborate dials, leading to time-awareness on the part of the general public that grew from a novelty to a necessity of life. One social historian regards not the steam engine but the clock as the key machine of the Industrial Age. Prestige associated with matching or bettering a neighbor's time-telling machine has from the start been a major force in the acquisition of tower clocks, which have undergone many changes (including electrification) but never fallen out of favor.

The early tower clock was large, crude. and expensive, good only to the nearest hour. Of hand-filed wrought iron, it took months or even years to make and often bound its maker to the clock's sponsor in a lifetime contract for winding, adjustment, and repair. Its precise origins are unknown. Gear trains, lantern pinions, and driving weights used for other purposes go back to antiquity; missing was a regulator to release power on a continuous and repeatable basis. This critical component appeared by the early thirteenth century, consisting of a verge escapement and an oscillating beam called the foliot. With some modification, this primitive regulator served the less demanding time standards of the general public for almost 400 years. It was replaced after 1656 by Christian Huygens' pendulum, enhanced a few years later by the invention of the recoil escapement. A monumental breakthrough, the pendulum improved clock accuracy from rough fractions of an hour to measurable seconds. It also sparked inventions to improve time accuracy by other Europeans to whom subsequent clockmakers owe a profound debt.[1] This rich horological legacy, plus the early immigration to our shores of skilled English and German clockmakers, provide the foundation on which the American tower clockmaking tradition is based.

The First American Tower Clocks

Brooks Palmer writes in *The Book of American Clocks,* "Aside from a very few foreign-made house clocks imported into the colonies, the first American clocks were Tower Clocks." The first town clocks appeared along our northeastern coastline and in major seaports from Boston to Charleston. References to town clocks at Boston in 1665 and nearby Ipswich in

---

1. Christian Huygens, pendulum (ca. 1656); Robert Hooke/ William Clement, recoil escapement (ca. 1675); Edward Barlow, rack-and-snail (1676); George Graham, deadbeat escapement and mercury compensated pendulum (ca. 1715); John Harrison, spring maintaining power and gridiron pendulum (1725); Henry Hindley, double frame and twin-spring suspension (ca. 1740); J.A. Lepaute, flatbed frame and pinwheel escapement (1753); B.L.Vuillamy, removable bushings (1825); E.B. Denison, double three-legged gravity escapement and cam-tooth strike wheel (1854).

1702 probably refer to small imported clocks of one kind or another used by the night watch. Later documentation is more specific. In 1714, William James of Portsmouth, Rhode Island, sold the Newport City Council a tower clock with a four-pound hammer that showed the time "rain or shine." In 1716, brass founder Joseph Phillips was paid £60 by the New York City Council for a pendulum-rated public clock with a nine-inch great wheel and two cedar dials having gilt numbers. In 1717, Peter Stretch, a skilled English emigrant, was paid £8/18/10 for the repair of Philadelphia's Town Clock, not otherwise identified. In 1717-18, another English-trained clockmaker, Benjamin Bagnall, installed a public clock on the roof of Boston's Brick Meeting House that he later converted to run a week on one winding. These mechanisms have not survived, the earliest known survivor being one made in 1726 by Ebenezer Parmelee for the meeting house at Guilford, Connecticut. Many other surviving tower clocks followed, listed chronologically in Part One.

Village Green, Norwich, Vermont.

The New England Meeting House

In the early days of the American colonies there was no separation of church and state. Township incorporation was contingent upon the services of a minister and the meeting house served equally for both religious and civil assembly. As the town's most prominent structure, the meeting house was usually placed facing the Town Green, the gathering place for military drills and other outdoor gatherings, and later the site of the town hall, post office, general store, whipping post and stocks. Town streets often radiated out from the Green, or, where a single main street prevailed, the meeting house was located as close as possible to where the most people lived. In short, these large buildings were made-to-order for installation of public clocks, even more so with their later addition of tall steeples which still punctuate the horizon. There was no problem installing a church-owned tower clock in the meeting

house; however, town clocks—those purchased with public funds or by subscription—required permission of the church elders. At issue for both parties were costs associated with a tower clock installation. Town selectmen willingly paid for the maintenance of clocks appearing on their inventory, but often contested repainting dials on meeting house walls they regarded as church property. These negotiations often appear in town or church records. In 1738, the town of Wallingford, Connecticut, granted "liberty to Mecock [*sic*] Ward to sett a clok in ye steeple; and if any damadge to ye belfre; hee will pay it and taik away ye clok." Eli Terry met with similar restrictions prior to his installation of a town clock in New Haven's Centre Church in 1826. On the other hand, the First Meeting House of Groton, Massachusetts, donated $30 to cover a shortfall in donations for a town clock installed in their steeple in 1809, and eventually fell heir to its ownership. In 1832, the town of Amherst, New Hampshire, sold its half of the meeting house to the newly formed Congregational Church, subject to the following conditions: "1st, the Town to reserve the right to use the house for all Town Meetings as long as they may want to use it for the purpose—2nd, the Town to Reserve the Bell, Clock and Belfry or Tower as the property of the Town—The [church] purchaser to have the right to pass and repass through the west doors as now used,— and also the right to ring the Bell for funerals, public worship and other public occasions without expense for the Town." In spite of this odd territorial schism, the Amherst town clock has run hand-wound both time and strike for over 180 years.

The Bell

A public signal at the noon hour, based on a sundial or a "noon mark," gave urban centers a standard by which watches and domestic clocks could be set to uniform local time. Early on, the signal came from a conch

Revere & Son bell, Groton, Massachusetts.

shell, a drum roll, or the firing of a heavy gun. As towns grew and prospered, these makeshift signals gave way to the ringing of a large meeting house bell, initially struck at noon by a man pulling on a rope, and later struck automatically on the hour by a hammer connected to the town clock. Quarter strikers were a rarity in the early colonies, except for a few made by early Pennsylvania clockmakers of German heritage. The sound of a good bell carried for miles around, far beyond the limited line-of-sight to steeple dials, and was, in fact, the best indicator of true tower clock time. Describing his 1855 tower clock installation, Ephraim Byram wrote to the people of Louisville, Kentucky, "...though the hands may not, through all the trials of the elements to which they are exposed, always point to the precise minute, yet the first blow of the hammer at the expiration of any hour will be found to give the time to the nearest swing of the pendulum, which is but two seconds." These large bells, weighing a half-ton or more and selling by the pound, often cost more than the clock itself. When flawed or broken, the precious metal fragments consisting of an alloy of 75% copper and 25% tin were painstakingly salvaged, then returned to the foundry to be recast into a new bell at reduced cost. The bell, although struck by a hammer connected directly to the clock movement, is usually considered a separate entity because it serves several masters. In addition to being struck by the clock hammer, it can be swung against its clapper by a rope-drawn wheel on special occasions, a second rope-drawn hammer serves to announce various church rituals, and a third possible hammer can be associated (after 1850) with the town's telegraphic fire alarm system.

A Different World

A tower clock is not simply an oversized house clock movement, although its clockwork shares some generic features. A tower clock is all business, representing unadorned functional horology with none of the furniture enhancements of domestic clocks or the jewelry enhancement of watches. Typically its only decorative elements are the gilt dial hands exposed to public view. The large sturdy movement is its most important component and much credit is due to those who have restored these irreplaceable machines, saving them from a sorry end as scrap metal. However, stand-alone movements provide few clues as to the variety, enormity and complexity of tower clocks considered in their entirety. Beyond movement differences, distinctive tower clock features include: a hostile working environment of falling dust, bird droppings, wayward drafts, building shifts and major changes in ambient temperature; plus long complex connections from the movement to the hands of remote multiple dials exposed to wind, rain, ice, and snow; plus the transmission of a public time signal for miles in every direc-

Church, North Orange, Massachusetts.

tion; plus the complex redirection of the weight line off the barrel to achieve sufficient vertical fall for weekly winding; and finally, the profound bonding that occurs between the custodian and *his* machine, babied for decades. To be truly appreciated, the different world of the tower clock must be seen or visualized in its "natural habitat," so to speak, as installed in a tower.

The average passer-by sees the dials alone as constituting "The Clock," with no thought given to what lies within the tower. The location of the bell is obvious from its exposed location or from louvered panels that free the sound. Otherwise, from outside the tower there is no telling the location of the movement, its remote bell hammer, dials, and weights, or their connections, most of which are typically supplied by the maker as part of the total tower clock package. The clock in its entirety can occupy significant portions of the tower interior from wall to wall and from top to bottom. The details of a given installation are unpredictable as no two are exactly alike, in most cases having been improvised based on obstacles found on-site. The adventure starts behind a door near the base of the tower. Unlocked, it reveals the first steps of an upward journey as simple as a spiral staircase, or as challenging as unpredictable numbers of high rise stairways, homemade ladders, hatches and structural beam hurdles. From bottom to top, the climb can reach the height of a seven-story building, although most towers are shorter. At some point along the way, one hears a distant beat that seems to say not tick-tock, but "CLOCK-CLOCK," a promise confirmed moments later by the sight of a swinging pendulum bob extending through the hole in a floor above. Arriving at the movement level with remote connections extending in all directions, one stands literally *inside* the tower clock. The movement itself is rooted to the tower structure, usually inside a small room or large cabinet that protects it from dust and falling particles that can turn its lubricant into an abrasive paste. As for the movement itself and its pendulum, there are as many variations as there are maker models, a subject covered in detail in Part One and summarized by **Chart 1, 1726-1870 Feature Comparison** (see page xv).

Movement connections to the remote bell hammer, dials, and falling weights are among a tower clock's most distinctive features; however, they do not necessarily represent the original arrangement as early movements were often moved to larger buildings to accommodate growing congregations. Although differing in detail, layouts can be described in a general way. The tower bell, weighing up to a ton or more, is located either below or above the movement. The hammer's bell crank lever is connected by rod, wire or light chain to a lever on the movement frame, acted upon by a rotating strike train pinwheel. A few minutes prior to strike, the hammer is drawn back at warning. It is released on the hour, falling by gravity to strike the bell, then recoils slightly not to deaden the sound. The bell area is hazardous during a strike sequence, but the sound is very tolerable on other tower levels. The end of a strike sequence is signaled by the distinctive winding-down sound of the fly's ratchet.

Outside dials of varying size, style and shape can be located above, below, or level with the movement. Observation of outside dial hand position from inside the tower, as may be required to reset the time, is provided for by dial ports and/or setting dials of various types on the movement itself. Outside dials having one hand are driven by direct connection to a time train takeoff making one revolution in 12 hours. Outside

Town Hall, Milford, New Hampshire.

dials having two hands require motion work behind each dial plate to convert the hourly minute hand rotation delivered by the movement to the 12-hour rotation of the hour hand. Occasionally minute hands are counter-balanced behind the dial, but a better arrangement balances both hands outside the dial. Pre-1840 American clocks having three outside dials are usually on the same level as the movement, driven by rods that radiate out from a simple contrate wheel transmission located on the frame. Four or more outside dials can be located just below or up to 20 or more feet above the movement. Hand rotation comes from leading-off rods that radiate out from one or more transmissions on the same level as the outside dials. Most transmissions consist of a nest of bevel gears driven by a vertical rod that extends above or below the movement dial takeoff. The leading-off rods used in these remote connections can be up to 25 or more feet in length, requiring roller wheel support; they are of wood, iron, or rolled and soldered sheet metal. Flexible universal joints, or U-joints, at each end of the rods allow for component misalignment, building shifts, and expansion or contraction due to changes in ambient temperature. Remote dial connections become complex when power must be angled around inner tower structure or a bell located between the movement and multiple outside dials. While generally effective, complex connections and part wear can result in minor disagreement between the position of the hands and the strike of the bell. In addition, complex connections mean added friction, which always pays a penalty in the need for increased driving weight.

Our earliest clocks were wound daily with natural fiber rope falling directly off wooden barrels. Later clocks provide the convenience of once-a-week winding, but require much longer vertical weight fall, particularly on the strike side, not available in most towers. As a consequence, 200 or more feet of line can run through a maze of rollers, traveling pulleys, levers, and guide pulleys to redirect the line off the barrels to the highest point in the tower, then still require weight compounding for weekly winding. (See **Chart 2. Tower Clock Schematic**, page xvi.) As with complex dial connections, friction associated with line redirection requires additional driving weight. Consequently, the optimum weight needed to drive the total tower clock system (plus something extra to allow for bad weather) cannot be determined until the hammer, remote dials and redirected weight line are completely rigged. In some installations, weights hang free in open tower space; in others, they are redirected to fall in wooden chutes running from high in the tower to ground level. A catch box is occasionally placed under the chutes to prevent catastrophic damage to the building below should the weight line break. Weight types include large single boulders, reinforced wood boxes filled with stone or iron rubble, cement blocks, slabs of

Town Hall, Topsfield, Massachusetts.

granite or soapstone, neat stacks of cast-iron segments, or single weights of cast-iron or lead. Almost all types provide for adjustment of clock weights.

Weight-winding aids to look for include reduction gearing (winding jacks) on the barrel arbors, and also various forms of maintaining power on the time side to keep the clock running during a time rewind cycle. Regardless of weight size, power reaching the escapement is light enough for finger pressure on the escape wheel arbor to stop the clock. For centuries, this feature was used to reset tower clock hands ahead, a process called freewheeling wherein the pallets are disengaged from the escape wheel, to allow fast-forwarding of the time train under manual control. The hands are set back simply by stopping the pendulum. Unfortunately, both maneuvers temporarily stop the clock, a drawback overcome by various clutch arrangements in later clocks that allow resetting the hands in either direction while the clock continues to run.

A Different World, a Different Language

We have seen how the tower clock differs from other timekeepers. As such, a distinctive tower clock language has evolved. Many terms are generally familiar to those acquainted with mechanical clocks, but terms such as *motion work*, *setting dial*, *catch box*, *winding jack*, *leading-off rods*, *transmission* and *freewheeling* are unique. There is the added challenge of redundant nomenclature. The language has developed in many countries over hundreds of years, resulting in multiple terms to describe the same clock feature. Simple examples are *barrel/drum* and *pillar/spacer*; more complex are *fly/fan/fan-fly/air governor/wind-vane*, and a tower clock frame variously referred to as *double/chair/armchair/extended barrel* and *upright piano*. It can be confusing even for experts. For this and other obvious reasons, a glossary of tower clock terms appears on page 217. Exercising editorial privilege, the word definition is led off by the term favored in this work, followed by known alternatives shown in parenthesis.

The Challenge

We know a great deal more about early American tower clocks than we did 50 years ago, particularly since the 1976 Bicentennial which heightened awareness of these fine old artifacts as important to local heritage. Increasingly, individuals, ad hoc teams of local enthusiasts, and professional restorers have risen to the challenge of returning disabled town clocks to working order. Once restored, many have been returned to their original towers to serve new generations of people. Others have been installed in innovative free-standing towers or in the lobbies of public buildings with the working movement displayed behind glass at ground level for public view. The restored movements of still others find welcome homes in museums or with private enthusiasts. Research has proceeded with similar enthusiasm, every discovery or new bit of information helping to complete the picture. Work done thus far particularly in villages, small towns, and cities is encouraging, but it just scratches the surface. Hundreds of urban centers remain largely unexplored territory. The history of public timekeeping in our largest cities is virtually an unwritten chapter. For every recent find, many surprises remain in old records and in the dark corners at the end of an adventurous tower climb. In short, tower clock exploration remains a fascinating last frontier of horological research and discovery.

Home Church, Old Salem, North Carolina.

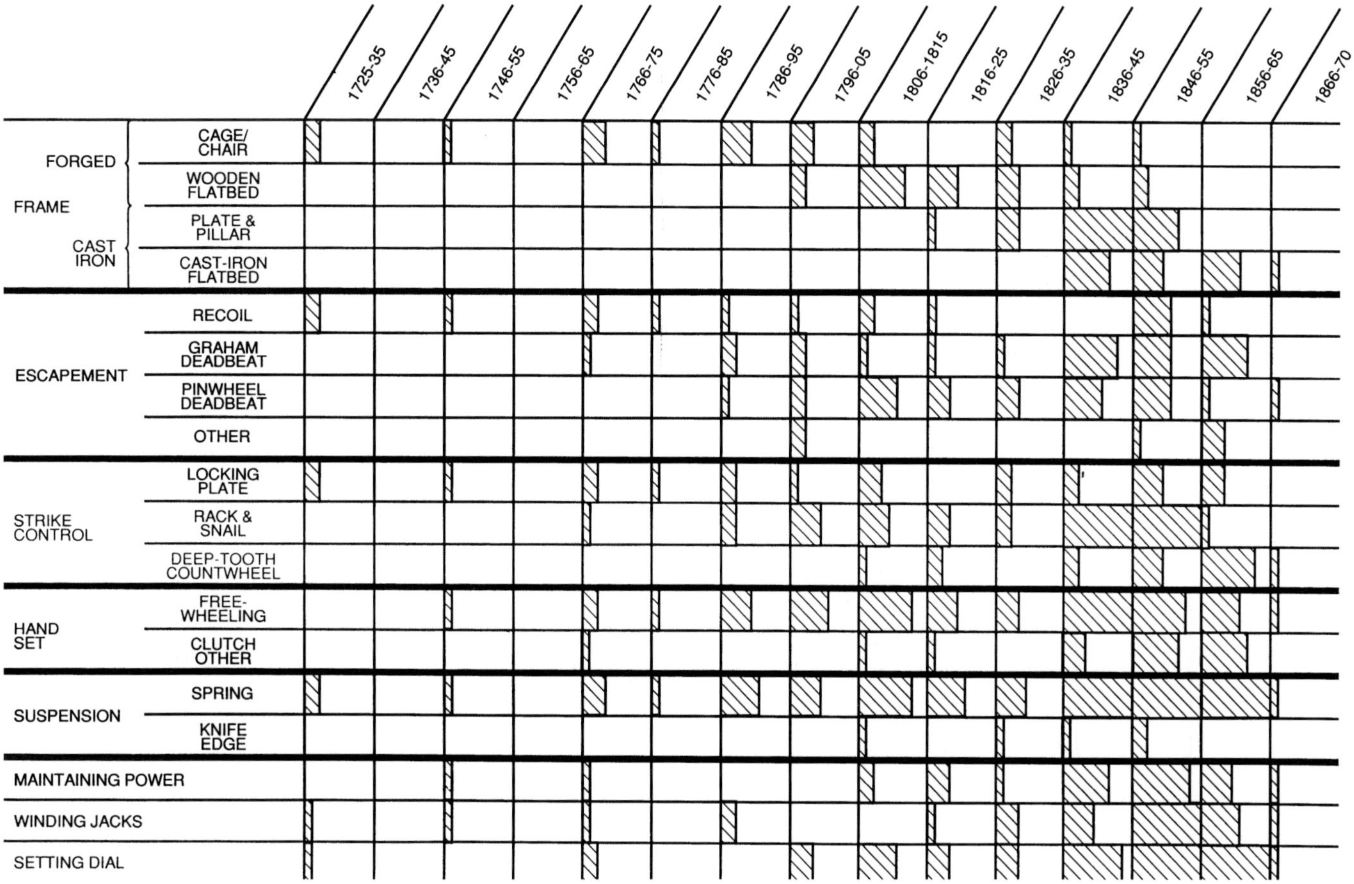

Chart I — 1726–1870 New Model Feature Comparison

Column headings (decade ranges): 1725-35 · 1736-45 · 1746-55 · 1756-65 · 1766-75 · 1776-85 · 1786-95 · 1796-05 · 1806-1815 · 1816-25 · 1826-35 · 1836-45 · 1846-55 · 1856-65 · 1866-70

Category	Sub-feature
FRAME — FORGED	CAGE/CHAIR
FRAME — CAST IRON	WOODEN FLATBED
	PLATE & PILLAR
	CAST-IRON FLATBED
ESCAPEMENT	RECOIL
	GRAHAM DEADBEAT
	PINWHEEL DEADBEAT
	OTHER
STRIKE CONTROL	LOCKING PLATE
	RACK & SNAIL
	DEEP-TOOTH COUNTWHEEL
HAND SET	FREE-WHEELING
	CLUTCH OTHER
SUSPENSION	SPRING
	KNIFE EDGE
MAINTAINING POWER	
WINDING JACKS	
SETTING DIAL	

Chart I. 1726-1870 New Model Feature Comparison. Clocks that survive before 1776, although few in number, reflect an English or German heritage of forged iron cage frames, recoil escapements and locking-plate strike control. Many originally wound daily were modified later to run eight days on a winding. After 1805, there is a significant shift to the wood beam horizontal flatbed frame having a deadbeat pinwheel escapement and rack-and-snail strike control (introduced by Stowell in 1799). By 1836, cast-iron plate-and-pillar and flatbed frames predominate, a change attributed to improved smelting and foundry practices. As for strike control, the locking-plate favored for centuries in Europe persists here in various forms, but as early as 1796 is overtaken by the rack-and-snail, and later by the deep-tooth count wheel. The centuries-old practice of freewheeling, for all its hazards, remains the favored dial-setting technique until 1856 when various clutch systems are introduced to reset the hands in either direction without stopping the clock. Flat-spring pendulum suspension is a clear favorite over the knife-edge, resurrected for no known reason by Meneely and Lukens. After 1870, added value features such as maintaining power, winding jacks, setting dials, and strike cutouts take on increasing importance, with engineered "factory" clocks generally standardized around accepted features of proven performance, durability and operator convenience.

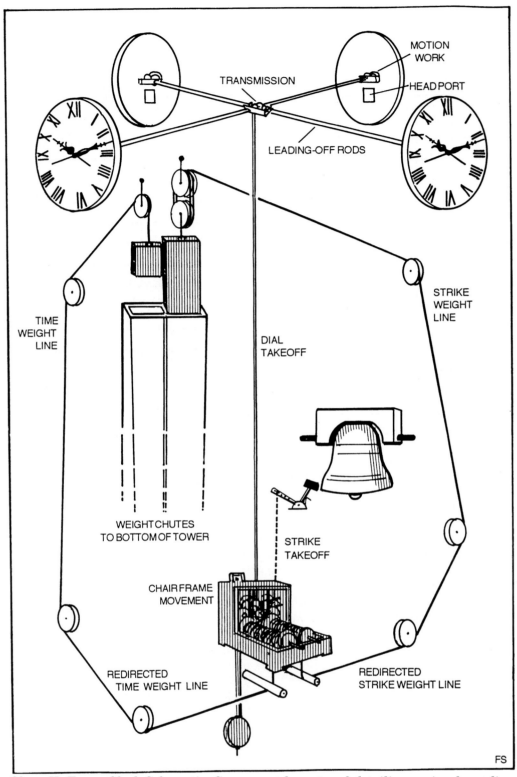

MOTION
WORK

TRANSMISSION

HEAD PORT

LEADING-OFF RODS

TIME
WEIGHT
LINE

STRIKE
WEIGHT
LINE

DIAL
TAKEOFF

WEIGHT CHUTES
TO BOTTOM OF TOWER

STRIKE
TAKEOFF

CHAIR FRAME
MOVEMENT

REDIRECTED
TIME WEIGHT LINE

REDIRECTED
STRIKE WEIGHT LINE

FS

Chart II. Tower Clock Schematic. Component layout and detailing varies depending on the clock and interior tower configuration. This schematic is hypothetical, one of many possible layouts.

EARLY AMERICAN TOWER CLOCKS
PART ONE
Chronology of surviving American tower clocks from 1726 to 1870,
with their maker profiles, technical descriptions, and illustrations.

1726 • EBENEZER PARMELEE

Ebenezer Parmelee was born on November 22, 1690, in the town of Guilford, Connecticut, about 10 miles east of New Haven on Long Island Sound. The son of Isaac and Elizabeth (Hyland) Parmelee, Ebenezer learned carpentry and cabinetmaking from his father, adding to his own natural skills as a mechanic. It is not known for sure where he learned clockmaking. On July 29, 1718, at the age of 27, he married Anna Crittenden of Guilford; a year later to the day he paid his parents £40 for about three acres and the former homestead of his maternal grandfather, George Hyland. Over the years Parmelee made a number of additions and changes to the house, which remains standing today. They had nine children, although six died at an early age, leaving only two daughters and one son, Ebenezer, born to them late in their marriage. Four boys were "taken by the epidemic" in 1836, and two other sons died under the age of 5. These terrible losses had to have cast a shadow over their lives.

In 1725, the First Church and Society of Guilford bought a large bell and shortly thereafter erected a 120-foot steeple on the west end of their meeting house. On December 10, 1726, they granted liberty "to any of the Inhabitants of this parish to set up & fix a suitable Clock in the meeting house, with a hammer to strike on the great bell;...provided the Charge of purchasing sd. clock be raised by a voluntary contribution." Parmelee, described as an ingenious mechanic, fashioned a single dial one-hand clock, making Guilford what was said to be the first town in Connecticut with a steeple, bell and clock. In 1829, the clock was moved to a new meeting house at the north end of the Guilford green. There are contemporary accounts which describe Parmelee's clock as a "big cumbersome affair made entirely of wood." This is unlikely based on the clock that has survived today in Guilford's Henry Whitfield House State Historical Museum. Undoubtedly, significant alterations have been made to the original cage frame mechanism, but its construction except for wood barrels is primarily of iron and brass. For many years Parmelee dutifully wound the clock and kept it in good repair, at some point adding a second one-hand dial. By 1741, he was excused from all other town duties while he remained its custodian. After long service the old clock was replaced in 1893 by a modern factory clock donated by a member of the congregation. Parmelee made at least one other town clock that has not survived but is well documented. He installed it about 1740 in the First Church of Milford, Connecticut, also on Long Island Sound a few miles west of New Haven. After a trial period of two years, a town meeting on December 12, 1742, authorized the selectmen to pay for Parmelee's clock, "which is now standing in ye meeting house, and if they can purchase ye same at reasonable rate, then to pay for ye same out of ye Town Treasury." Apparently the clock performed well, but was eventually replaced in 1825, when the town employed Barzillai Davison to make and set up wooden works. They cost $240 in addition to Parmelee's "good old brass wheel clock," for which Davison allowed $40, and then was reported to have set up in New York for $600.

In addition to steeple clocks, Parmelee made tall clocks, and their cases as well. Few have survived. He was also a skilled chair maker and shipwright. In his later years he operated a cargo sloop which regularly traded at ports of call on Long Island Sound. On December 15, 1841, the town approved his proposal to build a convenient wharf at the common landing place on the Guilford sluice, provided that he pay for it and that "it belonged to no particular man." During this period Connecticut was actively engaged in the trade of mules and "good Jamaican rum" with the West Indies. Ebenezer Parmelee died on September 17 (or 27), 1777, in Guilford where he was buried.

Ebenezer Parmelee Tower Clock

The Guilford clock is mounted in the Museum on a wood beam base measuring about four by two feet that is not original; nor are the bevel gears to its single outside dial. The eight-spoke cast-iron great wheels, their bearing blocks, pinions, and 19" long outboard wooden barrels are also probably later additions, typical of changes made to lengthen the winding interval of very old clocks from one day to a full week. The cage frame clockwork appears completely original, in the English tradition and with all parts left in as-found condition. It is of simple wrought-iron bar construction held together with nuts on end-threaded corner posts with turned brass capitals and bases. Brass train wheels with four spokes (time to the left, strike to the right) are mounted on steel arbors with cut leaf pinions. Arbors pivot in brass-bushed holes in strap iron risers that add to the frame support. The escapement is recoil, with a 5" diameter brass escape wheel. The recoil pallet arbor pivots in brass bushing blocks screwed to the top of the frame, as does the arbor of the four-blade ratchet-driven fly on the strike side. A 16" fork-ended crutch delivers impulses to a wood rod, lead bob pendulum with an effective length of about 56 inches. Winding ratchets are mounted on the time and strike second wheel arbors. The time second wheel arbor also trips a diagonal strike lever by means of a pin on the setting dial pointer which rotates against a fixed dial plate. The same arbor also drives contrate wheel take-off connections to the hand of the outside dial. The strike side second wheel arbor is also multi-functional, advancing both the strike locking plate, and turning the train hoop wheel. All strike control levers and the fly are iron. Clock weights, consisting of 9" square by 12" deep wood boxes filled with stone rubble, hang on natural fiber rope which falls directly off the winding barrels.

Above, EP Figure 1. *Front view (winding side) of Parmelee's Guilford Meeting House clock. Note between the barrels the contrate wheel with a vertical leading-off rod to the dial; it is driven by a pinion on the time train second wheel arbor which also trips the diagonal strike lever, and turns the setting dial pointer. The winding wheel at far right is not original.* **Below**, *EP Figure 2. Side view of the typical "American" outboard barrel configuration. Clock-work with short sturdy arbors is mounted in a tall shallow cage frame to the left while the great wheels and winding barrels are supported outboard. The fly, crutch, locking plate, and pendulum are outside the cage frame.*

EP Figure 3. Escapement detail: the brass escape wheel works on a steel recoil anchor, its arbor carrying the crutch and mounted in bearing blocks screwed above the frame. Frame corner columns have turned brass capitals and bases.

EP Figure 4. Strike train detail. The long diagonal lever is tripped hourly by the time second wheel arbor, unlocking the strike train. Strike number is controlled by notch spacing in the locking plate just visible behind the strike second wheel. Winding ratchets are located on the second wheel arbors of both trains.

1735 • CHRISTOPHER WITT

Christopher Witt, an English physician, was profoundly affected by his association with Johann Kelpius, a German mystic who preceded him as an immigrant to this country by 10 years. Kelpius and his Chapter of Pietists, or true Rosicrucians, had fled their native land to escape religious oppression. Arriving in Philadelphia in 1694, they settled to the north near what is now Germantown on the rugged banks of the Wissahickon River, land allotted by William Penn's European agents. The Theosophical Community built a tabernacle allowing nightly astronomical observations, monitoring what they believed to be the imminent Millennium. Their leader, Master Kelpius, took up residence in the nearby caves, where he lived for 14 years.

Dr. Christopher Witt, who was born in Wiltshire, England, in 1675, came to Philadelphia in 1704, and almost immediately set out for Germantown where he joined Kelpius in the caves. Although only 29 and inclined toward the occult, Witt was a trained physician and an expert naturalist, well-versed in mathematics, astronomy, and the practical sciences—skills which made him a welcome addition to the community, and highly regarded by all. During this period he also displayed talents as an artist and mechanic. His portrait painting of Kelpius in the caves has a clock in the background, thought to give evidence of Witt's clockmaking skills as early as 1706.

With the death of Kelpius in 1708, the Theosophical Community on the Wissahickon disbanded and its members scattered to other German sect communities. Witt received many of Kelpius' philosophical instruments and astronomical apparatus with which to continue his studies; however, he left the tabernacle in the woods, buying land in Germantown and building a small wooden house where he served the community as a doctor, or "Practitioner in Physic." Over the years he remained in contact with the scattered followers of Kelpius, particularly with those at the Ephrata Cloister north of Lancaster, who were virtual successors to the Germantown Mystics. A small tower clock signed "WC 1735," now on display at the Ephrata Cloister of the Pennsylvania Historical Museum Commission, is attributed to Witt. It was first installed in the late 1730s at the Cloister's Zion House, which served as a hospital during the Revolutionary War, and was later moved to the cupola of the Ephrata Academy, where it drove two 1-hand dials.

Witt lived in a stone mansion in Germantown, bequeathed to him by the Warmer family, where he worked, exercising his many skills for the rest of his long life. Large gardens on the estate enabled extensive biological experimentation with plants and medicinal herbs. He made an eight-foot telescope to continue his astronomical observations, drawing horoscopes, and on one occasion documenting the passage of a major comet through the heavens. A competent musician, Witt played the virginal and also a large pipe organ of his own construction. Time was set aside during the cold months for clockmaking, at which he was highly skilled. Witt's clocks were made of brass and iron, some running 30 hours with one weight on an endless chain, and the bell placed immediately above the works. These were wall clocks set on two brackets with all parts exposed, forerunners of the eight-day tall case clocks that came later. His large personal clock struck the quarters, and was one of three clocks valued in his estate inventory at from £15 to £25. The variety of smells, sights, and sounds that emanated from Witt's diverse activity caused his superstitious neighbors to regard him with respect bordering on fear, calling him, *hexen-meister*, the hex-master.

One day Witt returned home having bought himself a slave in Philadelphia. The man was a mulatto named Robert (Claymore), described as having a piercing black eye, light colored skin and curly hair. Robert looked after his master's personal needs, including the carrying of his lantern at night. He received certain unusual privileges in return, acting as Witt's business agent, and being instructed in the art of clockmaking. Witt's eyesight failed in his 80's, and Robert became even more important to his master's well-being, a loyal service rewarded by Witt in his last will and testament. The will manumitted (liberated) his trusty servant, providing him with the wherewithal to make a fresh start as a free man. His legacy included a bit of land, personal property including Witt's own clock that struck the quarters, plus all his clockmaking tools and engines.

Dr. Christopher Witt died in January 1765 at the age of 90, in Germantown, Pennsylvania, where he was buried.

Ephrata Cloister Tower Clock

The clock frame is entirely functional. It consists of two pairs of sturdy iron risers on the corners, spaced out by brazed strap iron spacers at top and bottom, and held together by riveting on one side and decoratively filed nuts on the other. The strike side vertical risers have outrider extensions in which the strike levers pivot. Overall, the frame measures 8½" wide by 5" deep by 14¾" high. The second-beat pendulum is suspended from a cock fastened to the top of the time side of the frame. Rating adjustment is provided for on the pendulum rod just above the brass-faced lead lenticular bob measuring 5½" in diameter. All wheels are brass, with steel arbors that taper down to cut pinions and pivot in brass-bushed holes. Trains are vertically aligned in the frame's iron risers, time to the left and strike to the right. The wooden barrels are conventional, with great wheels on one end and brass flanges on the other. As presently rigged, the clock runs about two days on a winding. The three-wheel time train includes a recoil escapement, an intermediate wheel and a great wheel. Two pins on the side of the time great wheel trip the hourly strike. The four-wheel strike train ends in a heavy gage brass fly, friction-mounted on an arbor inside the frame. The strike is controlled by three levers, a hoop wheel, and a plate type count wheel mounted on the back of the movement. A friction-mounted count wheel is driven by wheel-and-pinion

connections to the strike great wheel, which also serves as the strike pinwheel. The movement once drove single hands of two outside dials; the present take-off gearing, its single dial, and the movement and bell display stand are recent additions.

This tower clock, attributed to Christopher Witt because of his close connections with the Ephrata Cloister, is neatly engraved "WC 1735" on the frame. The reversal of initials weakens the attribution, but whoever its maker may have been, other than Witt, the clock is a worthy example of the period when Witt was one of Pennsylvania's earliest clockmakers.

Left, CW Figure 1. Ephrata Cloister tower clock, front view, time to the left, strike to the right. Note the engraved signature "WC 1735" on the upper right vertical riser and the decoratively filed nut fasteners. The pendulum's one-second beat is maintained by a fork-ended crutch, and is rated by an adjustable nut above its lenticular bob. *Right*, CW Figure 2. Frame connections on the back of the clock are riveted. Note the J-bolt fastening to the seat board. During a strike sequence the locking plate count wheel is advanced by a pinion-and-wheel connection to the strike great wheel with peripheral pins that lift the bell lever.

1747 • AUGUSTINE NEISSER

Augustine Neisser was born in 1717 in Sehlen, Moravia. When Augustine was six years old he and his family moved to Herrnhut, Saxony (eastern Germany), where he appears to have remained until July 1735. At the age of 18, he and his older brother, George Neisser, joined 22 members of the second colony of Moravians invited by the Trustees of Georgia to come to America, to join nine others that had emigrated in 1734. They sailed from Hamburg to England, then embarked from London on the ship *Simonds*, arriving in Savannah on February 20, 1736. Fellow passengers included General James Oglethorpe, the Governor of Georgia, and John Wesley, the founder of Methodism. Some Moravians returned to Europe and others died, but 23 migrated north to Pennsylvania; George went first in 1737, followed by Augustine and the others in 1738. Along the way Augustine decided to remain in Germantown, an early settlement now part of greater Philadelphia. His brother George continued north with the main party which by 1741 founded Bethlehem, Pennsylvania, located on high ground north of the Lehigh River at the mouth of Monocacy Creek.

Neisser established himself as a clock and watch repairer soon after settling in Germantown, where he was to live and work until he died in 1780. As early as 1739 he made an eight-day movement for Cornelius Weygandt, and at about the same time made another with time, strike, seconds and moon phase for John Wister of Philadelphia. Neisser made several clock types during his long career. Where or from whom he learned the skill is unknown, but his surviving tower clock suggests strong European influences.

Germantown was within reasonable traveling distance to Bethlehem, allowing Neisser to visit friends and his brother, a leading figure in the Moravian community. On such occasions he brought them special items from Philadelphia suppliers not available locally, such as "springs to bleed with," for which he was reimbursed £1/13/9. On April 16, 1746 (Julian calendar), the Bethlehem community engaged Augustine Neisser to make a large quarter-striking public clock with two dials. The details of his contract remain hidden in the old style German script of the Moravian Archives, but it is known that the clock was destined for installation in the cupola of the community's Bell House, completed on June 9, 1746 (Julian calendar). Before Neisser started on the project, over 58 pounds of brass work had been purchased for the sum of £18/4, an excessive cost for raw stock suggesting some finished clock parts. Neisser set to work by April of 1746 and was back in Bethlehem on December 30 to finish the clock, but it was actually not completed until February 15, 1747. In March, the settlement's leader, Bishop Cammerhof, wrote to his Moravian patron, Count Nicholaus Ludwig von Zinzendorf of Saxony, "We have a fine brass clock and three bells, of which one strikes the hours, and the other two in pleasant euphony strike the quarters."

After 74 years of operation, it was reported in May 1821 that members of the community had complained about the care of the clock. The brother in charge allowed that it was perhaps time to turn the job over to younger hands, as he had wound it daily for over 60 years! He was replaced by Jedediah Weiss (1790–1873), a noted Bethlehem clockmaker. In August 1824, it was suggested that the clock be moved from the Bell House to the tower of the new church building erected in 1803–06. A feasibility study showed the building was more than strong enough to support the clock, and a meeting of the congregation was called specifically to consider the matter. They decided not only to move the clock mechanism, but to provide it with four large dials, each having two gilt pierced sheet-metal hands, and, furthermore, to pay the added costs out of their Civic Treasury. Custodian Weiss moved the clock.

In December 1874, T. Floria Giering, a Bethlehem watchmaker, was appointed clock caretaker. He urged that after 127 years of daily winding the clock be modified to run a full week or more between windings. A special meeting of the governing board approved Giering's proposal on the condition that he would wind the clock and keep it in good order for five years without any expense to the congregation. The modification added frame outriders, wheels and pinions, winding jacks, and much longer barrels to carry the rope for an eight-day weight fall. These additions required installation of a large flatbed frame of channel iron railing upon which the extended mechanism could be mounted. The modified clock continued to be wound on a weekly basis until April 1946 when the time and strike trains were electrified, ending 199 years of hand-wound, weight-driven operation.

Bethlehem's Central Moravian Church is home to Augustine Neisser's only surviving tower clock. Now approaching its 250th anniversary and having endured significant changes over the years, it stands out as this country's oldest known tower clock in continuous operation. (C.L Woodbridge)

Augustine Neisser's Tower Clock

The core clockwork at the Bethlehem installation is basically as Neisser installed it, with some parts set aside due to changes made over its 250-year life. The European style cage frame of forged-iron bars measures 39" wide by 9" deep by 25" high, and supports three trains: hour strike, time and quarter-hour strike. All wheels are brass with four shaped spokes, and are mounted on steel arbors with cut pinions. Hour strike control is by locking plate, with iron control levers and ratchet-driven fly. Quarter-hour strike control is by a notched flange count wheel. The arbor of the time train second wheel extends beyond both its pivot holes, one end turning the hand of a replaced setting dial, and the other driving the bevel gear take off to a four-dial transmission located well overhead. During its long hand-wound years, the escapement was recoil, with provision made for freewheeling. Its 80" long wooden rod pendulum was rated by hand nuts at the frame cock of its suspension end and also under its brass-cased lenticular bob. After 1874, major additions were made to convert the clock from daily to weekly winding. New mostly solid brass parts include 20" diameter great wheels, pinions, 30" barrels with integral ratchets, winding jacks and maintaining power. These barrel assemblies extend outboard under the old cage frame. They are mounted in brass-bushed bearing blocks bolted to a massive 73" by 31" iron rail flatbed, which sits on heavy

wood beam trestles and is attached to the cage frame by curved forged-iron outriders. When the clock was electrified in 1946, a number of parts were removed from both the old cage frame and the post-1874 winding enhancement. Parts set aside included the pendulum, the pallet arbor and crutch, and certain portions of the 1874 time and quarter-strike barrel assemblies. The time train is now driven by a synchronous motor connected by gearing to the escape wheel arbor. Hour strike, tripped by a pin on the arbor of the time second wheel, is controlled by the old count wheel, and is driven by a small weight electrically rewound and connected by chain and sprocket wheel to the third wheel arbor of the strike train. This 250-year-old veteran is scheduled for honorable retirement and restoration free of all electrical entanglements.

AN Figure 1. Overall rear view, prior to electrification in 1946. Neisser's original cage frame was handwound daily for 127 years. After 1874, Floria Geiring's barrel assembly enhancements supported by a massive iron rail flatbed, reduced winding to once a week. Note Neisser's original cage frame is attached to the sturdy flatbed frame by curved iron outriders.

AN Figure 2. Overall front view following electrification in 1946. It served to eliminate hand-winding, but resulted in substantial removal of time and quarter strike parts. The strike train barrel assembly additions include large brass-bushed bearing blocks, a 20" diameter great wheel with 78 lifting pins, a 30" long brass barrel with an integral ratchet, and reduction gearing to aid winding.

AN Figure 3. Strike side, cage frame detail. Note vertical risers with decorative ends and fancy nut fasteners. The ratchet-driven fly and friction-mounted locking plate are original Neisser parts. Shaped spoking of the recoil escape wheel to the right is typical of all original cage frame wheels, as compared to the straight spokes of Geiring's 1874 enhancement.

AN Figure 4. Geiring's time great wheel removed prior to the Neisser tower clock electrification. Note the five straight spokes, added Harrison maintaining power, and the brass-bushed bearing block formerly bolted to the iron rail flatbed.

1766 • JOHANN EBERHARDT

Johann Ludwig (aka Lewis) Eberhardt was born on May 17, 1758, in the village of Alm, Schwarzburg-Rudelstadt, Thuringia, southeast Germany. At age 14 he went to work in the clockmaking shop of his father, Johann Gottfried Eberhardt. Afterward he joined the Moravian community in Gnadau, and continued to perfect his skills as a clockmaker, watch repairer, and silversmith, working off and on for his father and with other masters at various locations in Germany and Holland. In 1798, he became master in the clockmaking shop of the Brothers House in Gnadenfeldt, and the following year received his call from the Collegium of the Moravian Community in Salem, North Carolina.

Eberhardt landed in Philadelphia on September 28, 1799, at the age of 41, a skilled craftsman, but in debt and without savings. Arriving in Salem by November, 1799, he shared the forge of the community gunsmith before setting up his own clock, watch and silversmith shop. In 1800, he sought to "establish" himself, which meant having a house, getting married and raising a family. Eventually, the ruling elders accepted Julianna Michel, a woman 12 years younger than Eberhardt. The couple married on June 2, 1800, and had a daughter and four sons between May 1801 and June 1809. It was a stormy marriage, with Eberhardt often called before the ruling body for "scandalous behavior." Time and time again, the Collegium excluded Eberhardt

from community privileges, threatening expulsion, only to change their minds and readmit him for his good work, contrition, and genuine religious commitment. The Eberhardt's oldest son, Louis Ferdinand, eventually succeeded to the business, took over shop finances, and saved his squabbling parents from impoverishment in their old age. On his deathbed, just shy of 81 years old, Johann Eberhardt reaffirmed his dedication to Moravian beliefs, asking forgiveness for having been "at times perplexing, yes even shocking, in work and deed to my Brothers and Sisters...." He died on April 10, 1839, in Salem, North Carolina, where he was buried.

Eberhardt was a highly-skilled and industrious clockmaker, always happier at the work bench than dealing with people. Added to the normal run of general repairs, he made fine tall case clocks in the English tradition that found a ready market. In addition he is associated with three early North Carolina tower clocks, two of which still run hand wound. The **Home Church clock** was imported from Gnadau, Germany, and put up in the Salem tower in 1791. Its care and winding was Eberhardt's first responsibility when arriving here in 1799, a daily task he continued to the age of 78. In 1800, he moved the old iron mechanism from the Salem tower to the gable of the new Home Moravian Church. Over the years, he added significant improvements. **The Hillsborough clock**, reportedly the gift of King George III to the Hillsborough's Church of England, arrived on our shores in 1766. Eberhardt brought the clock to his shop for repairs in 1806, when it appeared in his inventory valued at $278. Shortly thereafter, he installed the clock at its second site, the tower of the old Hillsborough market house. In 1846 it was moved once more, with added gearing to drive four dials in the cupola of the Orange County Courthouse, where it remains to this day. A third tower clock listed in Eberhardt's 1835 inventory was sold to the village of Germanton for $95. Now missing, it was reported to be the size of a "two foot cube," and possibly made by Eberhardt himself.

Johann Eberhardt's Tower Clocks

The cage frame of the 1791 **Home Church clock** is of typical eighteenth century German style, a cage frame of forged vertical and horizontal iron bars held together by wedges, having bowed legs and curled finials. It measures about 39" wide, 25" deep by 35" high. All moving parts are iron, except for its wooden barrels, and a 9" diameter brass recoil escape wheel. Large lantern pinions with riveted trunions mounted on square arbors are used throughout. Wheel spokes are forged to the annulus with hand-filed teeth, in the old style. The three-wheel time and strike trains are mounted end-to-end, the strike great wheel being over 16" in diameter. An iron rod, lenticular bob pendulum

(38 beats to the minute) is suspended outside the time end of the frame. A leading-off rod extends from the time train to the motion work of a single dial on the front gable of the church. Eberhardt additions to the clock included a large 84-inch diameter outside dial with elegant hands and new dial motion work converting the old 24-hour one-hand dial to a conventional two-hand indicator. He also added quarter strike on a small bell to accompany the existing hour strike on a large bell. This required making a much larger count-wheel consisting of a huge 144-tooth ring wheel driven by a pinion on the strike barrel wheel arbor. It also required added strike triggering pins on the time train second wheel, and an ingenious mechanism to switch the single strike hammer between the hour and the quarter-hour bells. The hands are set by stopping the pendulum or disengaging it from the crutch to allow freewheeling of the time train. The driving weights are heavy stone posts, two-fall compounded on the time side and five-fall compounded on the strike. Both time and strike have ingenious winding jacks: their open-ended pinions on the winding square arbors can be disengaged when not in use. The clock runs 24-hours on a winding, but is customarily wound twice daily.

The 1766 **Hillsborough clock** is known in England as "pagoda style." Popular there in the last half of the eighteenth century, it was probably made by William Smith or Charles Penton of Upper Moorfields, London.

Overall, the frame measures 31½" wide, 13¼" deep, by 38½" high. Characteristic features, apart from the distinctive shape of the iron-bar cage frame, are splayed wheel spoking, meshed spur-tooth wheels in the transmission, and the frame outrigger in which strike control levers pivot. The dial motion work appears to be original; however, the overhead support structure for the transmission and the iron leading-off rods (with universal joints) were made by Eberhardt to provide added dials at this third installation site. The time second wheel drives a typical English friction-mounted center wheel that advances the snail, drives the setting dial and overhead transmission, while allowing the hands to be set back or ahead without stopping the clock. The recoil escapement is conventional, but lacks maintaining power. This clock's rack-and-snail strike control is not typical of most pagoda-style clocks. All wheels are brass with steel arbors and cut-leaf pinions, and the barrels are wood. The iron-rod pendulum, which beats 40 to the minute, is suspended from a cock on a center vertical riser; it is rated by a movable lenticular bob, fixed to the rod by a wing-head screw. Both driving weights are two-fall compounded on wooden pulleys, and are wound twice a week. The time and strike winding jacks are unusual and were probably added by Eberhardt based on similar devices on the clock at Salem.

JE Figure 1. Overview of the Salem clock, time to the left, strike to the right. At the upper left is its substantial recoil escapement. Note riveted iron lantern pinions, square arbors, wheels with spokes forged on the annulus, cage frame curled finials and wedged joints—all features typical of early European tower clocks.

Above, JE Figure 2. Salem clock strike train overview. Note bowed legs with pad feet and the wedged frame joints. Just visible at the far left end is the large 144-tooth hour and quarter-hour count wheel fashioned by Eberhardt. *Below*, JE Figure 3. Detail of the Salem clock strike side winding jack and count wheel. Once rewound, the open-end lantern pinion can be safely disengaged from the toothed rim on the winding barrel. Just visible is the barrel arbor pinion that meshes with the internal teeth of the count wheel ring gear.

Left, JE Figure 4. The Hillsborough English clock with its distinctive "pagoda-style" cage frame. Brass bushings are force fit and decoratively ringed. Strike levers pivot in characteristic frame outriders. The pendulum is suspended from a cock on the tall center riser that also supports a recoil escape wheel and a multi-function center wheel which drives a spur gear transmission located above the frame. *Right*, JE Figure 5. The awkward Hillsborough winding jack was probably added by Eberhardt based on the Salem arrangement (see JE Figure 3).

1768 • OBADIAH FRARY

Samson Frary, the grandfather of Obadiah, established himself by 1670 as an original proprietor of what is now Old Deerfield, then a wilderness in Massachusetts' fertile Pocumtuck River Valley. As with other pioneers, he was subjected to unexpected raids by hostile Native Americans encouraged by the French in Canada. After a number of incidents of no major consequence, combined French and Indian forces savagely attacked the sleeping town before daybreak on February 29, 1803. They killed Samson Frary, two young daughters, and, later, his wife who proved "lacking in vigor to endure" the captive march back to Canada.

These were not the last of the Frary losses. Obadiah's father managed to escape the Deerfield massacre, but Obadiah's oldest son, a soldier in the American Revolutionary War, was killed and scalped by savages in the 1777 retreat near Fort Edward, 40 miles north of Albany, New York.

Obadiah Frary led a peaceful life by comparison, surviving to the ripe old age of 87 with his scalp intact. He was born May 20, 1717, on his father's farm in Deerfield, the first of four children of Nathaniel and Mehitable (Dickinson) Frary. There is no record of his early training. He married twice, first to Eunice——, the mother of his six children, and second, in 1778, to Dinah Corse, whom he outlived by six years. Following a move and brief stay at Northampton, he went on to become an early settler of Southampton, where he operated a sawmill and lived most of his life. Frary became a skilled cabinetmaker, leaving his descendants some very fine furniture, including an elegant highboy.

The Deerfield Meeting House was renovated in 1768, with changes made to the exterior door frame and a tall steeple added in the old style to the side of the meeting house. Town records for 1768 show the following entry:

Town Clock—
Pd Obadiah Frary for putting
   up Town Clock   2/12/-
Boarding Frary 14 days @/8   9/4
Keeping his horse   4/8
                                    3/7/6

It is claimed that between 1745 and 1775 Frary made some good brass clocks for families and a few for meeting houses, so it is likely that he made the town clock as well as having put it up. The Deerfield clock, and at least one surviving tall case clock, appraised at $18,000 in 1979, supply tangible evidence of his skill in the trade. Later in life, he occupied himself with civic duties, serving as a constable, a church committeeman, and town moderator in matters regarding the trespass of hogs and deer. Too old to soldier during the American Revolution, he contributed by serving on the Committee of Correspondence, Safety and Inspection, which coordinated the town's war-related activities with those of neighboring towns. Obadiah Frary died on August 20, 1804, leaving most of his modest estate to Captain Nathan Frary, his son and executor.

Obadiah Frary Tower Clock

The Frary clock shows English influences, but its workmanship marks it as early American. Its cage frame is of forged strap iron, joined at the corners by square iron pillars threaded on each end, and decorated by turned brass capitals and bases. It is a small clock, measuring 15½" wide, 14" high, by only 7⅜" deep. The shallow depth, allowing short sturdy wheel arbors, results from the lack of winding barrels. The clock was wound, probably daily, by pulling down weight ropes which passed over spiked pulleys connected by ratchets to the great wheels. The clock's time and strike trains each have three wheels with unbushed pivot holes. All arbors and their pinions are iron. The wheels and their collets—plus the large count wheel and the train winding pulleys—are brass, decorated with concentric rings. During a strike sequence, the count wheel is advanced by an integral gear on its backside turned by a two-leaf pinion on the end of the strike great wheel arbor. Both the strike great wheel and its count wheel are 9" in diameter. The time great wheel is smaller, measuring 7¼" across; its arbor

turned the motion work (now missing) of a single outside dial measuring about 60" diameter. Other missing parts include the pendulum, the escapement anchor, and the vanes of a four-arm fly mounted behind the frame. There is no setting dial or maintaining power. The curled teeth of what appears to have been a recoil escape wheel suggest that wear and an escapement runaway ended this clock's career.

OF Figure 1. Overview of the Frary tower clock and its outside dial hands as displayed in the museum of the Pocumtuck Valley Memorial Association, Old Deerfield, Massachusetts.

Above, OF Figure 2. Mechanism overview, time to the left, strike to the right. The cage frame is of forged iron except for decorative brass capitals and bases on the corner columns. The dial take-off wheels, now missing, were mounted in the iron bridge at front center. Note the curled teeth of the escape wheel and the missing anchor, indicative of an escapement runaway.

Right, OF Figure 3. Strike train side view. The strike great wheel arbor is multi-functioned: during rewind its spiked pulley and ratchet serves to rewind the pull-up weight line; it also serves to control the strike sequence by advancing the count wheel and driving the train which spins the fly; and, finally, pins on the side of the great wheel lift the lever that strikes the bell. Note ratchet-driven fly arms with missing vanes at far right.

1769 • GAWEN BROWN

Gawen Brown (Browne) was born in England in 1719, and is said to have come originally from Penrith, a village 250 miles north of London. Like others from small towns, he made the most of his London credentials when he arrived in America at the age of 28:

GAWEN BROWN.—This is to give Notice to the Publick, That Gawen Brown, Clock and Watch Maker lately from London, keeps his Shop at Mr. Johnson's Japanner, in Brattle-Street, Boston, near the Rev. Mr. Cooper's Meeting House, where he makes and sells all sorts of plain, repeating and astronomical Clocks...Likewise does all sorts of Watch Work in the best Manner...*The Boston Evening Post*, January 16, 1749.

Brown specialized in imported English watches favored by his Boston clientele, and even some tall clocks of his own manufacture had English movements rather than his own, which are said to have been of poorer quality.

Brown has been referred to as "the Tory clockmaker" which is far from the truth. The Revolutionary War may have reduced his traffic in English goods for a few years, but Brown stood with the colonies and not against them. His wife at the time was the sister-in-law of Samuel Adams, the American patriot, and Brown himself had an outstanding military record. In 1752 he moved from his first address on Brattle Street to King (now State) Street, moving again the same year to Union Street. By 1760, he returned to King, setting up shop in a three-story building where he remained for almost 40 years. The 1798 Boston Directories place him finally on George (now Joy) Street near what is now Myrtle. Brown married several times: first, in 1750 to Mary Flagg who gave birth to six children; second, in 1760 to Elizabeth Byles, the daughter of his Hollis Street Church minister; and third, in 1764 to widow Elizabeth Hill Adams, who delivered six children, outlived her husband and was the executrix of his will. Gawen Brown died at age 82, with the funeral service held at his residence on George Street at 5 o'clock on Saturday, August 8, 1801.

No work of Gawen Brown's has attracted more attention than the town clock installed by him about 1769 in the tower of Boston's Old South Church. In 1750, Boston's north end, central Boston, and the southerly end of town all had church clocks. Further south on Washington at the corner of Milk Street, the Old South Church had a large bell and the set up for three dials, but no clock in its tower. In 1767 a town warrant stated that Bagnall's 1718 town clock in the Old Brick Church in central Boston was not worth repairing, but Brown took on the job anyway for "Forty Shillings Real Money." Simultaneously, he was mak-

ing a tower clock of his own, as reported by the *Massachusetts Gazette* of March 17, 1768:

GAWEN BROWNE.—Boston, March 17. At a Meeting of the Freeholders and other Inhabitants of this Town met at Faneuil Hall, on Monday last...were exhibited the Frame and principle Movements of a superb stately Town-Clock, Made by Mr. Gawen Browne, of this Town: the two great Wheels took nearly 90 lbs. weight of cast Brass: It is calculated for eight Days to shew the Hours and the Minutes; it will have three grand Dials, and a mechanic lever to preserve the Motion during the winding up. The Pendulum Wheel and Pallets to perform the dead Beat. The Works are nicely executed: The steel Pinions and Teeth of the Wheels are finely polished which must greatly abate the Friction, add to its Regularity and Duration. It will have a curious mathematical Pendulum that may be altered the 3500th Parts of one Inch while the Clock is going.—From the exquisite finishing of the Parts already done, good Judges are of Opinion it will be a Master piece of the Kind, and an Honor to America.

The evidence points to Brown's having installed a new *two-dial* clock in the Old South Church in mid-1769. The *Boston Gazette* noted on April 16, 1770, that his "great Clock" in the Old South Church had lost only two minutes in 14 weeks. Brown first refused to part with the clock for less than £100, but on March 30, 1774, he settled for £80 lawful money, with the promise to keep the clock in good order and wound up for seven years at his own expense. He also assured them he would add a third dial, a promise never kept. The clock is engraved "Gawen Brown 1766" on its count wheel, probably the date of its manufacture rather than when it became the official Boston Town Clock.

Gawen Brown Tower Clock

The plain cage frame consists of hand-forged horizontal and vertical flat iron bars, bolted together with decoratively filed nuts on the threaded ends of multiple iron bar spacers. Overall it measures 40" wide by 16" deep by 36" high, and stands on a wooden beam platform that raises it to convenient winding height. The functions of the "centre wheel" in English clocks are taken over by the time train second, or minute, wheel. It also replaces English bolt-and-shutter maintaining with a gravity bar inserted in the teeth of the time train minute wheel. The train pivots turn in brass bushings press fit into vertical risers, strike to the left and time to the right. Arbors are steel with cut-leaf pinions. The wheels are brass with uniform machine-cut teeth, but wheel spoking varies considerably. The Graham escape wheel has 25 finely cut teeth and dead-beat steel pallets on an anchor that can be disengaged to reset the hands by freewheeling. The setting dial is a replacement. Take-off power from the time train is via bevel gears connected by a vertical shaft to a two-dial transmission located above the frame. The iron rod pendulum is fine rated by a wing-nut screw at its suspension end. The fly and count wheel lever of the four-wheel strike train are missing, the strike side having been disabled some years ago when the bell tower was insulated. Both barrels are of wood, the strike side measuring 10" in diameter, the time side 8½". Winding of the heavier strike weight is aided by a lantern pinion winding jack of unusual design. The bell lever is lifted by pins on the strike train second wheel. The large brass count wheel is mounted outside the frame, turned by connections to the strike train.

It has been suggested that Brown imported the clock or its finer parts from England, which he then assembled in a strap-iron frame of his own making. Other experts doubt his technical ability to have made such a reliable design on the first try with little or no previous experience, and having succeeded, think it odd never to have made another. On the other hand, later technology features such as its use of Vuillamy bearings can be attributed to custodial repair over the years. "G.B. Boston" is stamped on one of the great wheels, and the clock is known to have been repaired by Aaron Willard Jr., in 1828 and by George M. Stevens in 1890. Undoubtedly other custodians made "improvements" to keep the clock running for over 225 years, but who did what and when is not documented. (Richard W. Husher)

GB Figure 1. Clock front view, strike left, time right. Note the variation in the number and shape of wheel spokes. The overall design of the Graham deadbeat escapement is typically English. At far right is the weighted end of a gravity bar maintaining power, its finger end inserted in the teeth of the time minute wheel during winding. The setting dial face is not original, nor are the Vuillamy bearings on the upper end of the time train. The long vertical bar drives an overhead transmission. The lantern pinion winding jack on the strike train barrel is unusual, probably a later addition.

GB Figure 2. Clock back view, time left, strike right. Again, the lantern pinion winding jack at the bottom right is unusual. Note layout, pivoting and counterbalance of the strike control levers on the upper end of the frame. The strike train second wheel is the pinwheel which acts on the bell lever pivoted in frame outriggers. The count wheel lever is missing as is the fly. At far left a fork-ended crutch impulses the iron rod pendulum which extends through the floor. The pendulum's suspension spring hangs from a cock which also supports a fine rating device.

1785 • JOHN EBERMAN JR.

Lancaster County, the Pennsylvania Dutch heartland about 60 miles west of Philadelphia, yielded more than 125 clock and watchmakers between 1750 and 1850, but only Eberman and his son, Joseph, made tower clocks. Born in 1749, John Eberman Jr. was the older son of a soap boiler/tallow chandler who had emigrated as a child with his family from Schwaigern, near Heilbronn, Germany. John Jr. is said to have been an apprentice of Lancaster's first clockmaker, Rudy Stoner (1728–1769), to have worked as a journeyman for George Hoff Sr. (1733–1816), and to have been master to Martin Schreiner Sr.

In 1772, John Eberman Jr. opened the shop in Lancaster Borough where he remained through 1807, dropping "Jr." from his name after his father's death in 1805. He made 30-hour and eight-day tall case time and strike clocks in the English tradition, and from 1772 to 1824 was custodian of the town's courthouse clock, said to have been imported from England. Between 1785 and 1811 he also made four known tower clocks, three of which have survived. On July 9, 1784, while Eberman was placing the driving weights of the courthouse clock into new wooden chutes, a fire broke out that totally destroyed the building. The cause was never determined. The following year he was commissioned to make a tower clock for the new courthouse at a cost of £550, representing 10% of the total cost of the building. When the building was razed in 1854, the clock was moved to the new larger courthouse. In 1898, it was replaced by one made by Seth Thomas Clock Co. The old clock, still on the county commissioner's inventory, was eventually loaned for display at Heritage Center on Lancaster's Center Square.

In 1791, Eberman estimated the cost of a tower clock for the Manor House at Nazareth, Pennsylvania, built for but never occupied by Count Nicholas Ludwig von Zinzendorf of Saxony, patron of the Moravians. Other priorities put off the clock acquisition until October 1798. Eberman proposed a single dial clock with two hands for £170, but the frugal Overseers Committee saved £20 by ordering a one-hand clock. In the course of installation Eberman ran over budget on materials. He asked for an additional £8, striking a deal to pay half the freight bill and his transportation back to Lancaster, provided he received free lodging and board during the installation in late 1799. In 1840, a large church building was erected on the same square as the Manor House and the clock was moved to its tower by Bethlehem clockmaker Jedediah Weiss (1795–1873), who added dial motion work and "a running mate for the lonely hour hand." In 1860, the present church was erected on the Circle, and the clock was moved by a

Weiss apprentice, Nazareth clockmaker Josiah Beitel (1811–1898). Eberman's clock became irregular in the 1920s and was replaced after a century of service. Now beautifully restored, it is displayed in Whitfield House of the Moravian Historical Society at Nazareth, Pennsylvania.

Eberman's 1801 clock for the Moravian Church at Lititz, Pennsylvania, was destroyed when the building burned in 1857; it was reported to have been a 30-hour, single dial clock with two hands.

Harmony, Pennsylvania, was founded in 1804 by German Harmonists led by George Rapp. The group erected a sturdy 75 by 45 foot church building, with an upper story that stored several thousand bushels of grain. In a letter dated July 16, 1810, to Rapp's adopted son and financial adviser, the 61-year-old Eberman wrote,

> I received your letter and see from it that you would like to have a clock and bell made by me...Materials are very expensive at this time...In general, I will make you a good clock, but as far as the price is concerned, I cannot well give you a statement, but I will deal with you in a brotherly manner, but if at your expense, my son and I are to put the clock at your place, purely from the point of time, the clock could not be made earlier than spring, for it takes my son and me from five to six months until everything is finished.

A year later on August 30, Eberman wrote again, worried about the placement of the single hands on the original two dials. The date of the clock's removal to the Harmony schoolhouse is unknown, but it is now displayed in the museum of the Harmonist Historical and Memorial Association at Harmony, Pennsylvania.

As his career as a clockmaker wound down, John Eberman (Jr.) engaged himself in politics. At 57, he was appointed Justice of the Peace for the First District. At other times he served in the state militia, failed in a bid for sheriff, was named clerk of the Orphan's Court, and had a term as Chief Burgess of Lancaster Borough, a position equal to that of town mayor. From 1829 to 1831, he was with the Branch Bank of Pennsylvania in Lancaster. (C.L. Woodbridge/Stacy Wood)

John Eberman Jr. Tower Clocks

All known surviving clocks made by Eberman were installed in Pennsylvania. They have similar wrought-iron frames, with square chamfered corner posts topped by decorative finials that vary slightly from clock to clock. Wheel trains are mounted between spearheaded risers bolted top and bottom to the horizontal frame rails. Eberman trains have only three brass wheels mounted on steel arbors that taper down to cut pinions. Strike levers are also iron. Strike control is by brass locking plates and large two-blade flies, both mounted outside the frame. Eberman pendulums, suspended on a cock outside the frame, have an open loop in the upper end of their iron rods for access to the time train winding square. No provision is made for setting dials or maintaining power.

Eberman's 1785 Lancaster installation (JEJ Model 1) is the largest of his surviving clocks, measuring 46" wide, 19" deep, by 53" high. The movement has been modified at least twice: first in 1854 by Eberman's son, Joseph, and second in 1878 by Godfried M. Zahn (1817–1895), a Lancaster clockmaker. Changes include: winding jacks added to both time and strike; replacement of the anchor deadbeat escapement with an offset pinwheel, and replacement of its decorative iron pendulum rod with a conventional wooden one.

The frame of the 1791 Nazareth clock (JEJ Model 2) measures 39" wide, 14" deep, by 42" high overall. It stands on splayed 5" feet. This three-train, 30-hour movement provides time on the center train with an anchor recoil escapement, quarter strike to the left and hour strike to the right. Both strike trains have ratchet-driven flies and locking plates mounted outboard of the frame. Dial hands are reset by freewheeling. The 1¼-second beat pendulum has an iron rod and a brass-faced 22½-pound lenticular bob. Winding barrels are of wood with their great wheels measuring 12⅜" inches in diameter. Quarter and hour strike levers are lifted by roller pins on the sides of their respective great wheels. The time great wheel serves as the minute wheel. It drives a dial take-off of brass bevel gears with a leading-off rod to an overhead four-dial transmission (probably a later addition). The clock works weighs 310 pounds.

Eberman's 30-hour striker (JEJ Model 3) was made in 1811 for the first of the three successive towns carved out of the American wilderness by the Harmony Society. The clock's wrought-iron cage frame has spearheaded risers, wedge-shaped feet, and square chamfered corner posts with decorative brass finials, features shared with all other Eberman tower clocks. Overall it measures 43" wide by 44" high by 18" deep. Its three-wheel time and strike trains have brass wheels with four spokes and tapered iron arbors with cut-leaf pinions. Lantern pinions with roller trundles on the time train are probably repairs. The recoil escapement has a 26-tooth brass escape wheel; the hands are set by freewheeling. The clock's dial take-off is a spur gear driven by a pinion on the time great wheel arbor. The single hands of two outside dials, originally above the movement, are of distinctive design. Strike control is by locking plate and a ratchet-driven fly mounted outside the frame. The 1¼-second pendulum has a lenticular bob and an iron rod with a large hole providing access to the time winding square. (See **1827 • The Harmony Society**, page 72.)

JEJ Figure 1. Eberman's 1785 Lancaster clock (JEJ Model 1). Added floor pillars are for museum display. The original clock alterations include time and strike winding jacks, a pendulum rating device, and a pinwheel deadbeat escapement.

Above, JEJ Figure 2. Front view of the 1791 quarter striker for Nazareth (JEJ Model 2). Note Eberman's distinctive pendulum rod, split and opened for access to the time winding square. The spearheaded vertical risers and square chamfered corner posts with decorative finials are also Eberman hallmarks. *Below*, JEJ Figure 3. Rear view of JEJ Model 2 showing the symmetrical layout of its three trains. Quarter-strike levers are missing. The 26-tooth wheel of the recoil escapement measures $5^1/2''$ across, and all great wheels are $12^3/8''$. A dial take-off of brass bevel gears is driven by the arbor of the time great wheel.

Above, JEJ Figure 4. Front view of Eberman's striker (JEJ Model 3), on display at Harmony, Pennsylvania, where it was first installed in 1811. The works are in basically unrestored condition. The wrought iron cage frame has all of Eberman's hallmark decorative features. **Below**, JEJ Figure 5. Museum display of JEJ Model 3 shows one of two dials originally mounted above the movement on diagonal sides of an octagonal belfry. The 1827 clock at the Harmony Society's third town, called Economy, has a similar belfry; however, the chapter spelling IIII shows up on Economy's dials as IV. (See HS Figure 1, p. 73.)

1786 • BENJAMIN DUDLEY

Benjamin Dudley was English born and trained. Few details survive about his personal life. He emigrated from Birmingham, England, to Savannah, Georgia, by March of 1768 when he opened a shop and advertised his location "next door to Mr. Rutherford's in Broughton-Street...on the Business of a Silversmith in all its branches. He also cleans and repairs all sorts of Clocks and Watches, Mathematical Instruments, &c...."

By August 6, 1785, or earlier, Dudley removed to Newport, Rhode Island, a sophisticated, enlightened community, where he greatly expanded his product line in a shop located at John C. Wanton's, near the State House. In addition to clock and watchmaking, he offered

> Plain, Quarter, and Chime Clocks kept in repair by the year, horizontal and repeating Watches kept in Repair by the Year, the same as in London; Watches that never wind up (commonly call'd perpetual Motion Watches) carefully repaired and warranted; Expansion slide Watches carefully examined—Also Barometers, Thermometers, and Hydrometers, Air-Pumps, Microscopes, Telliscopes, reflecting and refracting, and most Kind of philosophical Instruments....

Dudley's place of business was within the shadow of Newport's famous State House, redesignated the Colony House (Historic National Landmark). Formerly the chief seat of state government, it was badly damaged during the American Revolution, requiring extensive refurbishment in 1784–1785. As part of the process it was proposed that a large public clock be placed on the front facade of the building facing the city green. By March of 1785, over 200 subscribers had pledged £58/5/5 (about $200) to be "applied to purchase a clock for the State House in the City of Newport to be made by Mr. Dudley." There are no further records of the transaction or whether Dudley took on the duty of winding and maintaining the clock, but a significant portion of the mechanism has survived in the collection of the Newport Historical Society. Dudley's old clock was replaced by an interim clock, maker unknown, again replaced in 1853 by a precision time and strike mechanism made by J.R. Brown & Sharpe of Providence. This third clock, beautifully refurbished with minimal replacement of original parts, runs hand wound, time and strike, behind a handsome illuminated glass dial.

Benjamin Dudley's Tower Clock

Dudley's 1786 clock is an American variation on the English "pagoda style" cage frame popular in the last half of the eighteenth century. Dudley may well have seen this type of clock in the environs of London or thereabout. The frame consists of forged iron bars bolted together, its lower portion being topped by two boldly concave pediments which originally supported a now missing bridge for suspension of the pendulum. The pendulum measures about 100" in length overall, including an 11" suspension spring, an 82" wooden rod, and a 7½" lenticular bob riding on a rating nut. Overall, the frame and its base measures about 34" wide, 17" deep, by 37" high, providing 15" inches shoulder-to-shoulder. The pivot holes are brass bushed. All wheels are brass with high count well-cut teeth (possibly imported); on the other hand, the pinions on the forged iron arbors are crudely cut, or possibly just appear so due to corrosion. The escapement has a one-piece steel anchor with deadbeat pallets and a 7½" diameter brass escape wheel with 60 finely-shaped teeth. The crutch measures 17" inches in length. The snail of the clock's rack-and-snail strike control system is turned by an integral 12-tooth star wheel advanced by a lever on the extended arbor of the time train second wheel. Both snail and star wheel are intact but the star lever, the rack, and all strike control levers are missing. The time and strike barrels are turned wooden spools without metal end plates, the diameter of the time barrel being 6½", the strike 8⅝". The strike great wheel diameter is 12¼", the time great wheel 11". The bell strike lever is lifted by pins extending from the side of the strike second wheel. The wheel of a winding jack on the strike side is missing along with the ratchet-driven fly. Dudley's State House clock is unusual and interesting, but its missing parts and badly corroded iron work represent a major restoration challenge.

Above left, *BD Figure 1. Overview of Dudley's 1786 clock. The forged iron frame's pagoda-shaped top shows English design influences, but also provides for a bridge from which to suspend the long pendulum. In general, the sophisticated character of the wheel teeth and spoking suggests they are English imports; the balance of the work is well within domestic capabilities of the period.* ***Above right***, *BD Figure 2. Dudley's three-wheel time train. The nut connection of the upper frame outrider allows depthing adjustment of the escapement anchor. The train's second wheel arbor extending through the frame made one revolution per hour. It would have carried a lever to advance the star wheel over a 12-hour period. It also served as a take-off to drive the dial hand or hands. Dial motion work has not survived.* ***Left***, *BD Figure 3. Wheel and pinion detail. Compare the clean machine-cut teeth of the brass wheels with the crude pinions. However, much of the deformed appearance of the arbors and pinions is due to iron corrosion.*

BD Figure 4. Dudley's four-wheel strike train. The heavier strike weight was rewound with the aid of a winding jack, its pinion evident on the upper winding square. The jack's main gear (now missing) was mounted on the barrel arbor square below. The barrel ratchets feature unusually fine teeth. The second wheel is the strike pinwheel.

1791 • DANIEL BURNAP

Daniel Burnap was born on November 1, 1759, in Coventry, Connecticut, the second of three sons and a daughter of Captain Abraham and Irene (Wright) Burnap. It is said that by the age of 15 he worked for a brief time for Thomas Harland, the recently arrived English-trained silversmith, clock, and watchmaker who settled in Norwich, Connecticut, in 1773. It was Harland's practice to conduct academic classes as part of the apprenticeship of the boys under his instruction, providing the basis for Burnap to teach school in East Haddam for two winter seasons before returning briefly to Harland's shop as a journeyman clockmaker. He worked there from September 1779 to July 1780, recording many of Harland's techniques as a guide for his own self-employment. After 1780 he launched his

career in old East Windsor (now South Windsor), across the Connecticut River from Hartford, setting up a clockmaking shop near Bissell's Tavern. In 1782 he married Deliverance Kingsbury.

Burnap's clockmaking shop prospered slowly but at a steady rate. Penrose Hoopes, Burnap's biographer, estimates that Burnap's monthly income increased from less than £1 to more than £10 between 1787 and 1794. He was well enough off by 1786 to purchase a home for retirement two miles north of the old East Windsor Meeting House. The 1790 census substantiates an increase in shop activity, showing a number of boys of apprentice age to be part of the Burnap household. Over the years, his apprentices included Nathaniel Olmstead, Ela Burnap, Levi Pitkin, Lewis Curtis, and, most famous of all, Eli Terry, who pioneered low-cost clock mass production. Much of Burnap's time was taken up with the repair of watches, silverware and miscellaneous metal goods, but his main stock in trade was the production of high quality tall case clocks of varying degrees of complication.

Burnap also produced a limited number of tower clocks, referred to specifically in a March 14, 1791, advertisement in the *Connecticut Courant*:

> DANIEL BURNAP.—Brass Wheel'd Clocks. The subscriber...takes this method to inform the publick that although he works in many other branches common to those in the silversmith line, as also Surveyor's Compasses, Watch repairing, &c. yet notwithstanding Clock Making is intended as the governing business of his shop...Those persons that may be in want of public Clocks may be supplied at the above shop, and may depend on faithful performance, by the publick's faithful servant, Daniel Burnap....

It would have been at about the time of this notice that Burnap installed a tower clock in the meeting house at Suffield, Connecticut. He probably made others. On November 2, 1802, Ruggles Woodhouse, acting for a committee from South Hadley, Massachusetts, wrote to Burnap, "You would make a good clock to the Meeting-House and set it up for $200." Both agreed that the clock would be paid for after a year's trial use, and Burnap pledged "to make a good one."

Burnap continued the clockmaking at his shop in old East Windsor as late as 1805, when he virtually quit the business. As early as 1795, however, he had begun accumulating property at his birthplace, Coventry, Connecticut, where he planned to retire. Over the years he added considerable acreage to his farm there, eventually building a splendid two-story five-bay homestead which he occupied by the spring of 1805. The attic was fitted out as a shop where he could tinker with repairs for his own pleasure, and the dining room often doubled as a courtroom to accommodate his duties as a justice of the peace. At various times he also served as tax assessor and collector, as surveyor of roads, and as representative at the Connecticut General Assembly. By 1810, Burnap was regarded as one of the wealthiest men in town, free to amuse himself in his workshop, or to devote whatever time he chose to church, civic, or family affairs. Life was not all wine and roses however. His wife of 40 years remained childless, and died in 1822 after a long, debilitating illness. The following year, the 63-year-old Burnap married Mary Kingsbury, his first wife's niece just half his age. The marriage produced three children, their only son dying young as a student at Yale College. In 1826, Burnap broke a hip which left him partially crippled for the rest of his life. He died after a short illness on September 26, 1838, at age 78, leaving a sizable estate. It was inventoried at $16,855.54, the principle assets consisting of $10,000 in bank stocks and 259 acres of land with a house and outbuildings valued at $5,000.

Daniel Burnap Tower Clock

Burnap's tower clock for the Suffield Meeting House has survived, now in the collection of the Connecticut Historical Society. It is in rough condition, having been stored in a barn for over 100 years, finally as a roost for chickens. We have the benefit of the maker's own description of the mechanism:

Frame 19 inches high, 26 inches wide. Irons for the pivots 12 inches from each other centers. The iron for the bottom of the back part of the frame runs about half inch above the barrels, The barrels 7 inches diameter & 12½ inches long...Barrel wheels 11 inches diameter, 60 teeth. Center wheel 48 teeth, its pinion 10 leaves. 3rd wheel 40 teeth, pinion 8 leaves. Swing wheel 30, pinion 7 leaves. Pin wheel 49 teeth, pinion 10 leaves, 7

pins. 3rd wheel 36 teeth, pinion 7 leaves. 4th wheel 32 teeth, pinion 6. Fly pinion 7 leaves.

Large dial wheel 72 teeth, takes into a nut of 7 leaves which is put on the center pinion which turns the dial work. The large dial wheel runs one inch from the outside of the pivot hole, the snail ¾ of an inch further, and the small dial wheel 6 inches off the pivot hole. The whole length of the arbor is 11 inches. The inside of the pendulum hangs 2¼ inches from the frame. The length of the pendulum rod to the middle of the ball is 10 feet 2 inches. The heft of the ball is 30 lb. Length of the crutch 12 inches. Length of the hammer tail, the shortest is 4 inches, the other is 5½ inches.

The dials 7 feet diameter. The diameter of the outer circle of the figures is 5 feet 2 inches, the length of the figures is 10 inches. The breadth of the figures is one eighth of the length. N.B. Length of the pillars is 7 inches & ¾ of inch. The perpendicular irons of the frame all stand forward of the long bars next to the dial work. The barrel arbors at the end for the key are one inch square & run through the barrels. For the large pivots there is a piece of iron brazed on & also the shoulder of the pivot & the barrel and all brazed together. The pinion heads are all brazed on the arbors.

The following is also noteworthy. The cage frame of forged iron bars measures 7¾" shoulder-to-shoulder. The mechanism measures 27" wide by 17½" deep by 22" high. The escapement is deadbeat with a steel one-piece anchor. The transmission to the outside dials consists of two spur gears meshing at a right angle, a form also seen in some eighteenth century English tower clocks.

DB Figure 1. Front (winding square) view of the Suffield clock, time to the left, strike to the right. The clockwork cage frame, riveted on one side and bolted on the other is mounted by J-bolts to the wooden beam base that also supports the barrel arbors in brass bushed pivot holes. Note the fly with missing vanes at upper right.

Above, DB Figure 2. Rear view of the Suffield clock. The cage frame, arbors, cut leaf pinions, strike control levers, the rack, and the great wheels are iron; all other wheels, their bushings, and the sheet metal snail are brass. The strike trip pin on a perforated disk on the time second arbor is adjustable. Pinion and wheel gearing on the same arbor advances the snail one revolution in 12 hours, and also drives the two-dial spur gear transmission. Note the 30-tooth Graham deadbeat escapement, and above it the pendulum suspension cock extending outside the frame. **Right**, DB Figure 3. This surviving cast-iron driving weight of the Suffield clock is 42 inches long, and weighs about 75 pounds. The elongated shape is unusual, reducing weight fall, but was used by a few other early makers.

1791 • FREDERICK HEISELY

Frederick Heisely,[1] of "Pennsylvania Dutch" heritage, was born in Manheim Township, Lancaster County, on October 17, 1759, the fourth of five children of stone mason Conrad and Sophia Bernardtina (Wirth) Heisely. He learned the clock and watch making trade in the Lancaster shop of John George Hoff, who had been trained in his native Grunstadt, Germany. At the age of 17, Heisely's apprenticeship was interrupted briefly by military duty in a Lancaster Company that marched against New Jersey during the American Revolution. After discharge from the army, he is listed briefly as a single man at work in Hanover, where he made at least one tall clock before resuming work for Hoff at Lancaster. On November 6, 1783, he married Hoff's oldest daughter, Catharina Juliana, just as Hoff had married the daughter of his master in Germany years before. Between 1788 and 1800 they had seven children, including three sons, two of whom became skilled clock, watch and instrument makers, and silversmiths.

Shortly after their marriage, the Heiselys moved about 40 miles west of Baltimore to Fredericktown (now Frederick), Maryland, a gateway to the west. The move was apparently with Hoff's blessing as he helped to finance their purchase of a lot next to the German Presbyterian parish house. In 1786, Heisely advertised opening a clock shop in his house on Market Street where he offered, "Clocks of all kinds, as well as Musical Chime Clocks, as common and plain ones, likewise large Town-Clocks if required...also makes Surveyors Compasses and other Mathematical Instruments, such as Protractors, Scales of different sorts...pocket Compasses with Sun Dials &c. &c." About 1791, Heisely made and installed a town clock in the steeple of the Evangelical Lutheran Church of Frederick. The mechanism was unusual for its early use of the French pinwheel escapement in America, and its use of roller lantern pinions throughout. The clock survives in the collection of the Smithsonian in Washington D.C. It was originally paid for by public subscription in the form of a clock lottery. On July 5, 1791, Heisely, as lottery manager, served public notice that those failing to honor their pledges had better pay up or forfeit their chance at the prizes. By 1795, Heisely's business prospered. He took on apprentices to keep up with the demand, particularly for his fine surveying instru-

ments, which found a healthy market throughout Maryland and in Virginia and Kentucky as well.

His father-in-law saw Heisely's specialized skills as a profitable adjunct to the clockmaking operation in Lancaster. In 1796, he convinced Heisely to return to Lancaster as a partner in Hoff & Heisely, located at Hoff's shop in the first block of West King Street. Tall case clocks signed Hoff-Heisely have survived from the period. Hoff's sons also participated in the enterprise, which probably complicated matters; in any case the partnership "dissolved" 10 months later. Heisely set up his own shop two blocks away from Hoff's shop on West King Street, where he remained in business for a couple of years.

By September 1798, Heisely returned to Frederick, Maryland, where he advertised having "recommenced the Clock and Watch-making business in the house he formerly occupied, next door to the Post-Office." In 1802 he added jewelry and some silverware items to his line. While still in Frederick, the two older Heisely sons were instructed in the trade of their father, following which the oldest son, George Jacob, moved on to Lancaster and later Harrisburg. During the War of 1812 George Jacob served in the Pennsylvania Militia and Frederick Augustus in the Maryland Militia; Frederick Augustus took a musket ball in the hip joint which left him lame, necessitating that John, the youngest son, serve out the balance of the enlistment. In addition to meeting the demands of his business, Frederick Heisely Sr. was an active communicant in the Evangelical Lutheran Church of Frederick. His youngest living daughter Catherine was married in the church in 1816, and Heisely may well have maintained the town clock he installed in the church's steeple in 1791.

In 1816–1817, the Heiselys joined their son George Jacob who had settled in Harrisburg, Pennsylvania. Added motivation for the move was completion of the camelback bridge over the Susquehanna River, an engineering marvel that redirected east-west traffic through Harrisburg and brought great prosperity to the town. On September 10, 1817, Heisely paid $5,000 for a house with a courtyard and surrounding land on the northwest corner of Second and Chestnut streets. Details of his life in Harrisburg are sketchy. At various times he worked alone or in partnership with George Jacob as Frederick Heisely & Son or F. & G.J. Heisely, but always in the clock, instrument and watch repair business. In later years he became active in civic affairs, serving as assistant burgess, as a member of the town council, and, between the age of 68 and 70, as treasurer of Dauphin County. At the age of 70 Frederick Heisely and his son George Jacob installed a town clock costing $700 in the new town hall at Columbia, Pennsylvania, and shortly thereafter they made another one for $750 installed in the Market House (now City Hall) at Chambersburg, Pennsylvania. Undoubt-

---

[1]The family name is variously spelled, being an Americanized version of the baptismal "Haeusele." He signed his clocks, surveying instruments and last will "Heisely," the spelling used here.

edly other Heisely tower clocks were made that have yet to come to light. In his mid-seventies, he produced a number of innovative low-cost brass eight-day strike repeater movements for cheap Connecticut factory shelf cases. At the age of 80 he presented a gallery clock to the Zion Lutheran Church of Harrisburg, where he was an active member. Predeceased three years by his wife, Frederick Heisely died on March 12, 1843, at age 84. Both were buried in Harrisburg Cemetery. (Martha C. Lang, Henry LaFond, Charles E. Smart)

Frederick Heisely Tower Clock

FH Model 1. The clock made in 1791 by Heisely for Frederick, Maryland, employs an early type wrought-iron cage frame held together by wedges; its short bow legs show German influences. Overall, the frame measures (in inches) 40 wide by 30 deep by 45 high. Its long two-second pendulum has a wooden rod and a cannon-ball bob of about 86 pounds. Thumb screws on the crutch fork provide for pendulum beat adjustment. The driving weights are cast-iron cylinders, weighing about 100 pounds on the time side and 170 pounds on the strike. All train wheels are of brass with four spokes (the escape wheel has five) mounted on steel arbors running in brass-bushed pivot holes. The clock's use of roller lantern pinions throughout is unique: they consist of iron trundles with pivots on each end turning in brass shrouds. The sole exception is a lantern pinion with fixed pins on the escape wheel arbor. None of the roller pinions show any significant wear. Another unusual feature is the clock's deadbeat pinwheel escapement. Invented in France by Lepaute in 1753, it is modified here, as in most American applications, with pins extending from only one side of the escape wheel; its steel pallet arms are of the closed-caliper type with a depth-adjusting thumb screw. The escape wheel arbor has a winding square extending outside the frame to control the freewheeling of the time train when resetting the dials. Both two-blade fly and locking plate count wheel are located outside the frame. The dial take-off utilizes machine cut bevel gears (probably not original) with a vertical rod tapered down from its center leading to a dial transmission above the frame. (Robert S. Edwards)

(For **F & GH Model 2** see **1831 • George Jacob Heisely**, page 79.)

FH Figure 1. Back view of 1791 Heisely's cage frame clock with its locking plate count wheel and four-wheel trains, time to the left, strike to the right. The bow-legged frame's wrought-iron bars are held together with wedges. The clock's two-second pendulum was suspended from a bridge that also supports the crutch end of the pallet arbor. Note beat adjustment thumb screws on the crutch fork.

FH Figure 2. Time train front view. The workmanship is impeccable. Heisely's expertise as an instrument maker shows itself in the escapement's adjustable caliper pallet arms. The five-spoke escape pinwheel may be a later replacement, as also may be the machine-cut bevel gears of the dial take off. The conventional lantern pinion of the pinwheel arbor is the sole exception to general use of roller pinions on the wheel trains. Note square brass inserts in the vertical risers, drilled for pivot holes.

1799 • SIMEON JOCELIN

Simeon Jocelin, the son of Nathaniel and Anne Jocelin of East Haven, Connecticut, was born on October 22, 1746. Largely self-taught, he is said to have served as an apprentice to Isaac Doolittle of New Haven. Jocelin first married Hanna Willard, who died in 1786, then second to Luceanda Smith (1764–1843), who outlived him by 20 years.

Variously described as a mechanical genius, the counselor of Eli Whitney, a skilled mathematician, and one of the most scientific of early American clock makers, Jocelin set up shop on State Street in New Haven by 1771. Disruptions caused by the American Revolution limited the demand for expensive tall case clocks, but he made the best of hard times by offering, along with watch repair and clocks of all kinds, "the best Sort hard Metal Buttons," good homemade salt, and watch crystals fashioned from broken scraps of English crown glass. He also engaged in engraving and publishing, his best work appearing between 1782 and 1793 in *The Chorister's Companion*. Demand for good clocks improved by the mid-1780s, and, after collecting a number of small debts overdue for watch repair, the business prospered. In November 1796, he advertised in the *Connecticut Journal*, "some improvements in machinery for keeping time.—Time-pieces for Observatories as also house and steeple clocks, may be made to go more regular than those with the common escapements:—the latter may have an additional striking part to ring the Bell three times a day." In 1799 he again offered "steeple and house clocks...on the most approved plans in common use, or with some new improvements for keeping time more perfectly." Steeple clocks were cited in two more advertisements made in 1800, but Jocelin shifted the emphasis to his "Silent moving Time-Keeper," covered by U.S. Patent No. 287X, dated May 8, 1800. Models were offered for $20 to $50 in tall cases and in miniature, running eight-days to 12 months. Neither of these unusual movements nor their patent records have survived. Several beautiful Jocelin tall case clocks have, however, one revealing his taste for the unusual with a delicate pinwheel deadbeat escapement. Innovation also characterized his church clocks. One made for the Yale College Old Chapel before 1800 at a cost of $850 incorporated an equation device he invented to tell apparent time, as the college conducted its classes by the sun (see **Eli Terry**, page 85). This clock was moved to Yale's Lyceum in 1822 and was lost track of after the building was taken down in 1901. Fortunately, strong evidence points to Jocelin as the maker of two surviving church clocks with many unusual design features installed about 1800 in nearby Madison and Branford, Connecticut.

Simeon Jocelin died in New Haven on June 5, 1823, at the age of 77. He left a small estate of personal property valued at about $680. It consisted mostly of clock tools and supplies, plus $2250 in real estate encumbered by liens of $1400. He was survived by his wife, Luceanda, and two sons whose fame came to exceed that of their father: Nathaniel, a well-known engraver and portrait painter, and Simeon S., a leading abolitionist and advocate of black rights. The family name changed from Jocelin to Jocelyn after the old clockmaker's death.

Simeon Jocelin Tower Clocks

All that is known about Jocelin's steeple clock for Yale College is that it told apparent time, had a one-hand dial, possibly a compensated pendulum, and is now missing. The surviving town clocks from Madison (ca. 1799) and Branford (ca. 1804) are obviously the work of one ingenious American maker, the best candidate being Simeon Jocelin. Their physical proximity to New Haven and early installation dates coincide with Jocelin's most active clockmaking period and his well-advertised tower clock improvements. Their unusual roller pin pallet escapement may even have its origins in his patented "Silent Moving Timepiece." Finally, Jocelin, quite simply, was the only known maker with the reputation and expertise to get and do the job at that time and place.

Madison and Branford clock similarities include: integrated chair-frames of well-joined wild cherry beams; sand-cast brass work; forged iron work; rack-and-snail strike control; great wheel strike lifting pins; similar wheel spoking and tooth form; poured and drilled brass pivot holes; split bearing blocks; old style filed nuts; unusual time train layouts; $1\frac{1}{2}$-second wooden rod pendulums; and bevel gear dial take-offs connected by 20-foot vertical iron rods to overhead transmissions. Most noteworthy, both clocks employ *roller pallet* deadbeat escapements. Large rollers having small diameter pivots reduce friction to a minimum compared to the frictional "drag" of most deadbeat escapements. The roller pallet anchor at Madison is conventionally mounted above the escape wheel, spanning seven of 30 radial teeth and having the usual bent rod crutch to the pendulum. With the Branford clock, the roller pallets taper from 3 to 2 mm. and engage the diameter of an unusual contrate escape wheel with 30 outwardly-slanted teeth. The pallet anchor rocks back-and-forth on a vertical arbor. Its integral crutch, a *straight* iron rod extending at a right angle from the pallet arbor, engages the pendulum rod via a pin and slot connection. Both Branford and Madison escapements provide for freewheeling, and at both locations power is conveyed from the movement to a three-dial transmission high overhead by a $\frac{1}{4}$" iron rod about 20' in length. The **Madison clock** runs hand wound, time and strike, still keeping excellent time after almost 200 years. Its chair frame, constructed of 1³/₄" by 2³/₄" wild cherry beams with pinned box-joint corners, measures overall 28" wide, 28" deep, by 33¹/₂" high. The lower frame supports two 23" long wooden barrels which pivot in split brass bearing blocks (similar to those at Branford). Time and strike trains pivot in brass-bushed holes drilled in *vertical* iron bars bolted to the tall end portion of the chair frame. The clock's 1¹/₂-second pendulum has a mahogany rod and a brass-faced lenticular bob; it rides on a rating nut and is suspended by a flat spring fixed to an iron stud bolted to the frame structure. The escapement is as described above. Power from the time great wheel drives the escape wheel via a pinion on the second wheel arbor. Downstream the time train branches: first, to drive a wheel with two pins that trips the strike and a 120-minute setting dial (both making one revolution in two hours); and second, to drive the 12-hour rotation of the strike control snail and a bevel gear dial take-off. High in the tower, a bevel gear transmission turns the single hour hand of three outside dials. The most notable difference of the **Branford clock** is its more sophisticated roller pallet escapement, described above. In addition, its chair-frame is slightly larger, measuring 33¹/₂" wide, 37³/₄" deep by 32¹/₂" high overall, and is constructed of smaller dimension cherry wood beams with pinned dovetail corners. The pendulum is rated at its suspension end by a large brass hand knob. Train wheels are mounted between unusual *horizontal* iron bars. The Branford time train is similar to Madison's but adds a 34-tooth minute wheel (making one revolution per hour) that trips the strike and drives bevel gear dial take-off. The transmission high overhead transmits power to the motion work of three two-hand outside dials. The clock is now in the collection of the American Clock & Watch Museum, Bristol, Connecticut.

Above, SJ Figure 1. *Front overview of the Madison clock, installed just under the church roof line. Note smooth box-corner construction and the use of vertical iron bars to support the wheel trains. Clock weights are single boulders on 200 feet of rope, directed by pulley to fall inside Greek revival pillars of the church's front portico.* **Below**, SJ Figure 2. *Madison roller pallet escapement detail. The escape wheel is just one wheel and two pinions away from the great wheel driving force. Note the square rod pallet arbor, and also the wear pattern on the upper end of the radial deadbeat escapement teeth.*

Above, SJ Figure 3. Branford clock back overview. Note integrated chair frame construction with small dimension cherry beams and forged strap iron supports. The tall frame extension provides for suspension and fine rating of the pendulum. The pendulum bob and dial hands are not original. *Below*, SJ Figure 4. Branford clockwork detail, strike left, time right. The top bevel gear of the dial take-off, center foreground, also serves as a 60-minute setting dial turning against a fixed pointer. Note the forged-iron frame supports and the very unusual horizontal iron bars that support the train wheels.

SJ Figure 5. Jocelin's Branford escapement detail, top view. The roller pallet anchor, mounted on a vertical arbor, engages the slant-tooth escape wheel at right angles across its diameter. The resulting rocking motion is conveyed to the pendulum by a square straight crutch that extends at a right angle from the anchor's vertical arbor.

1799 • ABEL STOWELL

Abel Stowell was born on June 12, 1752, the first of nine children of the second marriage of Cornelius Stowell, a prosperous clothier, and Zurvillah Goulding. Unlike the Willard brothers of nearby Grafton who moved on to richer pastures near Boston, Abel Stowell was born, lived, died and was buried in Worcester, Massachusetts, the largest town in the heartland of the commonwealth, 40 miles west of Boston. Nothing is known about his early life. In 1781 at the age of 29, Abel Stowell married Relief Jennison. Her sister married Abel's younger brother, setting a pattern for two Stowell daughters who married brothers named Ridgway, one of whom installed a Stowell type tower clock in 1809 at Groton, Massachusetts. In all, Stowell and his wife had seven children, including two sons, Abel Jr. and John, trained by their father as clockmakers. He served as town constable for two terms, was town weigh master, was reimbursed for the care of the poor, and in 1787 helped establish a cotton manufactory on the Mill River. After 1800, he received patents for a wooden screw and a "Gauge Auger" that cut large diameter holes. In 1816, Abel took on Abel Jr. as a partner in A. Stowell & Son. They dealt in sheet and cast-iron stoves, tower clocks, and other machines of brass and iron, particularly those for the printing and wool-carding industries key to Worcester's economy.

Abel Stowell's first notice as a clock and watch maker did not appear in Worcester's *Massachusetts Spy* until 1783 when he was 31 years old. He may have learned the trade from his older half-brother as a surviving tall case clock signed "Stephen Stowel [sic.] Worcester 1773" has the same simple lines and lack of ornamentation as Abel's tall case clocks advertised as late as 1802. Several examples have survived, including one with a removable eight-inch base extension to accommodate either high or low ceiling rooms. Abel also made large, elegant gallery clocks and offered warranted gilt and silver watches at his shop on the corner of Park and Salem streets facing the Town Green. He was best remembered in the late 1800s, however, as "the noted clockmaker of the last century, maker of the clock in the Old South Church, the old Worcester bank clock, and others."

Early surviving American tower clocks were derivative of the forged-iron cage frames long used in England and on the Continent. In the 1740s, French clockmakers Lepaute and LeRoy introduced a new plan called *horloge horizontale*. It employed a variation of Amant's deadbeat pinwheel escapement and mounted the clockwork on a horizontal flatbed frame that facilitated setup and maintenance. Remarkably, Abel Stowell, a backwater American, beat England's best tower clockmakers to first use of the plan by over 30 years and official endorsement by 50 years! Other American makers flirted with the idea of tower clocks made on a "new plan," otherwise unspecified, but Stowell's town clock installed in the Old South Church steeple in 1800 was this country's earliest known example of a wood-frame horizontal flatbed with a deadbeat pinwheel escapement. Stowell not only abandoned the generally accepted iron cage frame, he broke another precedent by completing construction of the clock *before* clinching its sale, as revealed in a 1799 *Massachusetts Spy* advertisement:

> ABEL STOWELL, Clock and Watch maker, near the South Meeting House in WORCESTER, Has for Sale a Large EIGHT DAY TOWN CLOCK, which he will warrant to keep good time; it is constructed so as to admit of three outside Dials and one small one within; it is on the newest construction, on the horizontal plan, which is the most approved method....

A Revere and Son bell weighing 1787 pounds was added in 1802. In 1887, the clock was moved to a cupola on the roof of the adjacent city hall, then moved again about 10 years later to the tower of a Worcester factory on Coes Square, where it was destroyed by fire in January 1942.

In June of 1802, Stowell advertised a second steeple clock of the same construction, "warranted to be equal to any imported." All interested parties were invited to examine the Old South Church installation as reference. In 1807, he installed another steeple clock of the same type that has survived in near original condition at Hubbardston, Massachusetts. Undoubtedly he made others, as steeple clocks were offered by A. Stowell & Son as late as 1816, and the inventory of his estate in 1818 included, "1 steple [sic] clock frame." Stowell's flatbed had an immediate impact on the work of other makers, as demonstrated by surviving clocks of Simon Willard in 1802, Gardner Parker in 1806, James Ridgway in 1809, George Holbrook in 1810, and Thomas Woolson Jr. in 1815. A second generation of American makers using variations on Stowell's plan included Stephen Hasham, Benjamin Morrill, and G.H. Holbrook. The cast-iron flatbeds of Ephraim Byram, Edward Howard, Abel Stowell Jr., and A.S. Hotchkiss followed, all leading the way to the cast-iron "factory clock" flatbeds that dominated well into the twentieth century.

Abel Stowell died intestate at the age of 66 on August 3, 1818. His modest estate included many old books and an inventory of clockmaking tools, patterns, and spare wheels, plus blacksmith and foundry gear.

The headstones of hundreds of former Worcester residents lie buried flat under the sod of the Town Green. Among a token few remaining upright is one testifying to the passing of "MR. ABEL STOWELL," a reminder of his clock that regulated the city's social, civic and business life for 100 years.

Abel Stowell Tower Clocks

AS Model 1. The clock frame consists of a forged strap-iron flatbed screwed to a sturdy wood-beam table mounted on a 12½" high wood platform, with woodwork painted light blue. Overall it measures 61" wide by 21" deep by 24" high. Wood barrels with brass end-plates extend at opposite ends across the full depth of the flatbed. A bridge of iron bars, bolted together and anchored at mid-frame, extends above the flatbed, a forerunner of the A-frame. It provides for suspension of the pendulum and pivot holes for the escapement arbors and long forged-iron strike control levers that extend from the strike trip and snail on the time side to a conventional rack, rack hook, and gathering pallet on the strike side. Stowell's replaceable deadbeat pallet escapement with pins on one side of the wheel differs from French prototypes which have fixed pallets impulsed by pins on both sides of the wheel. Time and strike trains are mounted inline and end-to-end, rather than side-by-side in the European manner. Wheels are brass with six spokes and teeth with a rounded addendum. Forged-iron shafts, tapering down from a thick middle, have leaf pinions, and pivot in fancy brass bearing blocks screwed to the strap-iron flatbed. Dial hands are reset by stopping the pendulum or by free-wheeling the time train, while referring to a two-hand setting dial driven by motion work at the front end of the time second wheel arbor. The back end of the same arbor drives a contrate wheel transmission with leading-off rods to three outside dials on the same level as the mechanism. Head ports with removable covers give access to the outside dial hands. Maintaining power and winding jacks are not provided. A heavy ratchet-driven fly is protectively mounted beneath the flatbed. A conventional wooden rod pendulum, measuring 68" overall, extends through a slot in the floor, and is rated by a knurled brass nut under its 10" diameter lenticular bob. In general, the excellent finish of all parts, plus the symmetrical open layout of Stowell's functional design pleases the eye and simplifies maintenance and repair. It does occupy considerable floor space, not always available in church towers built later in the century.

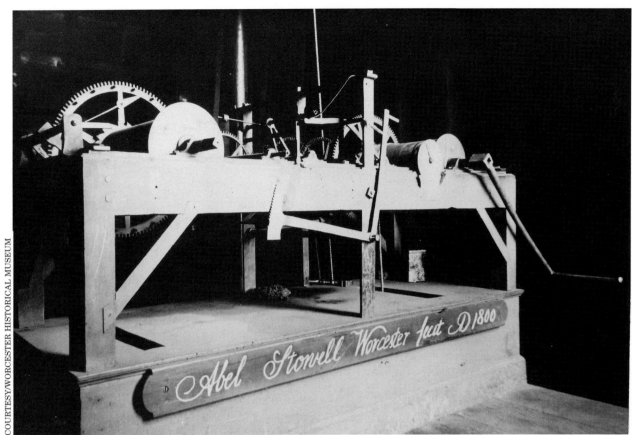

Above, *AS Figure 1. AS Model 1 overview. Stowell's landmark 1800 Worcester Town Clock, lost in a 1942 fire. Note the very long forged crank as a winding aid due to lack of reduction gearing.* ***Below***, *AS Figure 2. Stowell's 1807 installation at Hubbardston, Massachusetts. Strike is to the left, time to the right. The pendulum is suspended from behind the mid-frame bridge, which also supports the deadbeat pinwheel escapement and the long strike control levers. The winding jack wheel at far right is a later addition.*

Above left, AS Figure 3. Escapement detail. The steel deadbeat pallets of Stowell's escapement engage the 6'' diameter, 24-pin escape wheel at a tangential angle. Contrary to French prototypes, Stowell's pins extend from only one side of the wheel, the closed-caliper brass arms are joined at the end for rigidity, and worn steel pallets are easily replaced.

Above right, AS Figure 4. Time train second wheel detail. A pin on the wheel's arbor triggers warning and strike by contact with the crook-shaped lever which extends over to the strike train. The arbor also drives the motion work of a two-hand setting dial, advances the snail, and on its opposite end drives the contrate wheel take-off. Note the strike rack tail set to drop on the next snail step.

Right, AS Figure 5. Transmission detail. A wheel on the back end of the time second wheel arbor drives the contrate wheel transmission. Leading-off rods connected to contrate wheel followers radiate out to drive the motion work of three outside dials located on the same level as the mechanism.

AS Figure 6. Motion work detail. Large wheel, single pinion motion works were commonly used by most clockmakers until about 1830. To the right a dial port provides access to the outside dial and its hands.

AS Figure 7. Setting dial detail. The dial is a planished brass plate with an engraved chapter ring. The hands (hour hand missing) duplicate outside dial hand position, serving as a monitor while resetting the hands by freewheeling.

1802 • SIMON WILLARD

Simon Willard was born on April 3, 1753, at his father's farm in Grafton, Massachusetts, about 35 miles west of Boston. The eighth son of 12 children of Benjamin (Sr.) and Sarah (Brooks) Willard, he became the most famous of all the Willard clockmakers. Upon completion of his apprenticeship or shortly thereafter, he went in business for himself in the family workshop where he made tall case clocks similar to those of his 10-year-older brother Benjamin and some Massachusetts shelf clocks. While still at Grafton he invented a small 30-hour brass dial wall clock, the forerunner of the banjo timepiece, and also made improvements on the English clockwork roasting jack. In 1776, Simon married his cousin Hannah Willard, who died the following year. Years later at age 34 he married again to a Dorchester widow, Mrs. Mary (Bird) Leeds, who was the mother of his three talented sons, Simon Jr., John Mears, and Benjamin Franklin.

Between 1777 and 1780 Simon Willard established himself in Roxbury at what is now 2196 Washington Street in greater Boston. His workshop was connected to a house where it is said he lived until his retirement in 1839. His trade sign was a large double-dial public clock, hung on a neighbor's house as his own was too small to support it. A February 1784 notice in Thomas's *Massachusetts Spy* indicated that his shop was "on Roxbury-Street nearly opposite the road that turns off to Plymouth, where he carries on...Clock Making in all its branches." This included a full range of weight and spring-driven clocks running up to a year on one winding. He also offered "Willard's new constructed Astronomical Time Keeper," watch work of all sorts, perambulators (odometers), and a patented roasting-jack complete with kitchen dripping pan and skewers. Simon patented the Improved Wall Timepiece, nick-named the banjo. An instant success, popular for its fine appearance, compact size, and good time keeping, the banjo was widely copied by other makers for years, an invasion not seriously contested by its inventor. In 1819 he patented and made in limited numbers the "Lighthouse Alarm Clock."

As with other New England craftsmen, the influx of cheap Connecticut clocks cut into Simon's market. He met the competition by shifting to tailored variations on the patented timepiece, fancy gallery clocks, and church steeple clocks. He installed his first documented tower clock in 1785 at Newburyport, Massachusetts. It has not survived, but the sale was followed by a series of advertisements starting in 1789 promoting his manufacture of "large Clocks For Churches...Warranted as Cheap and as well executed as in any part of Europe." This bid for church clock commissions was repeated in 1792, and again in 1784 when he offered

steeple clocks so large the hands would never freeze up due to cold weather. In 1798, he advertised large steeple clocks featuring one, two, three, or four dials, with costs ranging from $500 for one-dial clocks to $900 for those with four dials. One assumes these solicitations attracted business, but no Simon Willard church clocks have survived from this early period. In 1802, he installed his earliest known surviving tower clock in the steeple of the North Church Meeting House at Portland, Maine. Ten other Simon Willard tower clocks are documented, but only three have survived, all restored to running condition. Missing clocks include the aforementioned installation in Newburyport (1785) plus those at Old Boyleston Market, Boston's Park Street Church, Roxbury's First Church (1806, $858), New York City's St. George's Church (1820, $900), Dedham's First Meeting House (1820), and Virginia's Jefferson College (1826). Clocks restored to running condition include an 1831 one-dial timepiece for Boston's Old State House, a large 1832 striker for the First Parish Unitarian Church in Cambridge, and an 1833 one-dial timepiece for Boston's Commercial Wharf Building. All three were made when Simon was past his 77th year and had abandoned the wooden flatbed in favor of the traditional English cage frame modified to trapezoidal form.

Simon Willard retired in 1839. A brilliant inventor who demanded uncompromising quality, he lacked the business acumen of his younger brother Aaron, retiring from a long and illustrious career a relatively poor man. In the last years, he lived with a succession of his children, tinkering at the vocation he loved in the workshops of a clockmaking son and a favorite apprentice. He died in Boston at the home of a daughter on August 30, 1848, at the age of 98.

Simon Willard Tower Clocks

SW Model 1. Willard's 1802 Portland clock is generally similar in design, size, materials and train layout to the wood beam, pinwheel escapement flatbed introduced in 1799 by Abel Stowell of Worcester, Massachusetts (see **AS Model 1**, page 36.) There are differences. Simon's flatbed frame is 6" higher, has a 1½-second beat pendulum and uses straight steel arbors (not tapered). Its deadbeat escapement has *open caliper* brass arms with replaceable steel pallets spanning the full diameter of the pinwheel. The hands are reset by freewheeling, but there is no setting dial integral to the movement. It originally had one westerly outside dial driven by direct connection to the time second wheel arbor. Later, two dials were added, one to the east driven by an idle gear on the second wheel, and another to the south driven by a contrate wheel and pinion on the third wheel arbor—a most unusual arrangement. The three outside dials of most flatbeds of this type and period utilize a simple 3-follower contrate wheel transmission driven by the second wheel arbor. The Portland clock, beautifully restored in 1996 with electric rewind and maintaining power enhancement, keeps excellent time.

SW Model 2. This large striking church clock made in Simon's 80th year, with its cluttered double cage trapezoidal frame, inappropriate finial, mix of leaf and lantern pinions, and wheel spokes of assorted shape and number, appears to have been put together by a committee. The frame measures 42" wide at its base, by 16" deep, by 48" high overall. While lacking the open design of SW Model 1, the clock does occupy less floor space and adds a number of enhancements. They include grooved winding barrels, a winding jack on the strike side, English bolt-and-shutter maintaining power, pallet depthing adjustment, a setting dial and a six-lobe cam on the strike second wheel to lift the bell strike lever. As with SW Model 1, this clock employs rack-and-snail strike control, and a pinwheel escapement with replaceable steel pallets in open caliper arms. However, with SW Model 2, vertical inline wheel

trains are mounted side-by-side in removable Vuillamy bushings screwed to iron bar risers of the inner cage. A small two-blade ratchet-driven fly is protectively mounted inside the frame. The 1¼-second pendulum, with a wooden rod and 100-pound cannonball bob, is fine-adjusted at its suspension end.

SW Model 3. This single-dial timepiece, installed at Boston's Commercial Wharf Building in 1833, is a trapezoidal iron bar cage frame of pleasing symmetry. The single ball finial seems appropriate here. The iron frame measures 27¾" at the base, 15" deep, by 48" high overall. A vertically-aligned wheel train is mounted in Vuillamy bushings on the frame's center riser. The great wheel measures 16" in diameter, and drives a lantern pinion consisting of leaf-shaped steel trundles let into slotted shrouds (invented by Englishman Henry Hindley, ca. 1750, and also used by Isaiah Lukens after 1828). The escapement is similar to earlier models except it employs an escape wheel with undercut teeth. Its 1½-second 35-pound cannonball bob pendulum is fine rated at its suspension end.

SW Figure 1. SW 1802 Model 1 front overview, strike left, time right. The far end of the time second wheel arbor drives a westerly dial; its near end turns the snail one revolution in 12 hours. The time second wheel also turns an idle wheel, its leading-off rod extending toward the viewer under the front flatbed beam to an easterly dial.

SW Figure 2. Model 1 pinwheel escapement and transmission detail. A contrate wheel turned by a pinion on the time third wheel arbor drives the southerly dial leading-off rod at upper right, an unusual arrangement. Note elegant brass bearing blocks with individually tailored square-head screws, suitable for wrench or screw-driver.

SW Figure 3. Rear view of the SW Model 2 trapezoidal cage frame. The slanted outer bars support inner cage frame vertical risers with Vuillamy bushings for the wheel trains mounted inline. An open caliper anchor with replaceable deadbeat pallets works outside the escape wheel pins.

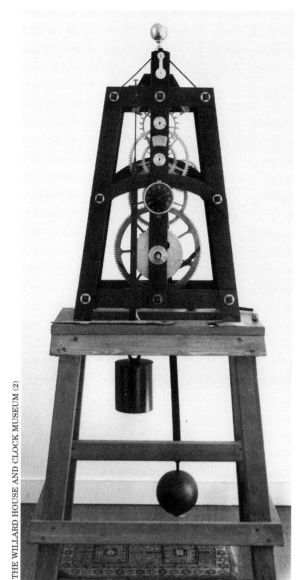

Left, *SW Figure 4. Front view of SW Model 3. The ball finial seems appropriate in this well-resolved trapezoidal frame of pleasing symmetry. The keyhole-shaped flap below the finial swings aside, allowing disengagement of the escapement to reset the hands by freewheeling. Note two-hand setting dial.* **Right**, *SW Figure 5. SW Model 3 lantern pinion detail. Leaf-shaped steel trundles are inserted and secured in slotted brass shrouds. The fancy corner great wheel spoking is most often found in clocks of the New York City School of tower clockmakers (See* **1851 •Reeve & Co.***, page 140.)*

1806 • GARDNER PARKER

Gardner Parker was born on March 14, 1772, in Hubbardston, Massachusetts, the second son of Isaac and Margery (Maynard) Parker. When Gardner was five years old, the family moved to Westborough, just east of Worcester, Massachusetts. His father built a large house on Maynard Street, and after a few years acquired the grist and saw mill on the Assabet River that gave Mill Street its name. Gardner and his brother worked at the mill with their father, and it was here where young Gardner first displayed his skill with tools, taking great pleasure in making any sort of repair. It was said that like Eli Whitney, also born in Westborough, he could take a watch apart and set it running when he put it back together again. Certainly he was more comfortable working in the mill than at the No. 7 schoolhouse that stood between his home and the river. His school teacher boarded at the Parker house, and after conferring with his father it was decided that the 14-year-old Gardner Parker would do better as an apprentice to the well-known Willard clockmakers of nearby Grafton. Training complete by 1790, he returned to Westborough where he set up a small shop at the corner of Main and Blake Streets.

Gardner Parker built country versions of the more sophisticated Roxbury tall case clocks using some parts imported from England. It is estimated he completed about a dozen a year, working for hire and often for barter. The last known serial number was No. 200, made about 1802. Like many small town clockmakers, he supplemented his income with other tasks, including gunsmithing, building wooden cabinets, and the repair of miscellaneous metal goods. In 1809 he built and installed a pipe organ in the Westborough Meeting House. He also made at least three large town clocks almost identical in design to the horizontal flatbeds made by Abel Stowell, the old clockmaker of neighboring Worcester, Massachusetts. Parker's first town clock, made for the Westborough Meeting House, was moved to the town hall in 1939. This clock has survived and has been restored to working condition in the collection of the Smithsonian Institution at Washington, D.C. Its elaborate sign board reads, "Made & Warranted by Gardner Parker 1801," but town historians claim it was first installed in 1806. Later, Parker made a second town clock put up in the Shrewsbury Meeting House. In 1808 he was paid $796.80 for a clock with three dials, said to have been installed the same year in the First Parish of West Cambridge, now Arlington, Massachusetts.

As early as 1805, Parker considered driving his clockmaking machinery by water power, a vision inspired by his work as a youth in the family grist mill. Consequently, he acquired land in Westborough at the end of Health Street which included a small tributary of the Assabet River that he planned to dam up as a mill pond for a proposed factory. Local experts cautioned him that the water supply was inadequate, but he persisted with the project which took about 10 years to complete. During the same period he greatly increased his inventory of clockmaking machines, foundry equipment, blacksmith gear, and hundreds of hand tools. In the same expansive spirit, he invested in shares of the Hopkinton and the Northborough Manufacturing Companies. He and his wife, Asenath (Sherman) Parker, moved to Northborough, where he speculated on three parcels of land on the Old Boston Post Road. His two-story clock factory was finally completed in 1815, and with high expectations he opened the mill race sluice gate to set the machines running. The water wheel stood dead in the running water. True to early warnings, the water fell short of what was needed to turn such a heavy wheel. The local population seemed to take a certain pleasure in his failure. They called the site Parker's Folly, and later renamed the road leading to the place Folly Lane. It was no joke to the bankrupt clockmaker. On the night of February 16, 1816, he ended his misery with a pistol shot to the head.

Gardner Parker Tower Clock

Of the several town clocks attributed to Gardner Parker, only the one from Westborough is signed by the maker. His town clocks are virtually identical to those made earlier by Abel Stowell who was 20 years senior to Parker. There is no known connection between the two men other than they lived in the same county, a short buggy ride apart. It seems likely that Parker inspected Stowell's well-advertised 1800 flatbed town clock in Worcester's Old South Church and was guided accordingly, along with many other tower clockmakers in the 30 years that followed.

As with Stowell's clocks, Parker's town clock frame is a horizontal flatbed painted light blue, consisting of a wood beam table, mortise-and-tenon joined, and mounted on a floor platform with edge molding. Parker's table dimensions are comparable, measuring about 61" wide by 21" deep by 15 high, but the floor platform is slightly higher, making an overall height of 28". The floor molding also differs from that used by Stowell. Parker's pendulum is about the same, having an iron rod measuring 74" long and a 12" diameter brass-faced lead bob. Most clock features of the two makers are similar if not identical, including the following: contrate wheel transmission; pinwheel deadbeat escapement with replaceable pallets in closed-caliper arms; freewheeling hand set; rack-and-snail strike control; end-to-end train layout of six-spoke brass wheels; and pendulum suspension from a mid-frame iron bridge. Both Stowell and Parker used kidney-shaped setting dials, identically configured strike levers, and wooden barrels. An unusual feature of the Westborough clock is what appears to be a recoil escape wheel with no mechanical connections fixed to the third wheel arbor of the time train, a Parker innovation or a feature added by some later custodian. Robert Edwards of the Smithsonian suggests that when rigged with a weighted saddle the wheel would have provided about 2.5 minutes power during winding of the time train. Stowell made no provision for either maintaining power or winding jacks.

Above*, GP Figure 1. Back view of Parker's Westborough town clock, time to the left strike to the right. Tooth form and spoking of the wheels and inline end-to-end train layout is identical to Stowell. Note the pendulum and crutch outside the iron bridge at mid-frame. The bridge also supports a Stowell-type pinwheel escapement, providing for setting the hands by freewheeling.* ***Below****, GP Figure 2. Top back view of the time train. Fancy shaped brass bearing blocks screwed to the strap-iron flatbed are typical of Stowell and his followers. The second wheel arbor drives a three-dial contrate wheel transmission at the bottom, and at the top trips the strike, drives the setting dial motion work, and advances the snail. Note at upper end of the third wheel arbor an escape wheel that serves no obvious purpose. (See GP Figure 3.)*

GP Figure 3. Top front view of the Parker strike train. The four-wheel strike train ends with a heavy iron fly safe-ly mounted inside the table frame. At bottom center is the rack and its gathering pallet. The maker's signature board spans the width of the frame in cursive script, "Made and Warranted by Gardner Parker 1801."

1809 • JAMES RIDGWAY

James Ridgway was born to a fifth generation Boston family of English ancestry in 1768. His early training is unknown, but at the age of 21, probably having completed an apprenticeship, his name appeared in Boston directories as a jeweler and gold-smith on Friend Street. He relocated often during his career, the first time to Worcester, Massachusetts, from 1793 to 1804, where he plied his trade in a shop nearly opposite the courthouse. Several events here touched directly on Ridgway's life. In 1800, Abel Stow-ell installed a town clock in the steeple of Worcester's Old South Meeting House. It was made on a new flatbed plan that significantly influenced the work of later tower clockmakers, such as Ridgway, who may have worked with Abel as he married his oldest daugh-

ter, Faithey Stowell, on January 12, 1802. Five months later they presented him with a granddaughter. The family connection was extended a few years later by the marriage of Ridgway's younger brother, John (also a silversmith), to another Stowell daughter, an alliance similar to that made by Abel Stowell and his younger brother who also married sisters. About 1817, the Ridgways moved on to Groton, Massachusetts, where he was described as a silversmith and clockmaker who carried on a large business during the War of 1812. His shop was located on Main Street nearly opposite the Groton Inn. His home, also on Main Street, consisted of half a two-family house a stone's throw away from the First Parish Meeting House where Ridgway installed a Stowell-type flatbed town clock in the spring of 1809. The town voted a sum not to exceed $70 for the town clock, and the church donated $30 to prepare a suitable room in the steeple. The price seems low considering the quality of Ridgway's clock compared to wood wheel tower clocks of the period which went for about $65. Ridgway was similarly frugal, as in 1815 he offered a 2¢ reward for the return of a runaway apprentice. While still in Groton they lost two namesake sons who died as infants. Both headstones read, "James, Son of Mr. James Ridgway and Mrs. Faithey Ridgway," an early manifestation of female liberation, as Faithy was a successful vendor of stylish hats, caps and custom millinery.

In 1817, the family removed to Keene, New Hampshire, and in October of the same year the *New Hampshire Sentinel* announced the opening of a new store called Ridgway & Rockwood located four doors south of Summer's Tavern. They offered gold and silver watches, watch repair, English and West Indies yard goods, apparel, glass and crockery, plus Faithey Ridgway's line of millinery and fancy goods. It was a short-lived partnership, the business taken over in late 1819 by Samuel Gerould, but both James and Faithey Ridgway continued in their respective trades at the same location. Keene's old town clock became very irregular during their time in town, but Ridgway is not known to have involved himself in its repair. It was replaced by a new clock at a different location after the Ridgways had moved on. They first relocated to Amherst, New Hampshire, in about 1823, then moved again in about 1834 to Nashua, New Hampshire. Ridgway and his son, Charles T., worked at both places as jewelers and makers of silver bowed spectacles. In Nashua, they occupied a store in the Nutt Block, and Ridgway converted property on Park Street into tenements where he lived until his death on September 11, 1850.

James Ridgway's Tower Clock

The 1809 Groton clock movement, located 72 steps high in the First Parish Meeting House tower, was obviously inspired by the pioneering work of Abel Stowell. Originally a town clock, it is currently owned and maintained by the First Parish Church. Over the years it has been the subject of a number of improvised additions and repairs, but runs today hand-wound with good accuracy, striking on an 1128-pound Revere & Son bell mounted in its original wooden yoke. A heavy forged iron bar flatbed and mid-frame bridge are held together by bolts and nuts, mounted on a wood beam table and floor platform painted pale blue. Overall, the frame measures 63" wide by 24" deep by 30" high, slightly larger than Stowell's clock. Both time and strike barrels are wound by the same nicely forged iron crank. The design and layout of the wheel trains, pendulum, deadbeat pinwheel escapement, and rack-and snail strike control components are similar to Stowell's. Differences include a 23-pin escape wheel, a distinctive pallet arm, a pendulum beat of something less than 1¼ seconds, and an unusual undercut strike-control snail. All wheels have four spokes rather than the customary six. Forged iron arbors, bulbous at the middle and tapered down to both ends, and the leaf pinions are similar to Stowell's, but decoratively shaped bearing blocks vary slightly in design. At some point, the clock train suffered a major failure; obvious repairs include strap-iron reinforcement of the wood beam frame corners, and replacement of two wheels and the fly of the strike train. The clock weights are slabs of soapstone, quarried locally and fitted with wheels to ride freely in angled wooden chutes that extend to the building basement. Dial hands are reset by stopping the pendulum or by freewheeling. The original two-hand setting dial, which would have covered the snail, has been replaced by a leading-off rod pointer that turns against a numbered 60-minute circle inscribed on the clock room wall. Bevel gears on the same leading-off rod are designed to drive the motion work of a slave gallery clock located in the assembly room below. This later addition is the work of Elijah Whiton (1779–1871), a skilled inventor and designer of engineering instruments, who also lived in Groton on the south side of Main Street, near its junction with Station Avenue.

Above, *JR Figure 1. Groton clock front overview, strike left, time right. The configuration of the frame, bridge, and clockwork is similar to Stowell. Obvious differences include the use of four rather than six-spoke wheels and the undercut snail profile. Note the poorly matched spoking of the two replaced strike wheels and the user-friendly location of the improvised setting dial on the back wall.* ***Below***, *JR Figure 2. Groton deadbeat pinwheel escapement detail. A hinged flap retainer over the near end of the pallot arbor allows escapement disengagement for free-wheeling. The steel deadbeat pallets, held by screws, are easily replaced. The shaped cutout of the pallet arm is unusual, but the tapered arbors are typical.*

Above, JR Figure 3. Groton dial take-off detail. As with Stowell, the contrate wheel transmission is driven by the extended arbor of the time train second wheel; power is distributed via leading-off rods to the motion work of three outside dials on the same level as the movement. At right, bevel gears drive a remote gallery clock mounted in the assembly room below. *Below*, JR Figure 4. Dial motion work detail. The large wheel, single pinion reduction gearing is typical of the Stowell era, but its spiral spoking may indicate a later replacement.

1810 • GEORGE HOLBROOK

George Holbrook was born on his father's farm in Wrentham, Massachusetts, on April 28, 1767, the son of Daniel and Esther (Hall) Holbrook. He had little formal schooling. He ventured as a teenager to Boston's North End as an apprentice to Paul Revere, from whom he claimed to have acquired his foundry, machinist and clockmaking skills. By 1795 he was on his own, established as a clock and watchmaker in Brookfield, Massachusetts, a small town a few miles west of Worcester. Before the American Revolution Brookfield was a Commonwealth foundry center, which may have drawn Holbrook to the places along with the charms of Miss Polly Wood, whom he married there on November 30, 1797. Their union marked the start of four generations of a very enterprising and musical family referred to as the Holbrook Dynasty.

Major George Holbrook got his title from service in the state militia. He was of striking physical appearance, described as strong as an ox, and large and rugged enough to be known as Hercules. Incongruously, he was also a skilled musician with a fine ear for pure tone. Notices in the *Brookfield Advertiser* starting in 1795, show him to have published the "Columbian Songster," and to be the maker of "Elegant Toned Base Viols, equal to any imported." His shop was located near the meeting house in Brookfield's south parish, and its main business was clock and watchmaking in its various branches. Advertisements during this early period did not offer Holbrook tower clocks or large church bells, but after 1800 he is known to have made both. In 1803, he put up a steeple clock and bell in the meeting house at Leicester, Massachusetts, and the following year sold a bell for $236 and a tower clock for about $100 to the Congregational Parish of Chester, New Hampshire. Both clocks performed poorly and had short lives. It would appear that Holbrook made design improvements, probably based on his observation of the tower clocks of Abel Stowell in neighboring Worcester, because his clock and bell installed in 1810 at the Scantic Meeting House in East Windsor, Connecticut, continues to run hand-wound time and strike to this day.

Major Holbrook prospered in Brookfield, building a comfortable home for his growing family and earning respect in town as a good citizen and man of property. His world collapsed in 1812. He co-signed loan agreements as a favor to a purported friend who reneged on payment when the notes came due, resulting in foreclosure on all of Holbrook's assets, including his home, land, and foundry. Depressed by this turn of events, the Major fell into ill health and the family retreated to New Hampshire to try their luck at farming. Failing at this and nearly penniless, Holbrook sought help from

relatives in Wrentham, Massachusetts. Word reached him of the need for a large bell in a newly built church in East Medway (renamed Millis in 1885), a small factory town 20 miles southwest of Boston. Major Holbrook offered his services as an experienced bell founder, and got the contract in 1815. A shoestring operation from the start, the work was done on borrowed land, in a shanty made of scrap wood, using condemned brick from a neighborhood kiln for a melting furnace. On the day of the pour, people came from miles around to watch the spectacle. Miraculously, considering the conditions, the East Medway bell was a perfect casting weighing over 1,200 pounds. First rung in the meeting house on May 15, 1816, it heralded salvation for the Holbrook family and the arrival of a great new industry for the town. Between 1816 and 1882, over 11,000 bells were cast by the East Medway foundry presided over by three generations of Holbrooks.

Major Holbrook retired in 1820 at age 53, turning over the family business to his son, 22-year-old George Handel Holbrook. It is not known how the Major spent his 25 years of retirement. He probably helped his son direct the course of the business, and may also have figured in the construction of "The Elms," a family homestead occupied by five generations of Holbrooks. He had the skill and experience to help set up the Holbrook Clock Shop which produced tall case, banjo and large tower clocks, the latter signed by the Major's son. A few details toward the end of his life are certain. In 1834, he lost his wife and also a favorite daughter, Mary Evalina, a lead singer in Boston's Handel & Haydn Society. In November of the same year he married a second time to Mrs. Roxana (Hills) McCray, a Connecticut widow. On September 29, 1846, the 79-year old Major George Holbrook died of complications due to palsy, in East Medway where he was buried.

George Holbrook Tower Clock

While at work in Brookfield, Major Holbrook was one of many early American tower clock makers influenced by the horizontal flatbed clock made in 1799 by Abel Stowell for Worcester's Old South Church. He had ample opportunity to examine "the new plan" which was open to public display a few miles east of the Major's shop in Brookfield. His surviving 1810 East Windsor clock is not only patterned on the early work of Stowell, in addition, escapement differences provide a direct link to the more sophisticated horizontal flatbeds produced after 1834 by the Major's son, George Handel Holbrook. As with Stowell, the Major's clock frame consists of a horizontal wood beam flatbed table mounted on a floor platform, measuring overall 60" wide by 21" deep by 31" high. Other similarities include: inline end-to-end trains of brass wheels with six spokes; wooden barrels spanning opposite ends of the frame; no maintaining power or winding jacks; and a sturdy strap-iron bridge at mid-frame supporting a pinwheel escapement, strike levers, and the pendulum; tapered steel arbors with cut-leaf pinions; fancy brass bushing blocks screwed to a strap-iron flatbed frame; rack-and-snail strike control; a three-dial contrate wheel transmission; plus a setting dial and freewheeling to adjust the dial hands. Holbrook's workmanship is sound but appears less highly finished than Stowell's. His 24-pin escapement pinwheel is also similar to Stowell's except for its pallets which consist of a one-piece, hardened *continuous arc of steel* with ground and polished deadbeat ends. The pallets engage the inside of pins located on opposite sides of the pinwheel rather than Stowell's tangential engagement of two pallets working on one side of the pinwheel. The one-piece pallet is replaceable, being screwed to the rounded bottom of a triangular brass anchor. The same unusual one-piece pallet arrangement was used in tower clocks made by George Handel Holbrook after 1834, by Aaron Willard Jr., in 1839, and by Benjamin Morrill, ca. 1854.

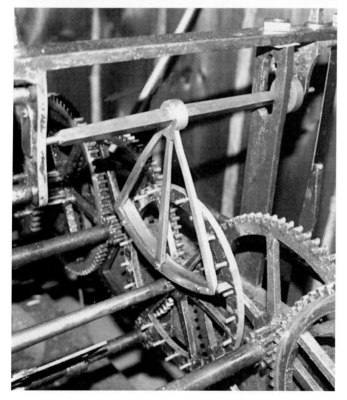

Above, *GH Figure 1. Overview of Major George Holbrook's 1810 tower clock. The style and layout are almost identical to the wood beam flatbeds introduced by Stowell in 1799. The signed, painted sheet metal setting dial in the foreground is original, its hands are crude replacements. Note the weight lines fall directly off the barrels.*

Left, *GH Figure 2. Holbrook pinwheel escapement detail. Deadbeat pallets ground on the ends of a continuous arc of steel are impulsed by pins on opposite sides of the escape wheel. Elongated pivots on the pallet arbor permit its disengagement from the pinwheel to set the dial hands ahead by freewheeling the time train.*

GH Figure 3. Holbrook pendulum detail. Pendulum length is adjusted at its lenticular bob end. Note the simple iron crutch and pendulum rod. The contrate wheel transmission, at center, is driven by the time second wheel arbor, and its leading-off rods drive three outside dials on the same level as the clock mechanism.

1811 • SAMUEL TERRY

Samuel Terry was born on January 24, 1774, in East Windsor, Connecticut, (redesignated South Windsor in 1845), a prosperous agricultural township on the eastern bank of the Connecticut River to the north of Hartford. The son of Samuel and Huldah (Burnham) Terry, he was first known as Samuel *Junior* to avoid confusion with his father, a tanner who taught him the trade and with whom he worked for a time. Unlike Eli Terry, his famous older brother who left early, Samuel Jr. lived and worked in his hometown until the age of 44. He married Esther Gillet of Canaan, Connecticut, and fathered their eight sons, all but one of whom became clockmakers.

Between 1797 and 1818, while still living in what was then called East Windsor, Samuel engaged mostly in leather work, from saddle and harness making to the repair of belts and shoes. In this connection, he also ran a small brass foundry. By 1808 his brisk trade in leather goods was interrupted occasionally by the sale or repair of clocks and watches. In 1811 he was discharged as a sergeant in the state militia, and the same year ventured into the manufacture of large wooden church clocks. At least three installations of this early model have been identified. On March 27, 1811, Samuel billed his hometown church for a tower clock costing $65 plus $2.25 for 13½ months of winding. Later the same year he put up a second clock in the First Church of Windsor, just across the Connecticut River. In 1813, he installed a third clock at Norfolk, Connecticut, the hometown of Samuel's South Windsor minister, Rev. Thomas Robbins, who paid the $65 cost and 20 years later arranged another sale in Massachusetts. Samuel's draft of a letter from about 1814 implies other installations as well:

> Sir Mr Barret informed me that you was in want of a steple Clock...I will make one and Carry it and set it up and furnish it with all necessary to make it go except dial and warrant it to perform to your satisfaction.. the clock will run one week at once winding and will be strong Enough to strike a heavy stroke the price will be $100, less than ¼ the expense of a mettle one and will perform quite as well and better in cold....

Meanwhile, Eli Terry's revolutionary techniques in the manufacture of low-cost wooden shelf clocks had created a demand that required added factory manpower. In September 1818, Samuel moved to Plymouth where he and the formidable work force represented by his older sons joined Eli's crew. By Samuel's accounting, Eli paid him a dollar a day and probably his sons considerably less, but everyone gained in the process. Samuel learned production and management techniques, his sons had a good clockmaking apprenticeship, and Eli was freed from the bench to expand his financial base. In 1823 he established what became the successful firm of Eli Terry & Sons. The following year he signed the three-year partnership contract of Eli & Samuel Terry, said to be in return for the six previous years of loyal and industrious service of Samuel and his sons. It did, in fact, establish their competence as independent clock manufacturers. Upon completion of the agreement, Samuel and his sons continued in business at Plymouth before relocating to Bristol in 1829. They sold from hundreds to a handful of movements and complete shelf clocks to many vendors in the Bristol area and elsewhere, earning Samuel the title, "The Clockmakers' Clockmaker."

The 1831 American Advertising Directory shows Samuel Terry of Bristol as a "Manufacturer of Patent 30 Hour Wood Clocks with various Patterns of fancy Cases, and Eight Day Church Steeple Clocks; also Brass Founder." His church clocks of this later period were of more compact design and superior finish. The earliest known examples of installations sold for $100 at Peekskill, New York, in 1829, and at Litchfield, Connecticut, in 1830. Other examples survive intact from 1832 installations at Bristol and Goshen, Connecticut, together with the dial motion work of an 1834 installation at Sag Harbor, New York. Complete clocks, original installation sites unknown, have survived at the Smithsonian, Ford, and Verdin museums. In addition, Samuel received church clock inquiries from Mattapoisett and Springfield, Massachusetts, from Lockport and Jamestown, New York, and from interested parties in Virginia, New York City and elsewhere. As far as is known, no multiple dial or brass church clocks were made, but in August 1835 he responded to one inquiry as follows:

> ...I have made wood church clocks for more than twenty years and find them to answer as well or better than brass and the price is one hundred dollars with those that move one pair pinters [hands] and for those that move three, it will be one hundred and thirty. I...have necessary preparations for making brass church clocks and would make one for you if you should wish...and the price will be three hundred dollars....

The letter went on to say that the Peekskill clock continued to perform well after five years, the Litchfield clock after six years and the Norfolk clock after 20 years. It concluded that he knew quite a number more, "not one that I have heard from but what gives full satisfaction."

Samuel retired in 1835, but continued to operate his Bristol saw mill until about 1840. Past the age of 70, he made his last tower clock in 1845, installing it himself in the Baptist Church at Waterbury, Connecticut, for $135 cash, plus board, keep, and transportation to and from his home. Samuel Terry died in Bristol at age 79 on May 4, 1853, almost two years after the death of his famous brother Eli at the same age.

Samuel Terry Tower Clocks

Samuel's tower clocks are unsigned but well-documented. Two distinct models have survived, **ST Model 1** dating from his East Windsor period, ca. 1810–1815, and **ST Model 2** dating from 1829 to 1845 after he had set up in Bristol. Layouts differ, but the wood beam flatbed frames of both models are approximately the same size, measuring about 48" wide by 24" deep by 20" high, both have wooden wheels, recoil escapements, and basically similar rack-and-snail strike control, consisting of both wood and metal parts. **ST Model 1** reflects influences of early American flatbeds in the Stowell tradition, including: wooden barrels at opposite ends of the flatbed, rack-and-snail strike control, decoratively cut bearing blocks, forged-iron arbors, a mid-flatbed A-frame, teeth milled with rounded addendum rather than the later pointed sawn teeth. The 15½" laminated great wheels of ST Model 1 are unusual, as is its 9-foot pendulum (theoretical length). Its recoil escapement anchor is located above the escape wheel rather than to one side, typical of the later model. The unprotected mounting of the fly, intermediate wheels, and strike control components outside the frame leaves them vulnerable to damage.

In general, **ST Model 2** is a more compact design of improved finish. Its arbors, pillars, and the sides of its cherry wood wheels are decorated with deeply turned concentric rings. The hardwood bushing blocks are streamlined. The steel recoil pallet anchor engages the brass escape wheel *from the side*, a distinctive feature of this model. The one-second pendulum is rated by a thumbscrew at its suspension end. Fly and strike control components are protectively mounted inside the flatbed frame. With all known Samuel Terry installations, a leading-off rod connected to the time train drives the wooden wheel motion work of a single outside dial on the same level as the movement.

Above, ST Figure 1. Model 1 overview. Distinctive features include rounded milled teeth, laminated great wheels, decorative hardwood bearing blocks, minimal decoration, iron arbors, and a fiddle back A-frame supporting portions of the time and strike train. A strike train wheel, the fly, and the pendulum are missing. Note the escapement anchor above the escape wheel. *Right*, ST Figure 2. Strike pinwheel detail. The wheel is laminated cross-grain for greater strength. Note the round milled tooth form and decorative bearing blocks. During strike a rope or wire from the hinged two-arm bell lever to the left raises the bell hammer, which falls by gravity to strike the bell.

Above, *ST Figure 3. Model 2 top view, time train left, strike train right. The compact design, almost totally contained within the frame and of superior finish, is an improvement over the earlier model. Note streamlined bearing blocks and the dimensional rings on the arbors, posts, and wheels.* ***Below left***, *ST Figure 4. Model 2 escapement detail. The recoil anchor engages the escape wheel from the side, a distinctive hallmark of Samuel Terry's later clocks. Extended above the pallet arbor is the pendulum cock, with provision for thumbscrew rating of the pendulum from its suspension end.* ***Below right***, *ST Figure 5. Model 2 strike control detail. The pointed, sawn tooth form and the decorative rings of the wheels are typical. Wood and metal strike components from left to right include: the pinwheel, strike trip lever, gathering pallet, rack hook, and the rack. The strike count is determined by the rack falling on a wooden snail on the back of the 78-tooth wheel seen at lower right.*

1812 • ISAIAH LUKENS

Isaiah Quimby Lukens, the second child of Seneca and Sarah (Quimby) Lukens was born April 24, 1779, on his father's farm near Horsham, Pennsylvania, 20 miles north of Philadelphia. As a boy Isaiah was trained by his father, a second generation tall clock maker with whom he worked until the age of 30. About 1811, he set up his own business in Philadelphia, a city entering a second renaissance of the mechanical arts and natural sciences in the tradition of Franklin and Rittenhouse. Lukens first lived and worked in a two-story stable behind a town house on Arch Street near 3rd, relocating after 1825 to the corner of High (now Market) and 9th Street.

Lukens produced tall case clocks, precision astronomical regulators, and at least one gold case pocket chronometer for his own use, but specialized in superior public clocks. Seven are known to have survived, with six others well-documented, suggesting 20 or more total installations. Surviving clocks include one in 1812 for Loller Academy at Hatboro, Pennsylvania, followed by clocks for Philadelphia's Head House Market (1819), Philadelphia's Second National Bank (1820), a 14-foot tall-case clock for Philadelphia Bank (date unknown), a town clock for Camden, South Carolina (1824) signed "LUKENS Nº 11 Philadᵃ", and a church clock for Norfolk, Virginia (1827). A series of tower clocks of improved design followed, starting with his State House (Independence Hall) installation in 1828, a crowning achievement that was replaced in 1876 and is now sadly abandoned to pigeons. His 1837 town clock for West Chester, Pennsylvania, was modified later by its custodian to toss out a ball at noon to children waiting below. Finally, Likens' 39-page probate file in 1847 lists two large and four small town clocks made for Washington D.C. and Louisville, Kentucky. One of these was later installed with five outside dials in the courthouse at York, Pennsylvania.

In 1825, Lukens left his shop in the hands of Joseph Saxton, and sailed for Europe to promote his improved French medical instrument called the "Lithontriptor." Snubbed by the Paris establishment, Lukens went to England where he worked a few years as a machinist/clockmaker on Adam Street, Adelphi, Middlesex. He also developed an improved method for hardening springs, highly endorsed by England's leading chronometer makers. He sold all rights to the process and departed from Liverpool on the ship *Montezuma*, arriving in Philadelphia on October 22, 1827. The following year he and Saxton completed a $2,000 tower clock for what is now Independence Hall. As clock custodian for years, he installed a transit in the tower to calculate standard uniform time for the city.

Lukens' varied interests and diverse connections led him in many directions. Typically, in the course of a year he would finish several small lathes and machine tool accessories. His five-shot .31-caliber air guns and canes were in great demand; one that shot 25 times without reloading went along with Lewis and Clark on their exploration of the far west. Lukens invented an odometer, developed a simple slide rest, and introduced the cast-iron wheel and flat belt that replaced grooved wooden wheels on treadle-driven machines. His mineral collection was spectacular. He also made scales, instruments of all kinds, barometers, spy glasses, pocket sextants, and cast commemorative medallions. He was one of Philadelphia's finest machinists and certainly the speediest. Late in life he lost an eye from a chip of steel while dressing a grindstone and thereafter shied away from fine work to save what sight remained. Rural origins were no barrier to his acceptance as an equal by Philadelphia's most elite organizations. He was the first vice president of the Franklin Institute, an honored astronomer with the American Philosophical Society, and curator of the Academy of Natural Sciences.

Lukens loved practical jokes. As a boy he shook up bee's nests with a long string to send strangers running down a country lane. In 1813 he caught Philadelphia's public eye by debunking Charles Redhoeffer's so-called perpetual motion machine. Twelve thousand handbills were circulated to advertise Lukens' replica, which appeared to work perpetually, albeit by a cleverly hidden spring. Even Redhoeffer was deceived and his fraud exposed. Lukens also had his dark side, riding off alone in his two-wheel gig before sun-up or by moonlight, and taking solitary summer excursions for six or eight weeks, with only a single change of clothes, a fishing rod and air-gun. Not even his best friends knew where he went and doubted he knew himself when starting out. Customarily, he ate at an ancient hostelry on Market Street and slept in a room off his shop (which he loved, calling it his wife). Naturally sociable, a speech impediment made him shy in the company of females. Late in life he developed an aneurysm of the aorta. When cautioned by the doctor that only a few days remained, Lukens took it calmly, continuing at the workbench where he died on November 12, 1846, it is said with tool in hand.

Isaiah Lukens Tower Clocks

Lukens public clock movements vary in size from oversized gallery or tall clock movements to seriously large machines driving five large dials or striking two ton bells. In general, they are all variations of the English cage frame. The earliest surviving clock (1812) is a chair frame of vertical and horizontal flat iron bars bolted together. It measures 37" wide by 24" deep by 34" high overall. Some years later, its original crutch-driven pendulum was retrofitted by Lukens to knife-edge suspension, the escape wheel working directly on deadbeat pallets attached to the upper end of the pendulum rod. Other clocks in the early period have box-type cage frames with conventional pendulum suspension and deadbeat anchor escapements. Clock frames after 1827 retain the flat iron bar risers and horizontal cross pieces, but end sections consist of two-inch diameter iron pipes, joined by sockets, and topped with ball finials. These frames measure about 52" wide by 35" deep by 54" high (plus an overhead transmission). Clocks of this later period feature Lukens' distinctive two-second pendulum suspended inside the frame on adjustable knife-edge suspension. Polished jewel deadbeat pallets mounted on a brass ring at the upper end of the pendulum rod are acted upon directly by the escape wheel, eliminating the need for a crutch. The pendulum is rated by a threaded hand bolt between the upper ring fixture and lower pendulum rod and large lenticular bob. Lantern pinions used in the early clocks have either rod or leaf-shaped trundles. Later clocks use machine-cut leaf pinions throughout.

Basic similarities: brass four-wheel trains with polished steel arbors and pivots turning in press-fit brass bushings; a 60-minute setting dial on the time second wheel arbor that also trips the strike and provides a clutch to reset the dial hands while the clock continues running; adjustable expansion joints on the leading-off rods; ratchet driven flies; locking plate count wheels and vertically aligned strike lever pivots.

Pre-1828 clock differences: gravity lever maintaining power; 10-inch diameter wooden barrels; a small four-vane fly mounted outside the frame; various pendulum lengths and lenticular bob sizes; mostly direct take-offs to a single outside dial.

IL Figure 1. Lukens' earliest 1812 tower clock retrofitted for knife edge suspension. The chair frame is an English design. Its primary advantage: its strong integrated frame accommodates both long barrels and short sturdy wheel train arbors. Note the need for a very long crank to wind the weights.

Post-1827 clock differences: Harrison maintaining power; 24-inch long grooved barrels; large three-blade fly inside the frame; crutch-less adjustable knife-edge suspension of two-second pendulums with 18-inch diameter lenticular cast-iron bobs; a pivoting winding jack clutch with one winding square; a multi-dial bevel gear transmission mounted above the frame.

IL Figure 2. This small cage frame movement drives the hands of a large gallery clock set high in the ceiling of Philadelphia's Second National Bank and strikes a bell set sidewise at 9 and 4 o'clock, bank hours. Note locking plate strike control, and Lukens' typical birdcage expansion joint on the leading-off rod to the dial.

Right, IL Figure 3. The York clock is typical of Lukens'
work after 1828. A combination of flat and round iron
bars with finials is Lukens' version of the English "bedstead" frame. Note aligned pivots of the strike control
levers, the overhead transmission, and a winding jack
clutch with one winding square serving both barrels.

Left, IL Figure 4. Figure 3 pendulum/escapement
detail. Lukens' two-second pendulum hangs inside the
frame from an adjustable knife-edge suspension. The
upper portion of the pendulum rod is a metal ring set
with deadbeat jeweled pallets impulsed directly by an
escape wheel also within the ring, thus eliminating the
need for a crutch.

1815 • THOMAS WOOLSON JR.

Thomas Woolson Jr., the youngest of five children of his father's first marriage, was born in 1777 at Danvers, Massachusetts. About 1783, the family moved to Amherst, New Hampshire, where young Woolson had the one room schoolhouse education typical of the day. With no record of having served an apprenticeship, he apparently depended on native intelligence and natural manual skills for his reputation as "the ingenious town mechanic who carried on the clock and watch-making business on the Plain." The Plain is an extensive sandy flat area on which Amherst was first settled. In 1803 Woolson took the oath of office as an Ensign of the 9th Company, 5th Regiment of the New Hampshire Militia, and was promoted to Lieutenant in 1804. At some point in his late 20's he began the manufacture of cards for wool carding, turning it into a cottage industry that provided work for the townsfolk of all ages when they were not otherwise occupied. Shortly thereafter he moved to Cavendish, Vermont, marrying Hannah Peabody Chandler of Chester, Vermont, in 1805. He continued established Amherst connections, making frequent excursions back from his home in Cavendish, as documented by a daughter-in-law, who also wrote, "I found Father Woolson to be a man of great intellectual ability, wonderful inventive powers, curious research into all manner of strange subjects, but very peculiar in his manners, stern and, at times, morose, and his younger children very much afraid of him."

In March 1812, an Amherst committee raised the question of financing a town clock for their meeting house on the common. It was proposed that certain space on the main floor of the building be set aside to build pews that could be sold, with the money allocated to purchase the clock. The plan was implemented, but insufficient funds were raised. The clock was said to have been designed by Woolson and made with the assistance of an employee named Luther Elliott. It is assumed that Woolson supervised clock construction during his regular visits back to Amherst from his home in Vermont. The actual installation date of the town clock is uncertain, but probably occurred about 1815. The matter of completing payment for the installation remained an issue until 1819. It was finally paid for when local contributions were spurred by a vote to sell the town clock unless the shortfall was made up within 60 days. The Amherst Meeting House served both civic and church needs, but in 1832 the Congregational Church Society was allowed to buy the building, except for its steeple, bell, and tower clock, which remained town property. The front doors were also held as town property, but church members were permitted to come and go, along with their use of the bell,

on appropriate occasions. Despite this odd arrangement, Woolson's clock has managed to survive, hand-wound and still running to this day, both time and strike.

About 1813, Woolson moved with his family from Vermont to Claremont, New Hampshire, where he was prominent in business, politics and the state militia. He operated out of a two-story wooden factory building on Sullivan Street, nearly opposite the house where he lived. Among his many enterprises, the main focus in Claremont was as a foundryman and stove manufacturer. He patented the first cast-iron cooking stove that sold well in America, as did the later Woolson parlor stove. He also introduced an early cast-iron plow that did less well, as farmers were reluctant to accept it. Woolson had a number of partners in these undertakings, including his son, Charles Jarvis Woolson, who joined him in stove manufacturing by 1823. He also continued in the manufacture of cards for wool begun in Amherst, a manual piece-work operation that kept half the population of Claremont busy until someone invented a machine that did the job automatically. Along with all the rest, Woolson made several more tower clocks in his factory, and in December 1827 placed one in the Claremont Town House. About 70 years later the clock was described as "marking the hours and the minutes into which the day is divided, with commendable accuracy, to the present time." It has since been replaced and is missing so that comparisons cannot be made with the surviving Amherst clock. In 1825 and 1826, Thomas Woolson Jr. served as a representative in the New Hampshire Legislature, in 1828 he was a state senator, and was one of seven presidential electors from New Hampshire who cast their vote for John Quincy Adams for President of the United States. Woolson died at the age of 60 on July 3, 1837, in Claremont.

Thomas Woolson Jr. Tower Clock

Woolson's clock in Amherst, New Hampshire, is the largest of the Stowell-type horizontal flatbeds, its wood beam table frame measuring 66" wide by 28" deep by 31" high overall (including a 10" high wood platform). Similarities with Stowell include the location of its long wood barrels, its six-spoke brass wheels on tapered steel arbors, the closed-caliper escapement arms with replaceable steel pallets, hand-set by free-wheeling, the decorative brass bearing blocks, and the three-dial contrate wheel transmission. At mid-frame a distinctive A-Frame measuring 10½" high is mounted on a heavy strap-iron flatbed bolted to the wooden frame; it supports the escapement arbors and provides for the flat spring suspension of a 1½-second pendulum with a lenticular bob. The Woolson clock also differs from Stowell in several ways. Its time train is unusual, having only three wheels, a very high tooth count second wheel making two revolutions per hour drives the arbor of an outsized escapement pinwheel measuring almost 11 inches across and having 48 pins. The strike train has the usual four wheels, including a typical ratchet-driven weighted fly safely tucked between the frame beams, and the typical great wheel pins lift the bell strike lever. The strike control system is unique. Reduction gearing added to the strike triggering mechanism compensates for the faster rotation of the time train second wheel which usually triggers strike based on one revolution per hour. The count wheel consists of a large wheel with 78 wolf teeth and 12 axial stop pins appropriately spaced around the side of its rim. During a strike sequence the count wheel is advanced one tooth for each bell stroke by a two-leaf gathering pallet. A spring-loaded count hook, actuated by a cam flange on the second wheel of the strike train, lifts and drops the lock lever until it encounters a stop pin on the count wheel. In general, the Woolson clock lacks the refined simplicity of Stowell's design, but it cannot be faulted for function or durability.

TW Figure 1. Overview of the time and strike clockwork, strike on the left and time on the right. Not shown are the clock's typical wood beam flatbed table and floor platform. The large wheel up front on the left is an unusual wolf-tooth count wheel with its spring-loaded count hook. Strike is tripped by complex rod and reduction gear connections from the time train second wheel at the upper right, across the horizontal rod in the front foreground, and back on the other side to a lever stopped by a pin on the strike train third wheel.

Above, *TW Figure 2. Strike train detail. Strike is initiated when the Z-shaped lever is lifted from its stop pin on the third wheel. This frees the train to rotate, with the Z-shaped lever riding on the cam flange of the strike second wheel. This motion lifts the count hook on the shark-tooth count wheel until a stop pin is encountered, dropping the Z-lever into the locked position shown in the picture. Note the fly at far left.* **Below**, *TW Figure 3. Transmission detail. This style contrate wheel transmission is typical of the period except that tooth count allowances have been made for faster rotation of the wheel which drives it. In turn, the transmission drives leading-off rods to three outside dials on the same level as the mechanism. Note use of decorative brass bearing blocks.*

1816 • STEPHEN HASHAM

Baptized in Boston on October 21, 1764, Stephen was the sixth of nine children born to Samuel (Jr.) and Hannah (Simpson) Hassam. As a boy he watched from afar the Revolutionary War battles of Breed's and Bunker Hills. During the siege of Boston, his father, who had remarried, moved his family to Grafton, Massachusetts. As early as 1777, the orphaned Stephen moved a few miles north to Worcester where he probably served as an apprentice to Abel Stowell, the town clockmaker. By 1785, Stephen succeeded as a clock and instrument maker in Charleston, New Hampshire, a gateway to the north. He married Theodosia Hastings in 1787, and soon after convinced his in-laws to sell him their extensive real estate for £500 and the promise of security in their old age. About this time he adopted use of the *Hasham* spelling from among 30 known variations of the Hassam family name. Childe Hassam, Stephen's great grandson, was America's leading impressionist painter.

Between 1787 and 1825, Stephen demonstrated his assorted talents with prodigious energy. The five children of his first marriage were all born by 1797. He registered over 30 real estate transactions. As a master builder, he literally changed the profile of Charlestown's Main Street, constructing large homes, the town bank, an imposing church, and a two-story hotel with stabling for 80 horses. Failing to sell the hotel, he moved in, set up a workshop, and established himself briefly as innkeeper. He called it the Eagle Hotel and carved a large gilt eagle signpost to put out front. When asked how he did it he said, "God Almighty put the bird in a branch which I took from a tree, and just took off a chip or two and there it was." The 1820 census shows Hasham as "manufacturer," presumably of town clocks, as in 1816–1823 he made and installed five clocks in four states, ranging in price from $200 to $500. In the 1830s, he resumed house construction, sometimes leaving his builder's trademark, a two-dial banjo mounted within a wall, telling time in adjacent rooms.

For all of his talent and energy, a devilish streak in Hasham alienated the community. His first wife managed to palliate her husband's eccentricities, but she died in 1841, and within weeks, Hasham was in hot pursuit of young Lucy Miller of Springfield, Vermont. Her parents objected to her marrying a professed atheist 50 years her senior, but the ever persuasive Hasham continued pursuit and they wed the same year. Tension ran high in the household as Hasham was overextended financially, and they produced five children in rapid order, the youngest born when Hasham was 86 years old! The crisis forced his return to a proven source of cash income, tower clockmaking.

By 1845, he installed improved tower clocks in four towns close to Charleston. This major achievement in his 80's was the sole bright spot in a gathering storm. First, he lost all equity in the Eagle Hotel, followed by a series of personal tragedies that dogged him in 1851. His young wife ran amuck in the neighborhood, was adjudged insane and committed to the asylum. A few months later the 87-year-old Hasham was accused of excessive drinking and idleness, a charge reduced to "Spendthrift," with the court appointing a custodian to oversee his assets. The same year his oldest son and heir died of causes unknown. In 1852, all Hasham assets were sold to pay off over 30 creditors. Making matters worse, Hasham alienated the ex-governor of New Hampshire, who offered him a choice between jail or a term in the asylum. Thereafter he vowed he would live to dance on the governor's grave, a vow eventually fulfilled. By the mid-1850s, an impoverished and wifeless Hasham rejoined his younger children under the roof of a relative. In his last years he was free to come and go as he wished, outliving both custodian and ex-governor. Stephen Hasham died on February 3, 1861, a few years shy of 100 years, and was buried in Charleston between the graves of his first wife and the Civil War soldier son of his second marriage.

Stephen Hasham Tower Clocks

Nine of the 10 Hasham tower clocks survive, most signed by their maker. Installation sites include: Charlestown (2), Haverhill, Alstead, and Cornish Flat, New Hampshire; Windsor, Norwich and Springfield, Vermont; Troy, New York; and his masterpiece at Pittsfield, Massachusetts. Hasham's innovative use of two levels of flatbed on wood beam frames results in a more compact clock. His clocks run eight days on a winding, time and strike, and drive three outside dials on the same level as the mechanism. Hasham escapements are pinwheel with replaceable steel pallets, and strike control by rack-and-snail. Along with a number of ingenious mechanical solutions, Hasham prided himself in an artistry apparent in the fine workmanship of his clocks. **Hasham Model 1 (1816–1820).** Three survive. Frames measure about 41" wide by 19" deep; height varies up to 41". The hardwood frames are edge-beaded and joined by bedstead hardware. Train wheels, time to the left and strike right, are cast iron, except for the brass escape pinwheel and the early use of a brass bevel gear transmission. Replaceable steel pallets are mounted in closed caliper brass arms. Cut leaf pinions are steel, as are the arbors which taper down from their "working" ends. Most operator interfaces (including the setting dial, rack-and-snail components, hand-setting adjustments, and gravity bar maintaining power) are on the back side of the mechanism, while the winding squares and pendulum are located up front. **Hasham Model X-1 (1820).** This ultimate early expression of the clockmaker as an artist was installed in Pittsfield, Massachusetts, in 1822. The wood frame with its massive reeded legs measures 68" wide by 33" deep by 35" high. Sheet metal sheathed wooden barrels with cast-iron great wheels extend across opposite ends of the table. Set back on the flatbed table are arabesque cast-iron arches that support a matched set of brass wheel trains, time to the left, strike to the right. Gravity bar maintaining power is provided, with the hands reset by freewheeling. On a frame center line, a two-second pendulum hangs from a sophisticated rating device with cycloidal chops. A handsome two-hand setting dial is at table center. Decorative components are brightly painted, and the table top is signed by the maker, embellished with gilt brush work.

Hasham Model X-2. Also one of a kind, the turned bedstead legs are its distinguishing feature. The frame measures about 50" wide by 20" deep by 42" high. Three parallel beams form the horizontal flatbed, which provides for short sturdy arbors on the wheel

trains and protection for both the pendulum and fly within the frame. Its six-spoke brass wheels are larger than earlier clocks, with the great wheels and their figured arbor brackets made of cast iron. It has the best of earlier clock features, plus a spring-loaded freewheeling device and a lever arrangement to rate the pendulum from the front of the clock.

Hasham Model 2 (1843–1845). Four Model 2 clocks survive. Flatbed construction is similar to Model 1 but strictly functional with no edge beading and the addition of iron leg braces. The frame is larger, measuring 54" wide by 20" deep by 35½" high. The clockwork is enhanced by cast-iron barrels, Harrison maintaining power, integral winding jacks, remote pendulum rating, and higher tooth-count bevel gears in the transmission. Train orientation is strike to the left and time right, typical of most makers. Its setting dial is angled back for better visibility, and all other machine interfaces, except the fly, are up front for operator convenience.

SH Figure 1. Front view of Hasham Model 1 clock installed in Norwich, Vermont, about the same time as its 1817 Revere bell. The decorative brackets and many wheels are cast iron. Most operator interfaces are located on the back of the clock.

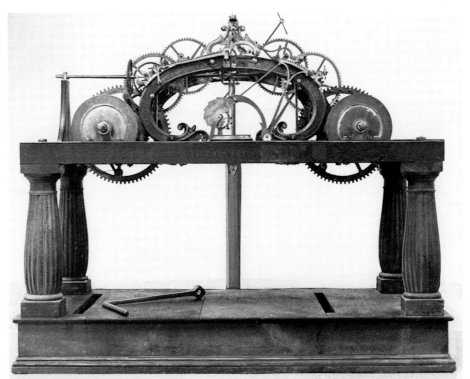

Above, SH Figure 2. Model X-1. In 1820 Hasham advertised this beautiful, symmetrical tower clock as "equal to any other in the United States." The weight line falls directly off the barrels through slots in the frame platform.
Below, SH Figure 3. Model X-2. The date is uncertain, and the frame distinct from other Hasham models. Added improvements include the three-beam flatbed construction and the location of all operator/clock interfaces on the front (winding side) of the clock. The setting dial is a replacement.

SH Figure 4. Hasham Model 2. Four survive. This example, now electrified, was installed in Charlestown, New Hampshire, in 1843. A winding jack and Harrison maintaining power have been added. Gear train arrangement is conventional: strike to the left and time right. Pendulum beat is 1 second.

SH Figure 5. Deadbeat pinwheel escapement detail. The reinforced closed-caliper arms with replaceable steel pallets and the escapement pinwheel are very similar to those used by Abel Stowell 40 years earlier. Above is the pendulum remote rating lever.

SH Figure 6. Hasham's setting dials are nonpareil. Housed under glass in a figured brass bezel, the elegant two-hand motion work is driven by geared connection to a transmission leading-off rod. On its right, note a typical Hasham fork expansion universal joint.

1820 • ELISHA HOTCHKISS JR.

Burlington, Connecticut, a hilly thinly-populated town about 12 miles west of Hartford, was set off from Bristol to the south in 1806. Primarily farming country, it produced a surprising number of clockmakers— one named James Frost as early as 1809, but more notably members of the Sperry and two branches of the Hotchkiss families—many of whom left town as young men and succeeded in the clock business in New York City in the first half of the nineteenth century. An exception was Elisha Hotchkiss Jr. who remained in Burlington to establish a clock business later called Hotchkiss & Fields. It became the largest manufactory the town ever had, employing 30 to 50 men making both cases and wood movements for several models of shelf clocks, and sending out young peddlers who brought back tales of fabulous prices paid by wealthy planters to the south and west.

Elisha Hotchkiss Jr. was born on May 4, 1787, in Burlington, the third son of seven children of Elisha and Lydia (Lee) Hotchkiss. His family was distantly related to another line of the Hotchkiss family in Burlington that produced A.S. Hotchkiss, a tower clock making genius who launched Seth Thomas in the business in 1872. Details about the life of Elisha Hotchkiss Jr. are spotty and the chronology of his business a roller coaster of success and bankruptcy. Even so he was one of the last holdouts in the business, producing wooden clock movements into the 1840s when brass works had taken over public demand. It is not known exactly when or from whom he learned his trade, but upon reaching majority in 1808, he paid his father $150 for 12 acres of land, and in 1813 married Lodema Upson in Goshen, Connecticut. In 1833 the oldest of their six daughters, also named Lodema, married Edward Fields who became her father's partner.

For a short period, Elisha Jr. worked in Bristol where he was assessed as a manufacturer in 1830, and his earliest known shelf clocks display a *Bristol* label. The following year he returned to manufacture in his hometown, using a *Burlington* label, first on 30-hour wood movement shelf clocks, soon after on eight-day wood wheel clocks added to the line. As with other entrepreneurs of the period, cash flow problems required constant financial juggling. Hotchkiss went bankrupt in 1834, after having mortgaged about 200 acres of land, plus his dwelling house, grist mill, saw mill, clock factory and other buildings. All debts were paid off by 1836, at which time he dropped "Jr." from his name and resumed the manufacture of wooden works clocks. Edward Fields was negotiating clock prices with customers in the absence of his father-in-law as early as 1834, a year after his marriage to Lodema Hotchkiss; however, the precise startup date of Hotchkiss & Fields is uncertain. It was probably established by October 17, 1837, the date when the two partners jointly executed a mortgage deed. They continued to produce various models of mantel clocks with 30-hour and eight-day wood movements, followed by OG clocks with 30-hour brass movements, some made by Hotchkiss & Fields and some by other vendors. In 1834 the partners joined a short-lived consortium organized for foreign trade called the Bristol Clock Co., which made at least one clock shipment to China. In 1845, serious financial difficulties forced Hotchkiss & Fields once again to mortgage all their assets. Collateral consisted of their land, homes, factories, water rights and, "all the tools and fixtures for making and manufacturing wood and brass clocks consisting of five upright drill lathes, five horizontal lathes, press and dies, leveler drop and dies, wheel engine and pinion engine, pinion lathe, drill box cutting round and flat. And four saw frames, veneering saw, mandrill and other saws belonging to said frames." By early 1847 the firm was defunct.

Little is heard about Hotchkiss or Fields after the bankruptcy proceedings. Elisha Hotchkiss and his wife retired to Hartford where she died in 1849. He joined her at the Spring Grove Cemetery in Hartford on May 9, 1882, at the age of 95. (Snowden Taylor)

Local historians claim that Elisha Jr. began clock-making as early as 1820, the date also assigned to the Burlington tower clock he was said to have made. They also claim the clock was first installed in the meeting house of the Ecclesiastical Society (now the Congregational Church) situated in "The Hollow," with the church and its clock being moved in 1836 to Burlington Center Village, where it remains today. Exhaustive research has failed to reveal *original source* documentation of the clock's purchase or gift, installation date, maker, or costs associated with its care and winding. It is also puzzling that neither Elisha Hotchkiss Jr. nor

his father were members of the Congregational Church where the clock was installed, but were active Methodists whose clock-less church building was also moved to Burlington Town Center about 1836. It is probable that Elisha Jr. did make the clock, considering his skills, facilities, and strong Burlington association, but more likely did so at a later date coincident with the moving of the Congregational Church to the Center Village in 1836.

Elisha Hotchkiss Tower Clock

The Burlington wooden tower clock is an excellent piece of work. Although not particularly innovative, the overall design is unusually compact, solidly built, and beautifully finished. The execution is strictly functional, lacking decorative frame detailing or rings on the wheels, arbors, and posts. The frame is an open box flatbed of well-joined native wild cherry measuring 42½" wide by 29" deep by 12" high. A mid-frame structure between the barrels provides for the rotation of a propeller-shaped wooden fly inside the frame, while allowing short sturdy arbors for the wheel trains. The wheels are native wild cherry with sawn teeth, mounted on turned hardwood arbors with milled pinions and steel pin pivots. Bearing block oil sinks and brass pivot hole bushings are probably restoration "improvements." A wooden bridge over the flatbed supports the recoil escapement and what was originally a one-second pendulum with a wooden rod and lenticular cast-iron bob. Strike control is by a conventional friction-mounted wooden count wheel. During a strike sequence a twin lobe paddle lifts the count hook which steps along the count wheel until dropping into the next deep slot. During its active life the clockwork drove two hands on a single dial. The original hands, wood wheel motion work, wood pulleys, and two cranks needed to wind the clock have survived. Its two-fall compounded weights were blocks of granite estimated to weigh about 300 pounds. The clock ran a week on a winding, but is claimed by a former custodian to have lost accuracy unless wound every other day. It was fully restored to working order in 1956, but was removed from the tower in 1970 when no volunteers came forward to wind it. The clock is a prized possession now encased and proudly displayed in the sanctuary of the Burlington Congregational Church.

Above, EHJ Figure 1. Clock rear overview, strike left, time right. An extension of the time second wheel arbor provides the take-off connection to the single outside dial. The original one-second pendulum rod has been shortened for display purposes. **Below**, EHJ Figure 2. Clock front view, strike train detail. Almost all clockwork is mounted in the shallow back section of the frame, providing short strong arbors and added space within the frame for the propeller-like fly, seen below. Note pointed, sawn teeth and, to the right, the twin lobe cam that lifts the count hook during strike.

Above, *EHJ Figure 3. Strike control detail. The deep slot count wheel integral to the back of this 78-tooth friction-mounted drive wheel is advanced during a strike sequence by a two-pin pinion on the extended end of the strike second wheel arbor.* ***Below***, *EHJ Figure 4. Recoil escapement detail. A 42-tooth brass escape wheel works on a steel anchor mounted above the wheel, conveying motion via a shaped iron crutch to a pendulum rated by a nut on the threaded rod below its bob end.*

1824 • AARON WILLARD JR.

Aaron Willard Jr., born June 29, 1783, in Roxbury, Massachusetts, was named for his father, the youngest of the famous clockmaking brothers of Grafton. His mother, Catherine (Gates) Willard, died in 1785 with the birth of her second child. The father, Aaron Willard (1757–1844), followed his older brother Simon to Roxbury after the American Revolution. Listed as the "clockmaker on the Neck," he never achieved Simon's prestige as a clockmaker, but his workmanship was excellent and he was the superior businessman. It is said that in later years he employed the services of 20 or 30 craftsmen, including both Aaron Jr. and the son of his second marriage, Henry (1802–1887).

Aaron Willard Jr. grew up enjoying the comforts afforded by his father's prosperity and the benefit of his instruction in clockmaking. His portrait, painted by John Ritto Penniman of Boston in 1804, shows a self-assured, fashionably dressed young man, pleasant-faced with unruly short hair. He was a fully fledged clockmaker by 1805–06, when records indicated he bought clock cases from John Doggett of Roxbury, and the following year painted clock tablets for Doggett. He also worked briefly for his uncle, Simon Willard, and from 1806 to 1809, was a partner in Willard & Nolan, clock dial and sign painters at Boston Neck. Thereafter he worked full time at his father's business. In 1815 he established a home at 815 Washington Street, Boston Neck, where he lived for over 30 years. Upon his father's retirement in 1823, the 40-year-old Aaron Jr. took over the business in his own name. The exact manufacturing site is uncertain, but he made tall case, banjo, regulator and gallery clocks, and is credited with having invented the widely copied lyre timepiece. He also made excellent tower clocks in two models, examples of which have survived in hand-wound working condition.

Among Aaron Willard Jr.'s apprentices from 1829 to 1834 were Edward Howard and David P. Davis, later partners in Howard & Davis. They lived in his house and worked in the factory attached to it. Years later Howard wrote, "His business was not large, no more than four or five workmen being employed, the most of whom were apprentices. The shop he occupied was thirty by fifty feet, and one story high...The aggregate production in money value would not exceed $8,000 per annum. During my five year apprenticeship not a single tower or hall striking clock was made by us...." The fact remains that Aaron Willard Jr. made excellent tower clocks of superior design and workmanship and was as good a businessman as his father before him.

By the late 1830s, the flood of cheap mass-produced common clocks from Connecticut factories captured much of the traditional marketplace of New England clockmakers like Aaron Jr. He remained in business by catering to the carriage trade, and by shifting emphasis to the manufacture of high quality gallery and tower clocks. Over time, he accumulated a comfortable fortune and retired from the business in 1850 at the age of 67. Little is known about the clockmaker's personal life other than his interest in flowers and gardening. A large greenhouse was attached to the residence on Washington Street and his flower beds on the property were the pride of the neighborhood. In January 1816, while working for his father in Boston, he married Ann Dorr, who died in 1842. They had two children: a daughter Emily, born December 27, 1816, who married a Boston cabinet maker, and a son, Anthony Maybin, born on July 11, 1819, who died young. Thirteen years after his first wife's death and five years into retirement, Aaron Jr. married Emiline, the daughter of Benjamin and Mehitabel Davenport of Newton, Massachusetts. He spent his last years at Cobbs Hill, Newton, probably indulging his taste for gardening. His house shows up on the 1855 Newton town map at the end of a country road in a heavily wooded area near a small pond. It was valued at $5,000, with taxes listed from $21 to $32. Aaron Willard Jr. died on May 2, 1864, in Newton at the age of 80. He bequeathed his estate to the four children of his daughter Emily, who had predeceased him, and to his second wife who outlived him by over 30 years.

Aaron Willard Jr. Tower Clocks

The earliest known surviving tower clock, **AWJ Model 1**, is signed and dated 1824 at Kennebunkport, Maine. A mock cage frame, it is actually a plate-and-pillar frame, consisting of two cast-iron skeletonized plates, spaced apart by five pillars, and held together by octagonal nuts. Overall it measures 34¾" wide by 16½" deep by 31" high. The great wheels and the winding jacks on both time and strike are of cast iron, the rest of the wheels are brass. Arbors and cut-leaf pinions are steel and pivot in Vuillamy bushings (probably not original). There is no maintaining power. The escapement is a Graham deadbeat with fixed pallets. Dial hands are reset by freewheeling. The 1½-second beat pendulum, with wooden rod and lenticular bob, hangs outside the frame and is rated at its suspension end. A large brass bevel gear take-off drives a three-dial bevel gear transmission mounted to the frame top. Leading-off rods are connected by expansion U-joints to the motion work of the outside dials. Strike control is by a disk type count wheel mounted on the strike great wheel arbor. Pins on the strike second wheel lift the bell strike lever. A fly with four small adjustable vanes is poorly located on the winding side of the clock. A second example of AWJ Model 1 was installed in Hagerstown, Maryland, in 1836. Major differences include its use of rack-and-snail rather than count wheel strike control, and its innovative use of a crutch with an adjustable elbow to put the clock in beat. Both clocks strike on bells made by G.H. Holbrook, whose foundry was located at East Medway, about 20 miles south of the Willard shop on Boston Neck.

AWJ Model 2 is a complete redesign of AWJ Model 1. Two nearly identical examples survive in Grafton, Massachusetts, dating from 1839 and 1840. The round-top cast-iron frame consists of multiple cast-iron sections assembled and bolted together. Its Federalist style (Pfyfe) incorporates a row of matched arches and graceful fluted legs. It measures 27" wide by 28" deep by 33½" high. A bridge centered across the arches provides for suspension of the pendulum and mounting for a three-dial bevel gear transmission. The pendulum is two-second beat, with a wooden rod and cast-iron cannonball bob. The dial take-off and motion work is similar to Model 1. Clockwork redesign includes three wheel time and strike trains mounted on short sturdy arbors which pivot in bushed holes or in bearing blocks screwed to the frame. The strike great wheel (strike pinwheel) measures 14" across, and the wooden barrels are 3¾" in diameter by 21" in length. Unusually large fly blades extend outside the frame. Strike control is by rack-and-snail, the snail advanced by a star wheel turned by pins extending from the time great wheel. Harrison maintaining power is provided. A major change is the conversion to pinwheel escapements using deadbeat pallets ground on the ends of a single arc of steel, an unusual arrangement devised by George Holbrook as early as 1810. Here, again, arrangements differ. The AWJ Model 2 installed in 1840 is conventional, with the pendulum suspended outside the frame, connected by the crutch to the escapement pallet arbor. The earlier 1839 clock is *crutch-less* (see **Lukens** and **Meneely**). The pendulum hangs inside the frame by knife-edge suspension. The upper end of the pendulum rod is a metal bracket with a large diamond-shaped hole in which the escapement pinwheel turns. Fixed to the same pendulum bracket are two deadbeat pallets impulsed directly by the escapement pinwheel, maintaining pendulum swing without benefit of a crutch.

Left, *AWJ Figure 1. Strike end view of AWJ Model 1. Bell hammer striking power can be increased by moving the cable connection toward the far end of the strike lever. Cast-iron great wheels and winding jacks are found on both the strike and time trains. Note three-dial transmission above the clock frame, and to its right the pendulum cock's rating nut.* *Right*, *AWJ Figure 2. AWJ Model 1 escapement detail, a classic Graham deadbeat. The use of Vuillamy bushings here in 1824 seems premature. Note ringed pillars and decorative elements on the frame plate vertical risers.*

AWJ Figure 3. Overview of AWJ Model 2, installed in 1839. The stylish frame and compact clockwork is in marked contrast to the bulky earlier model. Note the knife-edge suspension of the pendulum hanging inside the frame and rack-and-snail components outside the frame.

AWJ Figure 4. Overview of Aaron Willard's AWJ Model 2 installed in 1840. The pendulum is conventional, being crutch-driven, suspended from the extended bridge by a flat spring outside the frame. The winding jack on the disabled strike train is a later addition. The missing snail on the time side reveals its 12-point driving star wheel.

1827 • THE HARMONY SOCIETY

The Harmony Society was one of the most successful, wealthiest and longest-lived of all nineteenth century pre-Marxian communal groups who came to America seeking religious and economic freedom. In 1804, nearly 800 Harmonist farmers, skilled craftsmen, and their families emigrated here from Württemberg, near Stuttgart (now southwestern Germany). Their charismatic leader was George Rapp (1757-1847). He preached that the Society was the embodiment of St. John's vision of the Sunwoman,[1] who struggled with Satan, then fled into the wilderness to pre-

---

[1]Holy Bible, Book of *Revelation*, Chapter 12.

pare a place for the second coming of Christ. According to Rapp, this coming would restore the harmony of the Garden of Eden before the fall of Adam.

The Society was beautifully organized. Everyone worked for the common good and, in return, received the worldly goods they needed to live simply and comfortably. As the prominent leader of the Society, George Rapp lived in more elaborate quarters than his followers, but if he was a despot he was a benevolent one. According to a visitor in 1827, "The authority of Mr. Rapp over his colonists and their affection for him is unbounded. He is usually addressed 'Father,' and...the whole authority, executive and judicial, is vested in him from whom no appeal is ever made." Tobacco and whiskey were banned as useless, unnecessary, and harmful to health. There was no prohibition against marriage "at pleasure," but they saw mere physical enjoyment as below the dignity of man, and by 1807 adopted the celibacy that contributed to their eventual demise.

The Harmonists' most extraordinary achievement was their venture into the American wilderness, where they cleared vast tracts of land and established three virtually self-sufficient towns. Planning was carried out by Frederick Rapp (b. Reichert, 1775-1834), the adopted son of George Rapp and the Society's manager of business affairs. In 1804, they first settled 25 miles north of Pittsburgh on Connoquenessing Creek where they purchased 9,000 acres of land and erected the first town called Harmony. Seeking more low cost land and access to transport waterways, they sold the first Harmony at substantial profit, and by 1814, moved on to Posey County, Indiana. Here they purchased 30,000 acres of land on the Wabash River and built a second town called Harmony, also sold for substantial profit 10 years later. In 1824, the Harmonists made a final move, regarded by Father Rapp as ushering in the Age of the Divine Economy, or "Okeonomie." Their third and ultimate "paradise" was a town called Economy, cut from the primeval forest overlooking the Ohio River 18 miles northwest of Pittsburgh. Years in the building, the town had workshops for blacksmiths, tanners, hatters, wagon makers, cabinetmakers, weavers, potters, tinners, and yes, clockmakers. They also constructed a dairy, centralized steam laundries, and large cotton, wool, and silk factories powered and heated by steam engines. The Society gained worldwide recognition for its communal way of life, religious devotion and economic prosperity. As suggested by Thomas Jefferson, the Harmonists successfully "placed the manufacturer next to the agriculturalist."

Access to a uniform time standard was essential to harmonious interaction in a commune where *everyone* worked in different locations at wide-ranging tasks. Accordingly, each of the three Harmonist towns featured a tower clock. The first Harmony had a 30-hour striker with two one-hand dials, made in 1811 at the behest of Frederick Rapp by John Eberman of Lancaster, Pennsylvania (see **1785 • John Eberman**, page 19). The clock was sold along with the town in 1815, and remains on display in the local museum. The second Harmony in Posey County, Indiana, also had a town clock, now missing. The clockmaker is thought to have been an as yet unidentified craftsman in the Society who copied the 1811 Eberman clock. The same maker is credited with the large quarter-striker with two bells installed about 1827 in the third and last Harmonist town called Economy. It has survived in its brick church tower in hand-wound, running condition.

A growing reputation as fine clockmakers led to the Society's installation in 1829 of a four-dial town clock in the steeple of Pittsburgh's Trinity Episcopal Church, an imposing structure designed by Rev. John Hopkins, later Bishop of Vermont. In December 1832, the president of Jefferson College inquired if the Society would make a clock for Cannonsburgh, Pennsylvania. Frederick Rapp wrote back: "The person [still unnamed] who devoted himself mostly to that kind of work, has left our Society, and those remaining who understand clockmaking, are too much engaged in other work."

Harmony Society Tower Clocks

The two surviving Harmonist town clocks—a striker made in 1811 by John Eberman (JE Model 3) and the large quarter-striker made for Economy on the Ohio in 1827 (HS Model 1)—are similar with significant differences. Both clocks have forged iron cage frames joined by nuts and bolts, spearhead vertical risers, decorative brass finials, and strike control levers that pivot in parallel straps hanging from the top of the frame. Both clocks are powered by similarly shaped stone weights wound daily. Both clocks have 26-tooth recoil escapements that provide for freewheeling. Both have three-wheel trains, four-spoke brass wheels, and steel cut leaf pinions on tapered arbors that pivot in force-fit brass bushings. The hour strike trains of both clocks are similar, controlled by conventional brass locking plates and ratchet-driven flies mounted outside the frame. Both clocks have one-hand dials of similar design located on the diagonal corners of octagonal belfries.

There are also significant *differences*. Eberman's cage frame has the surface irregularities of forged iron, and features distinctive chamfered, square corner posts. The iron cage frame of HS Model 1 has a smoother finish and *round* corner posts with decorative rings. In general, the frame and all moving parts of HS Model 1 are more substantial and sophisticated, the wheel teeth appearing to be machine-cut and the great wheels being almost 20 inches in diameter. A stud on the side of the time great wheel trips the warning and strike of the quarters on a 518-pound bell. The 15-minute quarter strike interval is controlled by a small

timing gear, and its quarter strike count by a sophisticated rack-and-snail. Tripped by the minute strike system and under locking plate and fly control, hour strike occurs on a 2825-pound bell. Other HS Model 1 improvements include: winding jacks on all three barrels, one winding square on a clutch accommodating both the time and hour strike barrels; and a fine tooth brass dial take-off with an adjustable thrust bearing supporting a long leading off rod to a four-dial transmission located overhead above the bells.

The Harmony Society was dissolved by 1905. Its clock and bell now serve the congregations of St. John's Lutheran Church. What remains at Old Economy Village are most of the historic buildings and thousands of artifacts. The Village is a National Historic Landmark administered by the Pennsylvania Historical and Museum Commission.

HS Figure 1. Economy's tower clock, exterior view. Its one-hand dials and octagonal belfry are similar to Eberman's 1811 installation at the first town called Harmony, probably an architectural decision made by Frederick Rapp who designed both towns. The works are located at tower window level and the two bells mounted behind the louvered panels.

HS Figure 2. HS Model 1 cage frame overview, quarter strike train on the left, time center and hour strike right. The time train second wheel is not original. All three barrels have winding jacks, one that swivels between the time and hour strike barrels. An improvised "roof" shields the works against falling particles but not from drafts. Overall frame dimensions are 70" wide by 52" high by 24½" deep.

Left, HS Figure 3. Harmony Society's Model 1 recoil escapement detail. Note the replaceable steel pallet. Rubbing friction is reduced by passing the tips of the escape wheel through an improvised oil pan mounted under the wheel. *Right*, HS Figure 4. HS Model 1 quarter strike control detail. Each of the snail's 12 segments has three steps and a deep slot which along with the rack govern the quarter strike routine on the smaller bell. The smaller bell is struck once at quarter after the hour, twice at half after, thrice at quarter to the hour, and finally struck from one to 12 times to identify the upcoming hour. After a short pause, the hour strike, set up by the quarter strike and under locking plate control, repeats the same hour count on the large bell.

1828 • DAVID BROWN

David Brown was born April 17, 1781, at Attleboro, Massachusetts, the son of David Brown Sr. (1755–1849), originally of Newport, Rhode Island, and Chloe (Carpenter) Brown (1761–1848). As a farmer's son, he shared family farm chores until striking off on his own at age 14 to work for two years as a tavern-boy in Seekonk, Massachusetts. He then moved on to Providence, Rhode Island, where he first served as an apprentice to jeweler Nehemiah Dodge, and then to clock and watchmaker Payton Dana. In 1802, at the age of 21, Brown was hired by Obed Robinson to establish a plated jewelry business in Attleboro. Two years later Brown set up his own shop in Warren, Rhode Island, where he prospered as a dealer/manufacturer of clocks, watches, jewelry and especially silverware. On April 15, 1809, he married Patience Rogers (1791–1877) of Middletown, Rhode Island. They had six children, three of whom lived to maturity, including their first born, Joseph Rogers Brown, founder-to-be of the renowned Brown & Sharpe Manufacturing Co.

Financial reversals shortly after the marriage forced Brown to travel country roads as an itinerant peddler, selling his silver goods, and sharpening cutlery and tools with a treadle-powered grindstone on wheels that he had devised. After a few years he paid off his debts and managed to save a bit on the side. In 1828, he sold the property in Warren and moved to Pawtucket, Rhode Island, where he established himself as a clock and watchmaker. He was joined by his son, Joseph R. Brown, now 18 years old and already a trained machinist. Together they manufactured a series of tower clocks, noteworthy for their use of the so-called "tumbling pallet" escapement invented by David Brown. The father and son team is known to have made and installed town clocks in Pawtucket's Congregational Church in 1828–29 (for $500, by public subscription), in the Trinitarian Church of Taunton, Massachusetts (by public subscription), and in the North Congregational Church of New Bedford, Massachusetts, in 1836 (for $550 in public funds). Late in 1833, they established the partnership of David Brown & Son at 60 South Main Street in Providence. In addition to clockmaking and watch repair, they produced surveying and mathematical instruments and took on whatever light precision machine work that came their way. With some reversals, such as the total loss of their shop by fire in 1837, the firm grew steadily until the partnership ended in 1841 with the abrupt retirement of David Brown.

Brown was a strong-willed, determined Yankee, described as a skeptic if not a fire-breathing atheist. When asked to repair the clock of the old Methodist Meeting House in Providence, he did so begrudgingly, complaining, "One has to give the devil his due!" His early retirement was another case in point. He took a strong stand as regards Rhode Island's so-called "Dorr Rebellion," a battle of words against the state's adherence to an outmoded Colonial charter which disenfranchised everyone but the landed gentry from the vote. Fed up at last with what seemed an endless legal debate, Brown simply quit work and took leave of Rhode Island altogether, removing himself, wife and minor children to Arispa, Bureau County, Illinois. While there he set up his younger son, Peleg Brown, on a large tract of land which he had purchased. In 1856, Brown returned to Pawtucket where he paid $1,300 for a big lot with an unfinished house located on the west side of High Street. He enlarged the house to accommodate his family, which by then included his daughter's husband, and added a workshop to the rear for his own use. The state census for 1865 shows the family still living together on High Street, with 84-year-old David Brown, watchmaker, designated head-of-household. In his last years he remained cheerful and physically active, priding himself in particular on excellent eyesight. After his death on September 8, 1868, the *Pawtucket Gazette and Chronicle* eulogized, "We shall miss Mr. Brown, for almost everyone in Pawtucket knew him, and for every acquaintance he met he always had a smile, a cheerful word, and a hearty grasp of the hand."

David Brown's "Tumbling Pallet" Escapement

As indicated above, at least three town clocks made by David Brown and his son Joseph are documented. Based on Joseph's numbering system, a total of six could have been made. Their most intriguing feature was David Brown's "tumbling pallet" escapement. None have survived, but in 1890, Brown's clock for New Bedford, Massachusetts, was still in place and Charles Crossman, of the *Jewelers Circular and Horological Review*, decided to have a look at the rare escapement for himself. Subsequently he wrote that it was "a curiosity worth climbing up the old dusty stairs to examine, but one which baffled intelligible description." In 1849, Joseph R. Brown made town clock No. 7 for Warren, Rhode Island, which incorporated this escapement with the intriguing name. While inoperative, the clock has survived in sound condition, allowing a second look at the mysterious "tumbling pallet" escapement.

It belongs to the general class of deadbeat pin pallet escapements to which the Brocot, developed many years later, also belongs. Brown's arrangement consists of a 7½" brass escape wheel with 22 unusually shaped teeth separated by radial slots only slightly wider than the diameter of the roller pallets themselves. (The slots are comparable to the resting faces of conventional deadbeat escapements.) Brown's escapement anchor supports two large roller pallet assemblies that pivot, or "tumble," against adjustable fixed stops. The advantage of large roller pallets with small diameter pivots is *maximum impulse with minimum friction*, compared to the frictional drag of most escapements. A major concern with large round pallets is backside clearance, a problem handled by the slab-sided design of stationary Brocot pallets but hardly possible with rollers. Brown's solution was *pallet flexibility*. He solved his backside clearance problem with an arrangement capable of reducing or expanding pallet tooth span from 5½ teeth to five or to six teeth, respectively. Wear patterns on the escape wheel teeth indicate a distinctive impulse cycle: a locked roller rising in the radial slot between two teeth reaches maximum impulse as it unlocks and rolls over the front corner of the tooth's leading edge, with the impulse tapering off as the roller advances across the inclined plane of the tooth tip. As the opposing pallet locks in its next radial slot, the ongoing swing of the anchor frees the impulsed pallet to "tumble" by gravity against its other fixed stop. This positions its roller to fall into the next radial slot, where it "rests," awaiting the next impulse cycle. Brown's solidly-built escapement provides very positive action. Its connection to the pendulum rod is also unusual: a very short 4" crutch attached to the pallet arbor has a wide 4½" fork with two D-pins that impulse steel outriders attached to the pendulum rod. The pendulum is fine rated by an adjustable weight on a threaded rod extending above the escapement pallet arbor. These unique tower clock arrangements had too many adjustments for general acceptance; however, the 1849 Warren "tumbling pallet" church clock kept good time for over 100 years, with only one overhaul by the Brown & Sharpe factory in 1923. (Snowden Taylor/Michael Harrold) (See **1849 • Joseph R. Brown**, page 132.)

Above, DBP Figure 1. Exit roller pallet detail. Escape wheel rotation is counterclockwise; counterpoise A and pallet assembly stops B-B are adjustable. As seen here, the exit pallet has lifted out of a radial slot to engage the leading corner of escape wheel tooth C, where impulse begins. During impulse, which peaks as the pallet rolls over the tooth's leading edge corner, the exit pallet assembly is held by the turning escape wheel against its upper stop, as compared to the opposing entry pallet, which is held against its lower stop during its impulse phase. *Below*, DBP Figure 2. Tumbling pallet overview, Part 1. In the sequence that follows, escape wheel rotation is counterclockwise. Exit pallet A, moving down, remains locked in the radial slot between two escape wheel teeth. Entry pallet B, completing its impulse cycle about midway across the inclined tooth tip, remains held against its lower stop, but is poised to tumble against its upper stop. Roller pallet span is $5^1/_2$ teeth.

Above, DBP Figure 3. Tumbling pallet overview, Part 2. Rising in its slot, exit pallet A unlocks to engage the leading corner of the escape wheel tooth where maximum impulse begins. Entry pallet B, impulse cycle complete, has tumbled against its upper stop, positioned by gravity to enter the next radial slot. Pallet span extends to six teeth, thus providing backside clearance for roller pallet B. *Below*, DBP Figure 4. Tumbling pallet overview, Part 3. Impulse cycle complete, exit pallet A has tumbled by gravity against its lower stop, positioning it to drop in the next radial slot. Meanwhile, entry pallet B, riding in its radial slot, is pushed by the counterclockwise advance of the escape wheel against its lower stop (reducing pallet span to five teeth) where it remains locked awaiting its next impulse cycle. And so on.

1831 • GEORGE J. HEISELY

George Jacob Heisely, born November 29, 1789, in Frederick, Maryland, was the oldest son of the seven children of Frederick and Catharina (Hoff) Heisely. He served an apprenticeship with his father, a successful clock and instrument maker in Frederick, Maryland, followed by 11 months of additional training in Lancaster, Pennsylvania, possibly at the clock shop of his grandfather, John George Hoff. Thereafter, George Heisely set up his business in Harrisburg, Pennslyvania, where he specialized in surveying instruments and later in the manufacture of town clocks. On March 13, 1813, he married 17-year-old Anna Maria Kurtz in Harrisburg, but out of patriotism answered the call for the defense of Baltimore during the War of 1812 on August 29, 1814, just four months after the birth of the first of his five children. He served 99 days with the Harrisburg Volunteers, First Regiment, First Brigade, Pennsylvania Militia. An amateur musician, George brought along his flute for entertainment, and thereby hangs a family tradition.

Heisely and the Durang brothers found themselves among the 144 volunteers in Captain Walker's Company marching from Harrisburg to a rendezvous at York, thence to Baltimore. At some point, a copy of Francis Scott Key's poem describing the bombardment of Fort McHenry found its way into the Pennsylvania military camp. The Durangs, professional actors and singers, asked flutist George Heisely to play through his tune book and pick music suitable for Key's rousing words. They settled on an old German song adapted by the English as *Anacreon in Heaven*. Refinements to match the music to the words were made en route to a Baltimore encampment on Gallows Hill. When given leave, the Durang brothers headed for the stage of the Holliday Theatre in Baltimore, where they sang the patriotic song, enthusiastically received, that became our National Anthem. The story could be apocryphal, but it is a good one, and even the *World Book Encyclopedia* concedes that the Durang performance marked the first time the "Star Spangled Banner" was sung in public.

On his return, George Heisely set up in business at Harrisburg, Pennsylvania, and about 1816–17 was joined by Frederick Heisely and family who moved from Frederick, Maryland. For several years the father and son worked together as clock and instrument makers, offering town clocks by the late 1820s. At least two installations are known to have been made, but there are undoubtedly others. In 1829–30 "Frederick Heisely & Son of Harrisburg" made and put up a clock in the cupola of the new town hall at Columbia, Pennsylvania, located below Harrisburg on the east bank of the Susquehanna River. The clock, which has not survived, cost $700, an enormous sum at that time representing about 25% of the total cost of the town hall. The building was razed in the early 1870s, replaced by a larger structure that met the needs of a growing population. The second floor of the new hall had "one of the finest opera houses in the State," seating more than 1,000 people comfortably. The building, destroyed in 1947 by fire, was surmounted by a tower with a bell and clock, probably the original Heisely clock moved from the previous town hall. A second known Heisely town clock suffered a different fate. It was one of few landmarks left standing after Chambersburg, Pennsylvania, was burned to the ground by southern troops during the Civil War. The clock survived the war only to be maimed in recent years by electrification. On March 16, 1831, the commissioners of Chambersburg contracted with the Heiselys to make a four-dial tower clock for the newly constructed market house and town hall at the corner of Queen and Second Streets. Terms of the sale provided for payment of $375 on the day of installation, with the balance of $375 paid after a year's trial. In turn, the Heiselys agreed to cover transportation from Harrisburg, and also the expense of boarding two workers during installation of the clock. The clock's setting dial is signed "F. & G.J. Heisely Harrisburg," indicating that by the early 1830s George was the partner of his aging father. Some have written that George Heisely later made tower clocks on his own, an example cited being the first town clock of Waynesburg, Green County, Pennsylvania, but extensive research has failed to substantiate the claim.

In addition to instrument and clockmaking, George Heisely was as active in town affairs as his father before him. He served as town burgess and was a frequent member of the Harrisburg City Council. In 1820, he helped found the German Society and was active with its Relief Committee. When Pennsylvania was invaded by the Confederate Army, the 72-year-old George Heisely enlisted as a private in Captain Carlson's Company of the Home Guard in 1863. The same year he lost his wife of 50 years; his only son Frederick Kurtz Heisely died earlier at age 36. George Jacob Heisely died at 90 "of old age" on June 27, 1880, and was buried next to his wife in the Harrisburg Cemetery.

Heisely Tower Clocks

(For pictures and description of **FH Model 1**, a related clock, see **1791 • Frederick Heisely,** page 28.)

F/GH Model 1. The two surviving tower clocks of the father and son were made 40 years apart, yet have similarities, particularly the use of roller pinions and in the fine wheelwork. There are also differences, most notable being F/GH Model 1's exemplar chair frame of bolted horizontal and vertical heavy iron bars measuring 26" wide by 25" deep by 35" high overall. The lower part of the chair-shaped frame supports 19½" long, 10" diameter wooden barrels, the 12½" upper frame supports the balance of the clockwork on short sturdy arbors. Both trains have four wheels with five spiral spokes. The 16" diameter great wheels and their ratchets are iron; all other wheels are brass. Arbors pivot in brass-bushed holes and are made of steel as are the *roller* trundle lantern pinions used throughout. Even the 20 pins of the escape wheel have rollers. Description of certain features is limited by the loss of parts due to time train electrification in recent years. Loose parts include oddly shaped deadbeat pallets, one piece with the escapement anchor and a crutch that extends upward from the roller pinion escape wheel! The crutch/pendulum connection is uncertain due to missing parts. The slim 1¼" by ⅜" wooden pendulum rod measures 82" long, including a 9" flat suspension spring. The bob is missing, but the pendulum's computed beat is 1½ seconds. Dial hands are reset by free-wheeling. A fixed brass setting dial outside the frame is marked at the quarters, its single hand turned by the escape wheel arbor. The dial take-off is an old style pinion/contrate wheel combination, driven by the time second wheel arbor. Leading-off rod connections are missing along with the original 4-dial overhead transmission. The fly (now missing) and the locking plate count wheel are mounted outside the frame. The bell strike lever (now missing) is lifted by shaped pins sandwiched between the strike second wheel and an outer support ring. A superior clock of innovative design, more's the pity for sloppy electrification.

F/GH Figure 1. What remains of the time train after electrification. Metal shards below a modified contrate wheel take-off at lower right show resulting part wear. Roller pinions are used throughout.

F/GH Figure 2. Escapement detail. Twenty roller pins on the escape wheel engage unusually shaped deadbeat pallets, which appear to allow for over-swing. The pendulum crutch, unseen here, extends above the pallet arbor.

F/GH Figure 3. Overview of the strike train. The use of a sturdy chair frame provides a long barrel for weekly winding and short sturdy arbors for the wheel trains, a significant improvement over the cage frame of FH Model 1. The train is complete except for a missing fly at upper right. Roller pinions and spiral spoked brass wheels are used throughout. The brass locking plate is friction mounted.

1832 • GEORGE HANDEL HOLBROOK

George Handel Holbrook represents the second generation of four direct descendants, sometimes referred to as the Holbrook Dynasty, whose work spanned 100 years. Best known for their large church bells, the family also made fine pipe organs and probably more tower clocks than any other maker of the 1830–50 period.

George H. Holbrook was born July 21, 1798, in Brookfield, Massachusetts, the oldest child of Major George and Polly (Wood) Holbrook. He learned bell foundry and clockmaking from his father, who, in turn, had served an apprenticeship with Paul Revere of Boston. In 1812, the senior Holbrook suffered near bankruptcy, his health failing as a result. The family tried farming in New Hampshire for a brief period before settling in East Medway (now Millis), Massachusetts, by 1816. The citizens of this small factory town, 20 miles southwest of Boston, needed a large church bell, which the Major, along with his 17-year-old son and other helpers, managed to cast. It was the first of over 11,000 bells cast by three generations of Holbrooks. When the Major retired in 1820, George Handel Holbrook took over and was the family's prime mover for over 50 years. In 1867, he brought his grandson, Edwin Handel Holbrook, into the foundry, and upon his retirement in 1871, the grandson ran the operation until 1882, when the foundry and its patterns were sold to California interests.

Like his father before him, George H. was devoted to the military and classical music. He held every state militia rank up to colonel, for his own reasons refusing promotion to brigadier general when it was offered to him. He also served as the postmaster for 35 years, and as town representative in the 1835 state legislature. His enthusiasm for good music was foreordained, considering his family background and being the namesake of the famous composer George Frederick Handel. He was a skilled violinist and organist. Early in life he was offered the leadership of a theater orchestra in Boston, and later directed the musicians of Boston's Handel and Haydn Society at local musicals. The superior tone of Holbrook bells is attributed to his changing them from "noisy machines into musical instruments."

The year 1830 saw the first stirring of an entirely new enterprise. Working alone and with no previous experience, George H. Holbrook accomplished the monumental task of building a pipe organ for his own use. It turned out to be a fine instrument, and seeing the sale of Holbrook bells as an entree to the sale of church pipe organs as well, he began their manufacture. He joined with a cousin, J. Holbrook Ware, in the partnership of Holbrook & Ware, established in 1837 and set up across from the bell foundry on East Medway's Main Street. They met with considerable success. When Ware retired in 1850, George H. prevailed upon his son, Edwin Lafayette Holbrook, a music teacher in Bridgeport, Connecticut, to take over the East Medway organ manufactory. E.L. Holbrook, perfectly suited to the task, conducted a very successful operation along with his personal career as a traveling concert organist. He compiled a list of 101 E.L. Holbrook pipe organs built by the factory and claimed another 100 could be referred to. The business came to an end with his retirement in the late 1890s.

George H. Holbrook learned tall case, banjo, and tower clock making from his father, Major George Holbrook, and together they set up the Holbrook Clock Shop on Main Street in East Medway. Based on 10 known George H. Holbrook installations, it can be estimated that he made from 30–40 tower clocks between 1830 and 1850. The earliest known clock installation in 1832 at Holliston, Massachusetts, struck on an 1830 Holbrook bell, and by 1854 was accompanied by an E.L. Holbrook pipe organ claimed to be the third largest in the state at that time. In 1834, Holbrook tower clocks put up in West Townsend and Amherst, Massachusetts, joined earlier Holbrook bells in the same locations, as did Holbrook clocks installed in 1836 at Eastport and East Machias, Maine, and a Holbrook clock and bell put up in Chelsea, Vermont, in 1840. Exceptions to this multiple sale of Holbrook products were the 1835 clock installation at East Woodstock, Connecticut, and the 1839 town clock in Keene, New Hampshire, which struck on Meneely and Revere bells respectively. The date and origin of another Holbrook tower clock, now in a private collection, is unknown. The last known George H. Holbrook tower clock was installed in Medway Village Church in 1850, striking on a previously installed 1838 Holbrook bell, both of which were joined in 1861 by an E.L. Holbrook pipe organ, still in regular service and valued today at a quarter million dollars.

George H. Holbrook married Louisa Harding of East Medway on January 1, 1824. Only two of their five children reached adulthood: Edwin Lafayette, the organmaker, and Mary Louisa, who was married and sang with the Handel & Haydn Society of Boston. Tragically, another daughter and two sons, both named for their father, died young. On March 20, 1875, George Handel Holbrook died of tuberculosis in East Medway at the age of 76. For five decades he had directed the outstanding success of three Holbrook products critical to a church's inventory, an accomplishment not matched by any other bell founder, organ manufacturer, or tower clock maker in the world.

George Handel Holbrook Tower Clocks

George H. Holbrook's tower clocks are successors to clocks made 30 years earlier by his father, Major George Holbrook, who in turn was inspired by the horizontal wood-beam flatbeds of Abel Stowell of Worcester. Setting dials are signed in small type, "GEORGE H. HOLBROOK E. MEDWAY, MASS." While differing in some respects, the son's clocks owe a great deal to the layout, part design, and materials used earlier by his father, most noteworthy being the use of steel arc escapement pallets. Basically unchanged are outside dial hand design and its motion work, wheel train style and set-up, the deadbeat pinwheel escapement, rack-and-snail strike control, ratchet-driven fly, and provision for freewheeling. There are improvements. The same type of joined wood-beam frame with a strap-iron flatbed is used, but with longer legs added for comfortable winding height without recourse to the old floor platform. Frames are larger overall, measuring 63" wide by 24" deep by 33" high. The barrels remain mounted at opposite ends across the full flatbed width, but a mid-beam structure added between the barrels allows use of short sturdy arbors on core clockwork. Either 1 or 1½-second pendulums are employed. Other improvements include the addition of winding jacks, and replacement of the old contrate wheel transmission with one using a nest of bevel gears. Further improvements by 1850 include wheels with circular spoking and the necessary linkage to place outside dials well above clock movement level. The most obvious difference between the clocks made by father and son is the latter's decorative use of paint to dress up the overall appearance. Wood-beam frames painted light blue are highlighted with black trim. The strap-iron flatbed frame, the iron bridge, and the strike control levers are painted black with sinuous yellow striping. Paint traces on some brass work suggests that non-working surfaces were originally black.

GHH Figure 1. George Handel Holbrook tower clock overview. It changed very little over the years. The long legs, the mid-table structure between the barrels, added winding jacks, and the fancy paint job are the most obvious differences between this model and the clocks of his father.

GHH Figure 2. Time train second wheel detail. The arbor of this wheel also drives the motion work of a two-hand setting dial, advances the strike control snail, trips the strike, and, on its far end, drives a bevel gear dial take-off and transmission.

GHH Figure 3. Escapement detail. The pallet arrangement, consisting of one replaceable steel arc with deadbeat ends, was introduced by George Handel Holbrook's father as early as 1809. A swing-aside cap at the near end of the pallet arbor allows disengagement of the pallet arbor to set the hands ahead by freewheeling.

GHH Figure 4. Late model Holbrook tower clocks (ca. 1850) feature spiral spoking of the escape wheel and circle spoking of all other wheels including those in the winding jack, seen here and in the dial motion work.

1833 • ELI TERRY

Eli Terry, born on April 13, 1772, was the son of Samuel and Hildah Terry. They lived about eight miles northeast of Hartford, Connecticut, in East Windsor (redesignated South Windsor), where Eli served as apprentice to Daniel Burnap, and probably to the Cheneys of East Hartford. At 20 he set up on his own in East Windsor as a clockmaker, sharing space in the family workshop. About two years later he moved 30 miles southwest to Northbury (now Plymouth), seeking a less competitive marketplace than the Hartford area. It was hilly country with fast moving streams, a natural source of water power. He married Eunice Warner in 1795. Legend has it they were so poor they set up housekeeping with a single chair, but that it was sufficient for the honeymoon. Their children included Eli Jr. (1799–1841), Henry (1801–1877), and Silas Burnam (1807–1876), all instructed by their father and successful as clockmakers in their own right.

Early on, Eli Terry worked in the old way, as a craftsman making tall clocks to the order, or peddling them on horseback. His 1797 U.S. Patent for an "Equation Clock" was an impressive display of inventive powers, but did little to improve his income. By 1803, he abandoned itinerant peddling, turning by 1806 to volume production of wooden clock movements using water power to drive his saws and other clockmaking machinery. Craftsmen before Eli had made small lots of duplicate parts, but he pioneered in the manufacture of parts by the thousands. His completion of the 1806 Porter Contract—making 4,000 "hang-up" wood clock movements in three years time—was a seminal event in clockmaking history! Techniques developed in this period led to Eli's mass production of low-cost, 30-hour, time-and-strike, mantel clocks, shortly thereafter encased as the famous pillar and scroll which sold in the hundreds of thousands. The details of this most productive period in his life are well documented. Less familiar is the story of Eli's retirement when, according to Henry Terry, "He did not make clocks by the hundred, nor even by the dozen... He was during many years engaged in making now and then a church clock, a few watch-regulators and the like..."

Eli's first known tower clock was installed by 1825 at a cost of $250 in the Centre Church on the Town Green of New Haven, Connecticut. The clock had a compensated pendulum and was claimed by some to tell both mean and apparent time. In fact, the clock only told mean time as this was the cause of its early removal. Before 1800, Simeon Jocelin had put up on the same Town Green a tower clock for Yale College, with an attachment of his invention that showed *apparent* time as the college conducted classes by the sun. Having two public clocks located a few hundred yards apart, at best agreeing with the other only four times a year, brought about a spirited controversy in the press. Eli Terry joined the fray, writing to the editor, in part, that with mean time "all good clocks and watches can be kept nearly alike, and all appointments kept with a good degree of precision...a common clock cannot keep apparent time; the use of clocks and watches is to keep mean time..." He was correct, of course, but it did not halt the debate or the early removal of his church clock from the Town Green.

The rejected New Haven clock, or one like it, was donated by Eli in the early 1830s to the second Meeting House of the Congregational Church at Plymouth, Connecticut, where the Terry family were members. Before the building was torn down in 1837, its clock and bell (described as "practically new") were removed and reinstalled in a new third Meeting House on the Plymouth Green, where the clock runs today (discretely electrified). It is unsigned but its unique features correspond to Henry Terry's descriptions of his father's work:

> The church clocks were made in three independent parts...The time-keeping part was of the ordinary size, and moved by a separate weight. The striking part was moved by one large weight, and the dial-wheels by another, while that of the time-keeping part weighed only three or four pounds. The dial wheels, hands or pointers, moved only once in a minute...These clocks were made with compensation pendulum rods, of his own design, and the escapement after a model of his own.

Eli was also a member of the Congregational Church of Terryville, Connecticut, when it was organized in 1838. He contributed $300 to help raise the meeting house, and promised, "if my health permits, a Clock for the steeple." He did make such a clock. Pictures taken before a destructive 1967 church fire show it to have been of wooden flatbed construction similar to the one in Plymouth. A third clock having a wooden chair frame and some large cast-iron wheels, but working on the same three-part principle, has survived from neighboring Plymouth Hollow (now Thomaston).

Eli Terry emerges as a strong individualist who had visions and the genius to bring them about, leaving the accumulation of great wealth to those who followed. His rewards were substantial as he distributed over $100,000 to his beneficiaries, but he was content with a retirement income of $3,000 a year as sufficient for his temporal needs. Eli Terry died on February 24, 1852, at age 79 in Terryville.

Eli Terry Tower Clocks

The movement of the clock in the Congregational Church of Plymouth is located on the same level as a single outside dial on the building's front gable. The three principal parts, each driven by separate weights, consist of a brass regulator plus wild cherry time and strike trains. They are mounted on an open frame of upended cherry planks with dovetail corners measuring about 48" wide by 24" deep by 9" high. Winding barrels span the depth of the frame at opposite ends, strike to the left, time to the right. The rest of the sawn-teeth wheels and the strike control levers are mounted on a shallow, hardwood vertical structure, 21" high, set back at mid-frame between the barrels. Strike control is by a sheet metal count wheel. Centered up front and powered by its own 11-pound weight, the clock's most noteworthy feature is a brass wheel precision regulator. It features Harrison maintaining power and a very noteworthy deadbeat escapement. The regulator's one-second pendulum incorporates dual-spring suspension and bi-metal temperature compensation of Terry's own design. The strike train of the Plymouth clock is conventional. The time (or dial) train only runs when released by the time regulator, and it employs a separate fly to cushion the advance of the time train at one-minute intervals. Rotating outside the regulator front plate is a flanged wheel with 30 evenly spaced slots. One of six spokes of a "spider" trigger connected to the time train rides on a tooth of the flanged wheel until it passes through a slot. This unlocks the time train to advance the outside dial hands a full minute. As the next spoke of the rotating "spider" contacts the next tooth of the flanged wheel, the train is again locked for a minute until that spoke passes through the next slot, again releasing the time train to advance a full minute. And so on. Eli's Terryville clock is similar to the one described above at Plymouth; major differences being the use of a wood wheel time controller and also use of a rack-and-snail strike control, favored in the tower clocks of his brother, Samuel Terry. More sophisticated metal variations of Eli's three-part system were used by the Turret & Marine Clock Co. after 1858 and by Charles Fasoldt after 1872.

*Above, ET Figure 1. Overview of Eli Terry's Plymouth tower clock, strike train to the left and the time train to the right, each with a separate fly. Between the two is an independently powered brass time regulator, its 1-second pendulum swinging front-to-back rather than side-to-side. **Below**, ET Figure 2. Plymouth time regulator detail. Note one of six spokes of the triggering "spider" at rest on a tooth of the regulator's external slotted wheel. The triggering action is described in the text. To the left of the regulator is a friction-mounted sheet metal count wheel and its associated 78-tooth wooden drive wheel.*

Left, ET Figure 3. Plymouth time regulator pendulum detail. Eli Terry's bi-metal temperature compensation includes hinged levers. An 11-pound lead driving weight has a straight fall off the regulator barrel, passing through a hole in the floor of the clock room. **Right**, ET Figure 4. The experimental Thomaston church clock. A mixture of wood and metal components, the vertical portion of its wooden chair frame measures 36" high. Composed of assorted wood and cast-iron wheels and wood and iron arbors, its 6" by 11" wood wheel regulator operates by separate weight and incorporates a variation of the Plymouth triggering mechanism.

1835 • BENJAMIN MORRILL

Benjamin Morrill, the second son and next to the youngest of the six children of Samuel and Sarah Morrill, was born on January 16, 1794, in Boscawen, a village 10 miles north of Concord, New Hampshire. He had the usual education of the day, perhaps with greater emphasis on religion as his grandfather was an ordained minister and teacher who graduated from Harvard College in 1755. It is not known where Morrill learned clockmaking or if he served an apprenticeship, but he had a natural bent for mechanics and was reputedly a man of great ingenuity and skill, a fact borne out by the quality and diversity of his clockwork that has survived. He is best known for, and is consid-

ered by some to have originated, the distinctive New Hampshire mirror clock, but he also made fine tall case, Massachusetts shelf, and banjo clocks. In addition, he made at least three known tower clocks that introduce a number of original features. In the 1830s, the demand for hand-crafted clocks slackened in the face of competition from the low-cost Connecticut factory product. Joseph Chadwick, a fellow Boscawen clockmaker (and Morrill's brother-in-law) retired from the business and moved to Norwich, Vermont, but Morrill persisted in the town where he was born and lived all of his life. When clockmaking became unprofitable, he diversified his line to include counter scales of up to 100 pounds capacity. He also capitalized on his taste for good music and considerable talent in the field. About 1841, he began the manufacture of melodeons and seraphines, small vacuum-operated reed organs of

2 to 2½ octave range invented in the early 1800s. He was a founder of Boscawen's Martin Luther Society, a group for "the Cultivation of Music of a Higher Order" in which he sang for many years.

Morrill married twice, first before 1820 to Mehetable Eastman, probably of Boscawen. They had at least two children, although the 1830 and 1840 censuses show additional household minors that could have been Morrill children or apprentices. After his first wife's death, he married Mary Choat[e] of Derry, New Hampshire, who bore him a daughter, Mary F. on August 24, 1843. Apparently Benjamin Morrill lived out his last years quietly and in reasonable comfort in the residence erected by his minister grandfather. He died at home on April 21, 1857 at age 63.

Benjamin Morrill Tower Clocks

All three of Morrill's surviving tower clocks were first installed in the church towers of small New Hampshire towns. None are signed by Morrill, and all three vary in detail; however, two are well-documented as made by Morrill and all three clocks share common features which outweigh differences by far. Only a few telltale parts have survived from his earliest clock put up in 1835 for $300 in the First Parish Meeting House at Dover. A second clock, installed about the same time in the Congregational Church at Henniker, is intact, now displayed at the American Clock & Watch Museum in Bristol, Connecticut. The third Morrill church clock, a recent discovery, is hand-wound and running where it was installed in Orford, New Hampshire, probably around 1850.

Morrill's clock frames descend from the wood-beam horizontal frame flatbeds pioneered by Abel Stowell of Worcester, Massachusetts, however, as is the case with George Handel Holbrook, his use of longer legs eliminates the need for a floor platform. The Henniker flatbed table measures 57" wide by 26" deep by 31" high, topped by a 73" wood-beam vertical post that supports a four-dial transmission on its upper end. The frame's flatbed rails extend with decoratively cut "bumpers," a feature also used by fellow New Hampshire clockmaker Stephen Hasham. The addition of a mid-frame structure and two pair of distinctively shaped A-frames (spaced 12" shoulder-to-shoulder)

make for a compact core movement with short sturdy arbors. Morrill's minute wheels make two revolutions per hour, rather than the usual one, and the time trains vary from three wheels at Henniker to four wheels at Dover and Orford. Clock trains use a mix of high tooth count cast-iron and brass wheels, with almost all wheels, including those in the motion work, decoratively spoked. The arbors and cut-leaf pinions are highly polished. Barrel and great wheel placement varies from being mounted on the upper flatbed rails in Dover and Henniker, to below the flatbed in Orford's two-tier arrangement. All three clocks employ winding jacks but lack maintaining power. As originally installed, the Dover clock had a single outside dial driven directly from the mechanism; later Morrill added two additional outside dials, powered by rods with bevel gears angled back from the original motion work of the center dial. Dial hands are reset by freewheeling the time train, while referring to a setting dial on the dial take-off. Pinwheel escapements with steel deadbeat pallets are used throughout, but vary in pin counts from 18 to 46. Pallet style also differs, with the Henniker movement using separate pallets working on one side of the pinwheel, while at Orford pins on opposite sides of the wheel act on the deadbeat ends of a continuous arc of steel (see **Holbrook**). Pendulums also vary from 2 to 1¼ second beat, and are rated by nut adjustment under the bob. Morrill's notable contribution to strike control design is his introduction of a weight-driven *straight horizontal* rack and tail that bears directly on the snail. The non-working surfaces of his cast-iron wheels are painted black, as are the A-frames, and the winding jack gears. The steel arbors and cut-leaf pinions are highly polished, and the mortise-and-tenon joined rock maple frames are painted a light green. Variations in Morrill's tower clocks suggest experimentation to optimize cost, performance and ease of maintenance. His innovative placement of a four-dial transmission well above the movement was a significant advance over the conventional limit of only three outside dials. His horizontal strike rack and tail became an accepted form used by later makers such as Howard, Seth Thomas, and George Stevens. (Donn Haven Lathrop)

BM Figure 1. Overview of Morrill's tower clock from Henniker, New Hampshire. The rock maple frame is mortise-and-tenon joined. Both barrels are wood, with cast-iron great wheels and winding jacks. The strike great wheel is the bell lever pinwheel. Note compact core clockwork, and the four-dial transmission (bevel gears missing) mounted well above the movement.

BM Figure 2. Henniker time and strike train wheels, with unaccountably varied spoking, are mounted in frame bearing blocks and in bushed holes in cast and forged-iron A-frames of distinctive shape. The time train has only three wheels. Parallel to the flatbed's center beam is Morrill's innovative rack; when tripped, a counter weight slides the straight, one-piece rack and tail into contact with the snail.

BM Figure 3. Morrill's Henniker escapement/dial take-off detail. Two replaceable steel deadbeat pallets mounted on a single pallet arm are impulsed by pins on the one side of a high pin-count escape wheel. The vertical dial take-off, transmission, setting dial, and strike control snail are driven, and the strike is tripped, via the time second wheel arbor by a complex series of wheels, pinions and bevel gears.

1836 • JACOB CUSTER

Custer's inventive mind often changed course, leading him in many directions. Known as the mechanical wizard of Norristown, it was said he never saw a machine he could not improve upon. Jacob Detweiler Custer was born on March 5, 1805, in Worcester Township, Pennsylvania, about 20 miles northwest of Philadelphia. His Pennsylvania Dutch Mennonite father was a farmer whose "thunder" grist mill only worked after a major rain storm. Custer was largely self-educated, not attending the local schools until after the age of 16, and then only for a few months at a time.

When the farm chores were done he focused on machines of any kind. He is reported as a boy to have repaired the broken mainspring of his father's watch, and also the watch of a school teacher who spread the word of his mechanical skill. Eventually he peddled along country roads, then developed enough of a following by 1824 to set up a small repair shop near Shannonville. Five years later he moved to Lower Province Township and advertised in a Norristown newspaper, "JACOB CUSTER...will do all kinds of repairs to clocks and watches...Also gold and silver ware, made and repaired, and lettering [engraving] done at the shortest notice." In 1830 at the age of 25 he opened a larger shop at the corner of Egypt and Water Streets in Norristown, the Montgomery County seat and commercial center. The same year he bought the best tools from the estate sale of clockmaker Seneca Lukens and also received a U.S. Patent for a more easily repaired and regulated clock that used a third less machinery. The works of Custer's tall case and mantel clocks show ongoing experimentation, particularly in the simplification of motion work and strike control. He made about 30 so-called "Pennsylvania pillar & scrolls." Their cases are roughly comparable to Eli Terry's famous 30-hour shelf clocks, but feature brass works running eight days, moon phase, alarm, and a rotary bell hammer.

In 1832, Custer moved to Main and Swede Streets in Norristown, and shortly thereafter built a small factory at Main and Green. Nearby was a schoolhouse with a small tower for which Custer volunteered to build a clock. Before the job was done the Town Council commandeered it for their own use as a town clock in the courthouse cupola of Montgomery County. In the next 30 years Custer made well over a dozen tower clocks of his own unique design. Installations included town clocks in Pennsylvania—at Philadelphia, Norristown (2), Uniontown, Danville, Gettysburg, Waynesboro, Phoenixville, Coatesville, and Schuylkill Falls, in New Jersey—at Burlington and Glassboro, and as far away as South Carolina, Alabama, and Ohio. In 1856 he replaced the early courthouse clock with an improved model. As late as May 1861, he installed a town clock for $300, subscribed to by the citizens of Waynesboro. Many examples survive. His clock in Burlington is still hand-wound time and strike, and accurate within seconds a week. About 1850, clockmaker David Anderson paid tribute to Custer's design by making a modified, smaller version for Waynesburg (now Honey Brook), Pennsylvania.

Moving easily from the largest timekeepers to the smallest, Custer made about 15 watches of his own design between 1840 and 1845, fabricating the gold cases and *all parts* except hairsprings and fusee chains. In 1844 he sought a more affluent marketplace in Philadelphia, but soon returned to Norristown where he remained the rest of his life. The extent and range of Custer's achievements is astounding considering his limited resources. At one time he is at the Norristown wharf, working on improved riverboat propellers, and at another time building steam engines at the Stony Creek sawmill. His clockwork mechanisms rotated the lights on many coastal lighthouses, and 45 or more of his fog bell alarms (with patented maintaining power) were the government's machines of choice until the advent of the crane-striker after 1865. He invented a forced lubrication grease cup and a mini bullet-making machine used extensively during the Civil War. For diversion, he made his own shoes, and at one time fashioned a clockwork umbrella that opened and shut automatically to advertise a local parasol maker

For all of his hard work and genius, Custer lived modestly, charging only $1.50 a day for services regardless of the task. Even so he was often cheated, but, by constant application, was able to plead his own patent infringement claims. Late in life he professed atheism, turning his back on the faith he had long supported as an enthusiastic lay preacher. Custer married Mary B. Carlisle of York Mills, Pennsylvania, on April 14, 1842. He was known to be a devoted husband and father who often skipped work to play with his five children. In personal appearance, he was of medium height and of ruddy complexion with light colored hair. Jacob Custer died in Norristown on September 30, 1871, at the age of 66.

Jacob Custer Tower Clocks

All of Custer's surviving tower clocks are of the same type, being of substantial cast-iron plate-and-pillar construction held together with iron wedges. They measure 33½" wide by 22¾" deep by 50¼" high and are signed in raised letters, "J. CUSTER NORRISTOWN, PA." Moving parts are also cast iron, although later clocks make selective use of brass wheels. The 20-tooth escape wheel is brass, pivoting along with the fly in brass bushed holes. The escapement is deadbeat, employing a one-piece forged-iron anchor with hardened pallets. The two-second, lenticular bob pendulum has no crutch, being hung by a short stiff spring extending from the pallet arbor. Its wooden rod, of elaborate telescoping construction, permits rating the pendulum at mechanism level. Custer maintaining power is also unusual, being a steel coiled spring (flat or wire) wound around the time third wheel arbor. Time and strike barrels are wound by winding squares on the second wheel arbors. The 7" diameter strike barrels with 27" great wheels serve to take up the weight line, aided by a winding jack on the strike side. The strike train's second wheel is the strike pinwheel that lifts the bell lever. A large two-vane ratchet-driven fly is protected between the plates. Strike control is by a notched flange wheel with appropriate levers mounted outside the back of the frame. High on the same back side of the frame is the clock's most unique feature, a duplex bevel gear transmission that eliminates the need for reduction gearing behind each outside dial. Motion coming from two concentric nests of bevel gears conveys minute and hour rotation directly to the outside dial hands via iron rods (for minutes) inside sheet metal tubes (for hours). The concentric leading-off rods are supported on their dial end by two-wheel roller bearings. Provision is made at the transmission for resetting the hands in either direction without stopping the clock. Strangely missing in this ingenious arrangement is an integral setting dial.

JC Figure 1. Custer's tower clock, overall front view. Both plates are cast from the same pattern. Suspended between the frame plates, a two-second pendulum extends above the center of the front plate and through a hole in the floor below. Note the hand crank on the time side second wheel arbor and the winding jack aid on the strike side. The time train second wheel is not original.

JC Figure 2. Escapement detail. The 20-tooth wheel is brass; the anchor is formed from a single piece of iron bar stock with tempered deadbeat pallet ends. Provision is made for changes in anchor depthing.

JC Figure 3. Upper frame rear overview. At top center is a duplex bevel gear transmission and below it the 12-to-1 driving gear connections from the escape wheel arbor. At lower left, a friction mounted pinion with crank allows the hands to be reset in either direction without stopping the clock. To the lower right is the flange-type count wheel with associated strike control levers.

JC Figure 4. Custer's transmission detail. The hands of four outside dials are driven by leading-off rods from the two concentric nests of bevel gears mounted on the clock frame. Leading-off rods (consisting of iron rods inside of sheet metal tubes) radiate out to the outside dial minute and hour hands, eliminating all need for motion work behind each outside dial plate.

1836 • CHASE & QUIMBY

The town clock in the steeple of the First Church of Belfast stands alone as Maine's only tower clock made and kept in operation for over 150 years due entirely to hometown talent. In the early 1830s, town Selectmen wanted a clock befitting Belfast's role as the commercial center for a growing population around the shores of Penobscot Bay. Put off by the high price quoted for a "factory clock," they offered the job to local independent clockmakers Timothy Chase and Phineas P. Quimby.

Phineas Parkhurst Quimby was born on February 16, 1802, in Lebanon, New Hampshire, the son of Jonathan and Susannah (White) Quimby. His father was a poor blacksmith who moved his family to Belfast about 1804. After irregular schooling, Phineas probably served as apprentice to his older brother William, who succeeded in 1821 to a clockmaking business established in 1806 by Abiel Eastman of Belfast. By nature, Phineas was of an inventive turn of mind, experimenting with "photographic miniatures" (daguerreotypes), and receiving patents for "a machine for sawing coach-panels and veneer from logs" in 1829,

and for a "screw and compound steering apparatus for sailing vessels" in 1850. Phineas also made Willard-type banjos, and about 1835 joined with Chase in the design and construction of the Belfast town clock. Later, by dint of extensive reading and personal experimentation, he became expert in mesmerism and was called Dr. Quimby because of his astonishing ability to relieve pain and suffering by hypnotism. One disciple credited his notions on mental healing as the catalyst that changed her own thinking, but she abandoned him after a few years because of his hostility to religion. The disciple's name was Mary Baker Eddy, founder of the Christian Science faith. Quimby died in Belfast on January 16, 1866, leaving a wife and several children.

Timothy Chase was born in Charlton, Massachusetts, in 1793, and as a young man learned his trade working in a clock factory near Boston. The factory fell on hard times, and, as was the case with many hard pressed manufactories, paid off its employees with clocks in lieu of cash. Eventually Chase tired of the arrangement. He took his hoard of clocks, his wife, and his infant son by coastal schooner along the Maine coast, settling in Head Of Tide (North Belfast), where he set up shop as a clockmaker in 1818. In 1826, he moved into Belfast proper, establishing a jewelry store on Main Street where he prospered. Chase was highly regarded, not only for watch repair and his fine tall case clocks, complete with second hand, calendar and moonphase, but as a praise-worthy gunsmith, an expert in metallurgy and chemistry and, eventually, as Grand Master of the local Masonic Lodge. After his death in 1875, the jewelry store continued in business at the same location, run by his descendants until 1935, when it was sold to W.G. Stover, the establishment's watchmaker for 14 years. In 1960, he sold the business to his son, Henry C. Stover, the custodian of Belfast's town clock for almost 40 years, and the man who devised the electrical rewind system that now drives the mechanism.

When approached by the Selectmen, Timothy Chase and Phineas Quimby agreed to combine their talents to design and construct a town clock not to exceed the cost of about $200. A local machine shop located at Head of Tide made all the parts. Installed in the steeple of the imposing First Church of Belfast, the clock is on high ground, tolling the hours on a Revere & Son bell and displaying time on three 11-foot dials visible from Belfast harbor, plus a smaller eight-foot dial facing to the rear. It was first set running on October 3, 1836, and with some short rests, has run ever since, a testimonial to hometown ingenuity and dedication.

Chase & Quimby Tower Clock

The Belfast clock design—inline brass wheel trains with wood winding barrels, arbors running the full depth of the horizontal flatbed frame, large wheel dial motion work, and a pinwheel deadbeat escapement—reflects precedents set about 1800–1814 by earlier clockmakers working in the vicinity of Worcester, Massachusetts. Overall, the frame measures 59" wide by 23" deep by 28" high, with a 9" high iron bridge at mid-frame supporting the pallet arbor and pendulum suspension. Brass bearing blocks screwed to the flatbed are of plain functional design. Frame construction differs in its use of a wood-beam flatbed: two wood rails with spacers at each end are raised to convenient winding height by cast-iron arch-supported legs that run across the 59" flatbed dimension, front and back. A unique split click on the Harrison maintaining power ratchet has three pivoting blades of graduated length to avoid backlash. Power is delivered to the motion work of four outside dials set on two levels by a direct connection to the minute wheel arbor, plus bevel gear connections to a three-dial transmission at floor level. Leading-off rods employ unusual leather-pad universal joints and are supported at their dial ends by twin-wheel roller bearings. The strike is tripped by a crank-like extension on the minute wheel arbor, and the bell strike lever is lifted by pins on the rim of the strike second wheel. The clock's original rack-and-snail strike control was replaced in 1886 by a count wheel disk with axial stop pins. Other changes over the years include a counterpoise added to the angled pallet arms, and the addition in 1976 of electrical rewind systems on both time and strike. Otherwise, the original parts—including its wood rod lenticular bob pendulum—are as made.

C&Q Figure 1. Belfast clock front view prior to electrification, time train to the right. The train's second (or minute) wheel arbor also drives four outside dials on two levels, trips the strike, and, in the foreground, appears to have provided for a setting dial, now missing. At the bottom left is the strike's pin-type count wheel.

VIVIAN DON

Above, C&Q Figure 2. Harrison maintaining power detail. A flat spring brazed to the hub of the time great wheel bears on a stud of the maintaining power ratchet. To the left (displayed to show their graduated length) is the split click designed to assure catching a tooth on the Harrison maintaining power ratchet. ***Below***, C&Q Figure 3. Back view of the Belfast clock as seen today (obscured by electrification and supporting timber) time is to the left, strike to the right. The pendulum beats at 50 to the minute. The fly is protectively mounted within the frame. The clock strikes regularly on an 1819 Revere & Son bell located overhead.

1838 • EPHRAIM NILES BYRAM

Among those bringing fame to the whaling seaport of Sag Harbor, New York, on eastern Long Island, was clockmaker Ephraim Niles Byram, born on November 25, 1809, the son of master carpenter Eliab Byram and Cynthia (Clark) Byram. Ephraim did poorly at school and left early, educating himself in the natural sciences, astronomy, and mechanics by diligent reading. Like most boys, he was drawn to Sag Harbor's busy docks. An interest in navigation led to making his own tools to repair and maintain the compasses, telescopes and chronometers of the whaling ship masters, a skill that provided a steady source of income most of his working life. Astronomy was another lifelong interest. In his early 20's, he made a large celestial globe and shortly thereafter a spectacular clockwork planetarium. The machine occupied a space 15-feet square and incorporated an illuminated sun, around which the revolving planets and all their moons orbited, apparently unsupported in open space! It created a sensation in several neighboring states and won a gold medal at the 1836 American Institute Fair, establishing Byram's reputation as a mechanical genius.

In 1838, Byram made a tower clock for Sag Harbor's new Methodist Church for which he was paid $370, or about 84 cents a day. In November 1845, he put up a second clock in Sag Harbor's "Whaling Church." Its tall wooden steeple swayed in the wind, throwing the pendulum out of beat, so the clock was moved to nearby East Hampton Presbyterian Church, where it continues to run, gutted and electrified since 1969. These first tower clocks were extremely accurate (scoring 1 minute 16 seconds error in 6 months), establishing Byram as the maker of what *Scientific American* called "some of the finest clocks in the world." In June 1850, he installed a town clock in the Episcopal Church of Newtown (now Elmhurst), New York, at a cost of $500. This caught the eye of John Sherry, a Sag Harbor entrepreneur with a brass foundry called the Oakland Works. Between 1850 and 1854, they worked in partnership as Sherry & Byram, with Sherry the businessman and Byram the shop superintendent. Sherry's aggressive promotion of his partner's mechanical genius paid off quickly with far flung clock installations at increased prices: at LaGrange Female Institute in Georgia for $800; at Virginia Military Institute for $700; at New London, Connecticut, for $800; at Hempstead, New York, for $638; also town clocks at Belvidere, New Jersey, and McConnellsburg, Pennsylvania; and, in addition, 7-foot illuminated glass dials for New York City Hall at $2,000 and for Philadelphia's State House at $1,000. Finally in 1853, after long negotiations, $750 was agreed to for their most prestigious clock installation in New York City Hall.

In 1854 Byram broke off from Sherry, thereafter working alone. In 1855 he installed a $2,000 clock at the Walnut Street Church in Louisville, Kentucky; in 1856, a $1,050 clock at the Plymouth Church in Rochester, New York; and in 1858, his last tower clock for $940 at West Point's U.S. Military Academy (using cadet buttons for dial minute bits). Byram's final horological effort, an ornately carved tall case clock made for his own use, survives in the Sag Harbor Public Library. Unfortunately, the best of Byram's tower clocks have been lost to natural disasters or urban renewal over the years. Of five survivors (three in parts), only two of his smaller model clocks at Belvidere, New Jersey, and Hempstead, New York, continue to operate, the latter with electric rewind.

During and after his tower clock making period, Byram remained the village mechanic who could make or fix anything from umbrellas to fire engines. In the 1840s he bought land near the Oakland Works and finally completed a home on it in 1852. The house was of distinctive batten board architecture, with a privy to match, plus a tower for astronomical observations, and a wing for his library, the largest in town. In 1857 at the age of 45, Byram met and married 18-year-old Cornelia Pierce, a Cooper Union student and a gifted artist and musician. He was devoted to her and their two sons and a daughter, writing to them individually, often daily, when away on business. In later years a heart condition limited his labors to bookbinding, at which he was expert. On June 27, 1881, after a pleasant country excursion with his family, Ephraim Byram died in his home at the age of 71. His modest estate included an extensive library, bookbinding equipment, and $5,000 in the Seaman's Savings Bank.

Ephraim Byram Tower Clocks

Byram clock models vary in size and quality but all bear a family resemblance, the frames being of cast-iron plate-and-pillar construction with square corner posts. All run eight days, time and strike, with rack-and-snail strike control and Harrison maintaining power. The early Sag Harbor church clocks have ball finial corner posts and measure 42" wide by 18" deep by 25" high, the wheel trains running between plates in brass bushed pivot holes. Clocks from 1850 onward have decorative flat-top posts and are extremely compact, with arbors running in brass or gunmetal bearing blocks screwed flush to upper and lower cast-iron flatbed rails, and the movement separated from a skeletonized cast-iron floor stand by a base plate. Sherry & Byram offered five models ranging *down* in price and sophistication. For example, the lower end Model No. 4 measured 33" wide by 18" deep by 39" high, with a 1½-second pendulum and a four-dial transmission; it had a 50-year estimated life warranted not to exceed 12 minutes variation in a year. On the upper end,

Model No. 1 weighed 1,000 pounds and measured 48" wide by 24" deep by 54" high, offering special features and an estimated life of 300 years warranted not to exceed two minutes error a year. No top line models have survived, but *Scientific American* describes one made for New York City Hall, later lost by fire. All wheels and barrels were of the purest hardened brass, the great wheels being 20" in diameter and weighing 60 pounds each. Polished steel arbors with tempered pivots ran in gunmetal bushings, almost impervious to wear. Both barrels had winding jacks. The deadbeat escapement had jeweled pivot holes and pallets of highly polished agate. A two-second pendulum was suspended on a braced iron column independent of the frame, and featured Byram's unique temperature compensation and compound rating device. In short, *Scientific American* described Sherry & Byram's Model 1 as "equal if not superior to any in the world." The surviving clocks at Hempstead and Belvidere are of the smaller Model 4 type. Strike train is conventional, with the bell strike lever lifted by studs on the second wheel, and a heavy two-blade ratchet-driven fly mounted out-side the frame. Wheels added to the usual four-wheel time train drive a center wheel that turns a bevel gear take-off, trips the strike, and advances the strike control snail. The added wheels also drive a four-dial transmission located, at Belvidere, below the movement, and easily disconnected from the time train to reset the hands in either direction without stopping the clock. Neither clock has an integral setting dial. Replaceable steel pallets are of the *half-dead* type—all impulse comes from deadbeat pallet ends. Their curved resting faces add a slight recoil, said to be self-correcting in tower clocks typically subjected to great friction and variation in train force. Pendulums with round wood rods are rated below their cannonball bobs. They are suspended from a freestanding vertical beam and impulsed by a rod connection to the escapement crutch, as with Morbier clocks. The transmission of the surviving clock at Hempstead is located well above the movement. Its pendulum features Byram's unique compensator, a brass napkin ring free to move up or down on the round rod above the pendulum bob to compensate for changes in temperature.

ENB Figure 1. Overall rear view of the Belvidere Byram. Note corner newel posts, the upper and lower flatbeds, with inset bearing blocks at both levels. At left, the pendulum is suspended from a sturdy wooden beam apart from the clockwork, connected by a hinged rod to the escapement crutch.

Left, ENB Figure 2. Tooth form and dial resetting detail. Unscrewing the large hand knob and offsetting the wheel disconnects the transmission from the time train, allowing resetting of the dial hands forward or backward without stopping the clock. **Right**, ENB Figure 3. Byram's elegant escapements have fine long teeth and replaceable tempered steel pallets mortised into a decoratively cut brass anchor. The pallets are of the half-dead type, having deadbeat impulse faces, and resting sides curved to give a slight recoil. **Below**, ENB Figure 4. Front view detail. All strike control components, including the fly, are on the front (winding side) of the works. The snail drive wheel is advanced by an open-ended lantern pinion mounted on the center wheel arbor along with a strike trip cam. The rack is spring loaded for positive tail contact with the snail, and employs a one-tooth gathering pallet.

1839 • ANDREW MENEELY

Andrew Meneely and the family members who succeeded him (his wife, sons, grandsons and a brother-in-law) made the environs of Troy, New York, the bell foundry capital of America. Located a few miles north of Albany on the Hudson River, tens of thousands of bells were sold in a world market until the last of the Meneely-run enterprises shut down in the 1950s. In later years, Andrew Meneely, the patriarch of the clan, followed the lead of other bell foundrymen such as Benjamin Hanks and the Holbrooks by making a limited number of large tower clocks, an obvious adjunct of steeple bells.

Meneely was born in Washington, New York, in 1801, the son of a North Ireland immigrant who settled on the west bank of the Hudson River opposite Troy in 1795. Washington joined with neighboring Gibbonsville and Port Schuyler in 1836 as the town of West Troy, renamed Watervliet in 1899. At the age of 17, Meneely started as an apprentice to Julius Hanks, who ran the Gibbonsville brass foundry established in 1808 by his father, Benjamin Hanks. The foundry offered large bells of all sizes, cannons, tower clocks and surveying instruments. In 1824, Meneely went to Auburn, New York, to improve his instrument-making skills with Horatio Hanks, Julius' younger brother. Toward the middle of 1826, Meneely returned to Gibbonsville where he established his own foundry at Broad and Rochester Streets, several blocks northeast of the earlier Hanks site. In November of the same year, he married Philena Hanks, the oldest child of Benjamin Hanks' youngest brother. Their five children included Edwin, George, and Clinton Hanks Meneely, all of whom played an active role in the bell foundry business, either working with their father, or together, or in a diehard fraternal competition which ended up in court as Meneely vs. Meneely.

Andrew Meneely ran a very successful establishment. He first rented and then bought a shop and its contents on property Lot 14, then expanded his holdings to eight or more lots over the next two decades. The principal manufactory consisted of a large cluster of one and two-story buildings with many chimneys. He sold bells of all sizes for churches, steamboats and factories, town clocks, transit instruments, plus improved surveyor's levels and compasses. He also supplied to order church and parlor organs, along with brass and copper castings of all sorts. At the 1842-43 American Institute Fair, his bells won a silver medal and his town clock a diploma. A Meneely handbill headed "CHURCH BELLS AND TOWN CLOCKS" proclaimed that in the two-year period ending January 1, 1847, 645 bells had been cast, one being the largest ever cast in this country. Meneely agents covered the territory around Baltimore, Montreal, New Orleans, and New York City.

Sales boomed in the mid-1830s, although there may have been problems with cash flow, as Meneely took on a partner, Jonas Oothout (Meneely & Oothout) in 1836. They were entrepreneurs of kindred vigor, with Jonas Oothout participating in all business decisions, including a generous expansion of property holdings. The partnership ended in March 1841, with Meneely buying out Oothout's share for $5000, and splitting profits from pending sales. In 1849, his son Edwin joined the partnership of Andrew Meneely & Son, and sales continued to climb, reaching $122,255.36 by 1850.

Company records show that at least 10 Meneely church clocks were installed between 1845 and 1852, excluding at least one other known to have survived from about 1839. It is likely that Andrew Meneely learned what he knew about horology from Benjamin and Julius Hanks, who were both documented tower clock makers, although none of their work is known to have survived so comparisons can be made. While most Meneely clocks were sold to small towns in upstate New York, installations have been identified as far away as Virginia, Ohio, and Tennessee. Examples have survived in New York State at New Paltz, Eaton, Salem, and Trumansburg. Unfortunately, all are inoperative and largely abandoned.

In addition to attending to business, Meneely was twice president of the village and an ardent Presbyterian, serving as a lifetime ruling elder of the church. His portrait shows a slim, handsome, balding man with a sensitive face. In February 1851, while in Cuba with his wife, Meneely caught what he described as "a severe cold being overtaken by a shower while in the country visiting sugar plantations." On the trip back home in June he wrote that his health had been improving. But it was temporary. Andrew Meneely died at West Troy in October of 1851 at the age of 49. His substantial estate was probated at over $75,000. And the business he founded continued in operation for another 100 years. (Russell Oechsle/Winthrop Warren)

Andrew Meneely Tower Clocks

The surviving Meneely tower clocks differ slightly in detail and construction, but most are signed by their maker and all share common characteristics. Frames and moving parts are predominantly cast iron, exceptions being the time and strike wooden barrels, brass pivot hole plates, and a brass escape wheel. He uses a variation of the chair frame, long barrels extending completely outboard of a vertical free-standing clockwork frame measuring (in inches) about 31 wide by 9 deep by 33 high. The strike winding square usually has a winding jack. His earliest known clock was installed in a New Paltz church built in 1839. An 1841 installation in Salem, New York, is signed "MENEELY &

OOTHOUT," reflecting that brief partnership. The vertical frames of models installed before 1849 are of a cage type, built of cast-iron components, with decorative column risers and ornamental corner finials. A later model at Trumansburg is of plate-and-pillar construction, the front and back plates having a beehive-on-box shape, with "A. MENEELY,W.TROY" cast in the arched cross piece of its front plate. Typical Meneely tower clock features include the following: rack-and-snail strike control, a scallop-tooth cam wheel to lift the bell strike lever, an integral bevel gear transmission driving the motion work of three outside dials (four dials from an overhead transmission at Trumansburg), and occasional use of spiral spoking. The snail and the pointer of a fixed setting dial are driven by connections to the minute wheel arbor. Meneely's escapement and pendulum suspension are the clock's most distinctive features. The suspension is knife-edge, its two-second pendulum rated under a lenticular bob. The pendulum's long tapered wooden rod hangs in the narrow six to eight-inch shoulder-to-shoulder space between the front and back plates of the vertical frame. There is no crutch; wedge-shaped steel pallets attached to the pendulum rod itself are impulsed directly by escape wheel pins. With the early New Paltz clock, pins extend from only one side of the wheel. With the later clocks, Meneely's escapement pinwheels are similar to French prototypes, the pendulum pallets being impulsed by pins mounted alternately front and back, on both sides of the escape wheel.

AM Figure 1. The earliest surviving Meneely, ca. 1839. Pallets on the knife-edge suspended pendulum are impulsed by 45 iron pins on one side of a brass escape wheel. The outboard barrels are missing. Note the floral finials and the use of both straight and spiral spoked wheels.

HUGUENOT HISTORICAL SOCIETY, NEW PALTZ, NY

Above, AM Figure 2. The Eaton Town Clock (purchased by public subscription for $250 in 1848) is very similar to the Meneely clock installed in Salem, New York. Note the finial urn-shape variation. The outboard wooden barrels measure 22^1/$_2$'' long, by 6'' in diameter. *Below*, AM Figure 3. Eaton pendulum knife-edge suspension/pinwheel escapement detail. Deadbeat pallets attached to the pendulum rod engage 72 pins extending alternately on both sides of the escape wheel. Note the maker's nameplate at top center, and the use of easily replaced brass bushing plates on the vertical risers.

AM Figure 4. Trumansburg Town Clock (bought in 1849 for $263.66 by public subscription). Meneely updated the cage frame to a simpler, more stylish plate-and-pillar design, but the clockwork remains essentially the same. The scallop-tooth cam wheel, at center, lifts the bell lever during strike, an arrangement used by other upstate New York makers in addition to Meneely.

1842 • AARON L. DENNISON

Aaron Lufkin Dennison was born on March 6, 1812, in Topsham Village, Maine, the third child of Colonel Andrew and Lydia (Lufkin) Dennison. He worked hard with little schooling as a lad. At 18 he began three years as apprentice to clock and watchmaker James Carey of nearby Brunswick. In 1833 he moved to Boston, then briefly on to New York, refining his skills at a number of establishments before returning to Boston in 1839. He set up in business at 116 Washington Street in 1841 as a dealer in watches, tools, and materials. Apparently he was open to more ambitious projects when the opportunity presented itself, as in 1842 when he installed an impressive three-dial town clock in Christ's Church, Shepherdstown, West Virginia. It was the gift of Rezin D. Shepherd, a wealthy

benefactor of the town and the grandson of its founder. In 1859–1860, after some squabbling over ownership, the clock was moved to the cupola of a new town hall, also donated by Shepherd. Renamed McMurran Hall, it became the first building of Shepherdstown College where Dennison's clock remains to this day, hand-wound and running both time and strike. Dennison's fascination with mass production showed itself early and lasted a lifetime, but never found expression in the manufacture of tower clocks.

As a boy Dennison urged his cobbler father to make shoes in lots of a half dozen or more rather than his customary practice of making up cowhide boots one day, woman's shoes the next day, and something for infants on the day following. Later as a clockmaking apprentice he urged on his master the practicality of making a half-dozen clocks at a time with identical wheels and pinions. He described how in 1845 he stood by a workman at the Springfield Armory and commented that one day watches would be mass produced in the same way as guns, an idea dismissed by the workman as impossible due to the small size of the works. Three years later he met with Edward Howard of Howard & Davis, who along with financier Samuel Curtis, found his ideas very persuasive. Howard wrote, "Dennison being a watch repairer, and myself a clock-maker, we made a good combination to systematize watchmaking, and to invent labor-saving machinery for producing perfect and interchangeable parts. With such views and intentions we began the watch business in the spring of 1850, building a factory in Roxbury, Mass." Starting as Dennison, Howard & Davis, it became the Boston Watch Company in 1853. Due to limited financial backing, the new venture encountered unsurmountable startup difficulties which Howard claimed would make going through hell "a species of pleasure" by comparison. In 1856, they moved the operation to Waltham, just north of Boston, but failed the following year, with almost all assets being sold at a sheriff's auction to Philadelphia interests. The ever persuasive and resilient Dennison was kept on the payroll by the new owners, eventually becoming superintendent of works and a stockholder. At odds with management by late 1861, Dennison quit what eventually became the prestigious Waltham Watch Company. He sued in 1863, settling out of court for $4,000, and later the same year moved his family abroad. The details of Dennison's career in England and Switzerland are beyond the scope of this work, other than to say that in 1874 at the age of 62 he turned to the mass production of watch cases. After a shaky start, he achieved his first financial success of long duration as senior partner in Dennison & Howard and in Dennison, Wigley & Co. In 1887, Waltham UK alone took delivery of 50,000 Dennison cases. In 1890, 200 hands were employed and he introduced gold cases, by chance on the very year of his own golden wedding anniversary.

Dennison had married Charlotte W. Foster in Boston on January 15, 1840, and was a dedicated family man. They had five children, including two sons who later figured in the watch case business. Aaron Lufkin Dennison died at his home in Birmingham, England, on January 9, 1895, just two months shy of the age of 83. He left a tidy estate of £6,238.

A.L. Dennison Tower Clock

Surprisingly, the 1842 Dennison tower clock has little in common with those of the leading makers of the day, including those of his partner-to-be, Edward Howard. The clock's flatbed frame and component layout are more a throwback to Stowell and his followers, but with a number of interesting differences. The frame size is 57" wide by 22" deep by 25" high. Its flatbed wood beam table is in the early Stowell tradition, as is the mounting of the wooden winding barrels with their great wheels at opposite ends of the frame. The heavy gauge well-defined cast-iron flatbed and triple section A-frame with a bridge to match are substantial construction improvements. A mid-frame structure between the barrels separates the wheel train clockwork mounted at the back from the strike control components mounted at the winding side, or front, of the clock. The escapement is a conventional Graham deadbeat with fixed steel pallets, and a brass escape wheel (recently replaced). The pallet arbor can be disengaged for freewheeling to reset the hands while monitoring an integral setting dial. The wheels are brass with short, sturdy steel arbors and cut-leaf pinions. All train wheels (including the escape wheel) pivot in old style decorative brass bearing blocks attached by cheese-head screws to the cast-iron flatbed frame. The pallet arbor and strike control levers pivot in brass bushed holes in the A-frame. The 1½-second pendulum, having a wooden rod and cannonball bob, is rated at its suspension end and put in beat by a thumb screw device on the crutch. The clock's brass bevel gear transmission is at the flatbed level, with leading off rods to the old style large wheel motion work of three outside dials (on the same level as the movement). Power to a fourth outside dial, added in 1859, is transmitted by sprocket-and-chain connections from the time second wheel arbor. The bell strike lever is not lifted by the usual strike train pinwheel, but by a cam-tooth secondary wheel screwed to the strike great wheel. In general, the workmanship and finish on all clock parts is excellent.

ALD Figure 1. Front view of the Shepherdstown clock, strike to the left, time to the right. The clock is tightly encased, making overall photography impossible. The strike wheel with cam-shaped teeth is on the far left. On the right, behind the setting dial, is the sprocket-and-chain drive of a fourth outside dial added later.

ALD Figure 2. Pendulum and crutch adjustment detail. The pendulum is rated by thumb-nut at the upper end of its very long suspension spring. To the left is the precision crutch adjustment device to fine tune the pendulum beat.

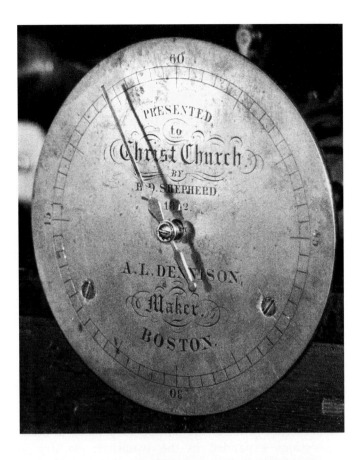

ALD Figure 3. Setting dial detail. A single fancy hand on the end of the minute wheel arbor turns against a fixed brass setting dial. The dial is beautifully engraved with the minute circle and with details associated with the original installation site, plus the clock's date, donor, and maker.

ALD Figure 4. Strike control details. The polished steel rack, rack hook, brass snail and associated levers are mounted in the front partition of the flatbed frame. The unusual gathering pallet is a disk with two pins.

1842 • THE VERDIN COMPANY

The Verdin Company—five generations in the same family business and still going strong—traces its roots to the coming to America of Michael and Francois de Sales Verdin from Marlenheim, Alsace, France in 1835. The brothers were part of the great European immigration to the Ohio Territory, settling first in the small town of Yorkville near Cincinnati. They were iron-mongers and trained blacksmiths who found a market for their trade in the repair, and eventually in the construction of tower clocks. Their 1842 clock made for Cincinnati's Old St. Mary's Church, now in the Verdin Clock and Bell Museum, is one of the brother's three known early installations. By the mid-1800s, the Verdins moved into Cincinnati itself, relocating several times but never far from their fellow craftsmen in the historical German Over-the-Rhine district. Francois de Sales Verdin died in 1884. He left his share of the business to his son, Alois Nicholas Verdin, who was succeeded by three successive generations of the same family who made the company what it is today. Product diversification began in the late 1800s with the manufacture of hardware for the suspension of bells. Operations expanded in the twentieth century to include electric bell-ringers and with the electrification of many old turret clocks of other makers, formerly wound by hand. They also installed and maintained bells made in this country by established foundries until their suppliers went out of business due to the shortage of brass during the wars. After World War II, Verdin made an agreement with the Royal Dutch Bell Foundry of Petit and Fritsen, expanding its business to include the casting and precise tuning of bronze bells. Today, the company claims to have provided bells for over 30,000 churches, and to be the largest producer of bells, carillons, and electric public clocks in the world.

Verdin Tower Clock

Of functional design with limited decoration, the clock reflects the European origins of the Verdin brothers. Its cage frame, of forged strap-iron bars held together by hex nuts, measures 24½" wide by 19" deep by 20" high, including the European style bowed legs. The frame is mounted on a sturdy wood beam stand, providing floor clearance for a pendulum which measures 64" overall. The vertical bars supporting the time train extend above the top of the cage to a shaped horizontal bar from which the pendulum is suspended, hanging outside the frame at the back of the clock. The pendulum rod is iron, and is rated by a nut under its large lenticular bob. The time train consists of three wheels ending in a deadbeat pinwheel escapement.

The single take-off connected to the time great wheel arbor probably indicates a single outside dial and frequent winding. Maintaining power is not evident. The strike control count wheel is of the deep-tooth type, and the three wheel strike train ends in a ratchet-driven two-vane fly mounted outside the back of the frame. Except for iron winding jack reduction gears on the strike barrel, all wheels are of brass with four spokes, driving lantern pinions on iron arbors that pivot in square hole brass bushes force-fit into vertical risers of the forged-iron cage frame.

VC Figure 1. As may be expected, the old clock appears to have undergone some restoration, as the hexagonal nuts and the deep-tooth count wheel probably date from a period after its original construction. The cage frame iron work, although completely functional in purpose, is expertly done with careful attention paid to uniformity of the cutouts, the bowed legs, and the graceful detailing of the horizontal cross piece supporting the pendulum.

108

1842 • SMITH'S CLOCK ESTABLISHMENT

Many clockmakers named Smith appeared in nineteenth century New York City Directories; however, between 1835 and early 1851 several stood out as working at the same 7½ Bowery Street address, located at the corner of Division Street on the lower east side of Manhattan. The first listed Smith was Andrew B. in 1835–39, followed by Smith & Brothers in 1840–41, Smith's Clock Establishment in 1841–42, and finally Ransom Smith from 1842 through 1851. The distinctive wedge-shaped building they occupied at 7½ Bowery was pictured on the labels of mantel clocks made by Smith & Brothers, and also appeared in a full-page directory advertisement when Ransom Smith led the operation. The building was also occupied by a map establishment and a furniture warehouse, plus assorted small shops in street level store fronts. Smith's Clock Establishment stood out on the third floor of the four-story building due to its display of two large public clocks and the company name painted in large letters across the full length of two sides of the building. Ransom Smith's directory advertisements specify his expertise in "Clocks for Steeples, Banks, &c." made to order, and his offer to manufacture and warrant "Clocks and Time-Pieces, Large and Small, for Banks, Churches, and Public Buildings Generally." As late as 1849 his specialty appeared as "Tower clock manufacturer."

The Smith brothers offered a variety of merchandise, probably much of it purchased elsewhere and marketed by them as New York City dealers. Their general line of products is beyond the scope of this work; however, amplification of one aspect of the business is warranted by the documentation and survival of specific examples of their tower clocks. In 1848, the city officials of Hartford, Connecticut, appropriated $100 toward the purchase of a four-dial town clock for the cupola of the Hartford State House. An additional $200 was raised by public subscription. A man named Penfield, described as "the agent for Smith's Town Clocks," had previously installed one of Smith's clocks in Hartford's Center Church, giving him an edge for the State House contract awarded on November 14, 1848. Sylvester Penfield was a New York City clockmaker at 385 3rd Avenue who supplemented his income selling and probably installing Smith's tower clocks in the hinterlands. The clock he put up in Hartford's State House developed problems, apparently not serious enough to deter improvement of the original dials with expensive ground glass replacements having gilt numbers. Even so, the Smith movement was replaced in May 1868 after only 20 years service. Local

newspapers reported it had never told acceptable time, with each of its four dials on its own usually varying from other public clocks. Both Hartford clocks are lost, but two other Smith's installations in widely separated locations have survived. Parts are missing due to electrification in recent years, but both clocks have the same features, starting with their distinctive cast-iron A-frames. The clock surviving in the tower of the First Presbyterian Church of Natchez, Mississippi, is unsigned, but it is said to have been made by "Smith" in 1842 to replace an earlier clock lost in the tornado of 1840. A nearly identical clock in the cupola of the old courthouse at Canandaigua, New York, carries on its setting dial the name of its maker, "Smith & Co., New York." This surviving Smith's Establishment hardware is almost identical to the A-frame clocks made by Reeve & Co, also of New York, who started business in 1850 about the time when Smith's shut down. Smith's former field agent, Sylvester Penfield, provides an added nexus: after 1851 his name appears on the setting dials of several A-frame clocks also signed "REEVE & CO. NEW YORK" on their front plate casting. The Penfield/Reeve connection is further substantiated on February 19, 1851, when the commissioners of Berks County, Pennsylvania, awarded "S. Penfield of New York" a contract for $480 to put a clock in the new Reading courthouse. He installed a new Meneely bell, and what was undoubtedly a Reeve clock, considering the date and the clockmakers' guarantee that it would be a good timekeeper for five years. Given the similarities of their hardware, Reeve & Co. were either successors to Smith's, or Joseph and Thomas Reeve, as skilled mechanics, were employed one way or another in the manufacture of Smith's town clocks until 1850 when Smith's closed down and Reeve & Co. set up in business.

Smith's Tower Clocks

The two surviving Smith tower clocks are identical to each other, although both are missing their outboard barrels and other parts due to electrification. In addition, they are almost identical to those made by Reeve & Co in the 1850s, the clocks of both companies being clearly distinguishable from other makers by their use of distinctive A-frames and unique escapement arrangements. The A-frames of both makers are of plate-and-pillar cast-iron construction, measuring 24" at the base by 37" high by 9½" deep. They differ in detail: Smith's plates are flawed castings, skeletonized with four curved cross pieces; Reeve's plates are immaculate castings with beaded edges and only *three* curved cross pieces, "REEVE & CO. NEW YORK" displayed in raised letters on the bottom cross piece. As for the escapement, a platform extending from the upper part of a very long crutch supports deadbeat pallets of polished agate which are acted upon directly by the escapement pinwheel. This is only a step away from the Lukens, A. Willard Jr., and Meneely escapement arrangement, where the crutch is eliminated altogether and pallets are attached to the pendulum rod itself. Noteworthy differences between Smith's and Reeve's include the following: Smith's 15½" long outboard wooden barrels are 5" shorter than Reeve's; the size, form, and location of the setting dials of both makers is the same, but Smith's dial plates are engraved brass and Reeve's are painted white with black details; Reeve's fly blades are considerably larger than Smith's; and Reeve uses coiled spring Harrison maintaining power not found on Smith's clocks. The following features employed by both Smith's and Reeve & Co. also appear in the work of other members of the New York City School of tower clockmakers: decorative spoke corners; deep-tooth count wheel; strike side winding jack via the second wheel winding square; offset escapement pinwheel with agate deadbeat pallets; elongated pendulum rating nut; and a distinctive cast-iron transmission. (See **1851 •Reeve & Co.**, page 140.)

Right, SCE Figure 1. Natchez A-frame detail, strike on the left, time right. Smith's plates are skeletonized with four cross pieces, compared to Reeve's three. Note the typical deep-tooth count wheel, friction mounted on the great wheel arbor.

Below, SCE Figure 2. Natchez bevel gear transmission detail. Smith's use of the cast-iron ring configuration is typical of that used by other New York City School makers.

Left, SCE Figure 3. Smith's Canandaigua time train detail. This recent electrical rewind system is a superior modification as it leaves the clockwork intact; however, the outboard barrels have been removed. The dual purpose pendulum crutch is the same as that used by Reeve & Co. **Right**, SCE Figure 4. Canandaigua setting dial detail. The brass dial is engraved with the chapter ring and maker identification "Smith & Co. New York." Two-hand dial in the glass covered brass pill box case is driven by motion work on an extension of the time second wheel arbor.

1843 •EDWARD HOWARD

Edward Howard, born October 6, 1813, was the son of Edward (Ned) and Lucy (Mayo) Howard of Hingham, Massachusetts, a harbor town 12 miles by water and 14 miles by land south of Boston. After his father's death at sea in 1825, young Edward worked first in his uncle's plow shop, then as a mackerel fisherman. Between 1829 and 1834 he apprenticed to clockmaker Aaron Willard Jr., along with David Porter Davis, his partner-to-be. Apprenticeship complete, Howard worked briefly in the butter and eggs business before six years employment by Henry Plympton of Boston, where he became expert at precision scale making.

According to Howard, "I went in business for myself, as a clock-maker, in 1840, continuing up to 1882, when I retired from active industry. I started in a shop not over thirty feet square and ended with a number of buildings, one of which was...seven stories high." He appeared in 1841 Boston Directories with Kenney & Howard at 88 State Street. Howard and Davis, listed separately as Boston clockmakers in 1842 and 1843, joined forces by 1844 in the firm of Stephenson, Howard & Davis, balance and clockmakers. Stephenson withdrew in 1847, precipitating the Howard & Davis partnership the same year. Undoubtedly, Edward Howard contributed to the design and production of distinctive tower clocks made by both companies. (See **1845 • Stephenson, Howard & Davis**, page 116, and **1847 •Howard & Davis**, page 128.)

The Howard & Davis period was one of continuous growth, with primary emphasis on the manufacture of a wide range of profitable balances and clocks. It appears likely that Howard, who dominated most of his business relationships, was the moving force in the company's expansion into a range of unrelated products from fire engines to leather-splitting and sewing machines. The large scale manufacture of steam locomotives was also seriously considered, but by 1848 Howard was diverted from this path by Boston watchmaker A.L. Dennison (1812–1895). His revolutionary idea was to systematize watchmaking under one roof with machines that made perfect and interchangeable parts. Later Howard described the challenge as an experience that would make going though hell seem "a pleasurable experience." The Yankee grit he displayed to achieve this goal is well documented. It will not be repeated here, except to say that Howard's shift in focus to watch mass production allowed little time for the business of balances and clocks. That was left to Davis and his staff, who moved across the street from the old wooden manufactory to a new brick building at the corner of East and Prescott Streets in Roxbury. In December 1858, Howard, in association with his cousin, formed a stock company called "E. Howard & Co. Boston." By 1860 the new corporation appeared as "Successors to Howard & Davis" and became a generic trademark for both Howard watches and clocks regardless of subsequent changes in corporate title. Davis is thought to have broken off from Howard about 1865, probably during one of the many watch company reorganizations.

Howard wrote in 1895, "The tower-clock business has had a wonderful growth in the past thirty years,... Some that I made fifty years ago are now running, still in good working order." However, in general it may be said that 1870 was a watershed in American tower clock making. It represented a shift from the day when a few innovative clocks were made by widely scattered craftsmen to an era when beautifully engineered but replicated *factory clocks* were made, marketed, and sold by two large corporations. When production ceased in 1964, E. Howard & Co. alone had produced about 4,000 tower clocks, by far the largest portion being sold after their founder's retirement.

In his later years, a cantankerous Edward Howard insisted on perfection in every watch that bore his name. "I would not tolerate a botch of any kind. I would rather break up a watch movement than have it go out imperfect," he said. It was a noble manifesto but one that did not endear the man to his workers or those paying the bills. In 1882, the board of E. Howard Watch & Clock Co. bought out its founder's interest in the company for $81,000. He insisted on cash, saying, "No notes or promises for me," retiring at the age of 72. Later he is reported to have lost everything due to poor

investments, and to have lived in rather straitened circumstances.

Little is known about Howard's personal life. After his marriage to Harriet McAllister, he moved from Boston to suburban Roxbury in 1845 where his first children were born. Later, he moved to 708 Washington Street, Dorchester, an upscale town south of Boston, where he lived out his days. He was a life member of the Massachusetts Charitable Mechanic Association, the old Central Club of Boston, and the Mercantile Library Association. Howard's second wife was Helen M. Taylor of St. John, New Brunswick, and his third wife was Elizabeth Weeks of New York City. He had eight children from his first two marriages, but left no male heirs, being survived by his last wife and three daughters. Edward Howard died in his 91st year, on March 4, 1904, in Dorchester.

Edward Howard Tower Clocks

Howard's earliest known tower clock, **EH Model 1**, was installed in 1843 in Bucksport, Maine. Its balanced design and high finish are a treat to the eye. The same model, with a four-dial transmission placed above the bridge, was also sold by Stephenson, Howard and Davis, and also appears in the advertisements of Howard & Davis. The cast-iron frame consists of a horizontal flatbed on decorative cast legs, measuring 48" wide by 21" deep by 25" high. A pair of cast-iron arches (10" high at their apex), with integral A-frames topped by a sturdy iron bridge, span the width of the flatbed. All wheels are brass with six spokes. Polished steel arbors with cut leaf pinions pivot in brass bearing blocks held by cheese-head screws. Cast-iron winding barrels with 15" diameter great wheels are mounted on the flatbed under the arches. The rest of the wheel trains are arrayed on the curved top of the arch superstructure, strike to the left and time to the right, a design similar to that used by Stephen Hasham 20 years earlier. The long-toothed brass escape wheel works on replaceable steel deadbeat pallets and provides for resetting the dial hands by freewheeling. The $1\frac{1}{2}$-second pendulum has a wooden rod and cannonball bob. A ratchet-driven fly is located outside the frame to the rear of the clock, as is a bevel gear transmission which drives the motion work of *three* outside dials on the same level as the mechanism. The minute setting dial, engraved "E. Howard/Maker/Boston," is poorly located for ready visibility. Strike control is by rack-and-snail, with the strike levers following the same curve as the front cast-iron arch on which they are mounted.

After the departure of Davis, the popular square-sided flatbed, **H&D Model 2** (see page 129) continued to see production with "E. Howard & Co. Boston" painted on its side. A new model was introduced in 1870 with clockwork essentially the same as H&D Model 2, but having a more stylish frame with colorful, painted detailing. It set a trend in frame design for other tower clock makers, and also led to the very popular Howard No. 2 and families of Howard flatbeds that included three-train quarter-strikers. Howard's general purpose "round top" tower clocks, of plate-and-pillar construction, sold in the hundreds. Other models ran the gamut from clocks small enough to fit in the base of street clocks, to customized giant mechanisms that drove the hands of four 30-foot dials and struck on bells weighing up to six tons. Customized options included gravity escapements, scheduled dial illumination, strike cutouts, automatic rewind, and electrical drives to multiple slave dials, all of which occurred after 1870, and is therefore beyond the scope of this work.

*EH Figure 1. Overview of **EH Model 1** symmetry. Critical operator interfaces, except for the poorly placed setting dial, are conveniently located on the winding square side of the clock. Note old style decorative bearing blocks and spokes machined flush with the wheel rims, the latter being a Howard hallmark more for show than utility.*

EH Figure 2. Pendulum suspension details: a pendulum rating nut on the suspension cock, and an adjustable crutch pin to put the pendulum in beat. There are no winding jacks, extra leverage acquired by an exceptionally long winding crank, its handle just clearing the floor.

EH Figure 3. Deadbeat escapement detail. The long, finely cut teeth of the brass escape wheel engage replaceable steel deadbeat pallets mounted on the ends of open caliper brass arms. The hinged pivot hole cap, at upper left, allows pallet disengagement for free-wheeling.

Above, *EH Figure 4. Shown here flanking the pendulum's cannonball bob, the Bucksport clock is driven by two-fall compounded blocks of native stone weighing about 250 pounds for time and 400 pounds for strike.* ***Below***, *EH Figure 5. Howard clock illustrations, 1869–1870. The 1869 model to the left is almost identical to H&D Model 2 except for a change in maker signature. The 1870 clock on the right makes few mechanism changes, but introduces a more stylish flatbed with cyma-curved sides and cabriole legs.*

1844 • STEPHENSON, HOWARD & DAVIS

Edward Howard and David P. Davis, young independent Boston clockmakers in the early 1840s, knew each other very well as both had served as apprentices to Aaron Willard Jr. at the same time. In late 1843 or early 1844 they joined with Luther S. Stephenson to establish the firm of Stephenson, Howard & Davis, first listed in the Boston Directory in 1844. Davis, a year younger than Howard, was primarily a clockmaker. In addition to his clockmaking skills, Howard had gained a substantial reputation as a precision scale maker during six years employment with Henry Plympton, a manufacturer of "Dearborn's Patent Balances" at 10 Theatre Alley, Boston. Stephenson, a brother-in-law of Plympton, brought to the partnership an established business, as he had been making Dearborn's Patent Balances for some time at his shop on Main Street in Hingham, Massachusetts, Howard's hometown.

Stephenson, Howard & Davis first set to work in Plympton's former shop at 10 Theatre Alley and Stephenson's shop in Hingham, adding a sales room at 42 Congress Street in Boston. In 1845, the firm moved from Theatre Alley to a new wooden factory in Roxbury that greatly increased their manufacturing facilities. In addition to precision balances they sold a general line of weighing scales, plus church tower and gallery clocks, regulators, and banjo timepieces. A gallery clock made by Stephenson, Howard & Davis survives in the sanctuary of the church at Bucksport, Maine, where Howard first placed a steeple clock in 1843. At least three tower clocks made by Stephenson, Howard & Davis have also survived, two in hand-wound, running condition. An advertising handbill found nailed to the wall of the clock room of an 1846 installation reads:

"CHURCH CLOCKS Manufactured by STEVENSON, HOWARD AND DAVIS, OF AN ENTIRELY NEW CONSTRUCTION. Warranted to perform equal to any other as a TIME KEEPER. Superior to all others in its FORCE upon the BELL and its price ONE THIRD LESS. The inhabitants of Towns and Villages wanting such articles either for Churches, School Houses or other Public Buildings with one or more Dials are requested to call upon us, either at the Manufactory ———— or at ———— Boston, Mass."

The company's 1844 manufactory address at 10 Theatre Alley and the sales office at 72 Water Street sales room are deleted and the later addresses at Roxbury and 72 Water Street are penciled in.

Stephenson, Howard, & Davis prospered in what appears to have been a compatible partnership, however, its short duration suggests possible discord. One can speculate that Howard, who appears to be the dominant personality in all of his business relationships, aspired to company diversification that went beyond what the senior partner had in mind. In any case, Luther Stephenson withdrew in 1847 to continue on his own as L. Stephenson & Co., keeping as his share of the company's assets the sales office at 72 Water Street and his original shop at Hingham. For their part, the two remaining partners continued with the manufacture of both balances and clocks, their share of the former business being the wooden factory building at the corner of East and Prescott Streets in Roxbury. In addition, they opened a new sales office at 34 Water Street, Boston, thus marking the start of an association of almost 20 years, well known as Howard & Davis.

Stephenson, Howard & Davis Tower Clocks

Stephenson, Howard & Davis made at least two tower clock models, designated here, SH&D Model 1 and SH&D Model 2. An example of **SH&D Model 1** in restored condition is on display in the municipal offices of Manchester, New Hampshire. Signed "Stephenson, Howard & Davis/Boston 1845," the mechanism is virtually identical to one at Bucksport, Maine, made and signed by Edward Howard in 1842–43 when he worked alone in Boston. Significant improvements include the addition of a winding jack to aid in winding the heavier strike weight, and the elevation of a *four*-dial transmission above the bridge, overcoming the three outside dial limitation of the earlier EH Model 1. The main frame is a cast-iron flatbed with decoratively turned legs. The highly finished brass and steel clockwork is beautifully made but conventional, except for its being mounted on the curve of the 10" high arched castings, with an integral A-frame that spans the width of the flatbed. (For details, see **1843 • Edward Howard**, page 111.) The same clock model is offered in early Howard & Davis advertisements, although no examples signed by the firm are known to have survived.

SH&D Model 2 is a rare and wonderful clock. It is unique. Examples, signed by the maker, are still hand-wound where originally installed in 1846 at Ashby, Massachusetts, and Richmond, Maine. The legs of the model's cast-iron horizontal flatbed frame are braced by highly decorative flora aprons of pierced cast-iron (nickel-plated at Ashby where the clock strikes on a Revere bell). The flatbed frame measures 65" wide by 31" deep by 26" high, or 74" high overall including the angular A-frame, centered on the flatbed and surmounted by a bridge. The bridge supports the overhead transmission and a cock for the fine rating of a two-second wooden rod pendulum with a cast-iron cannonball bob. Time and strike winding barrels are wood; all arbors and cut pinions are steel. There are only three principal wheels: two elaborately spoked cast-iron great wheels 25" in diameter for time and strike, and an unusually large brass escape wheel having 150 iron pins and measuring 18" in diameter. Deadbeat pallets of shaped steel are screwed to the end of a brass goose-neck pallet arm signed and dated by the maker. A 60-minute setting dial stamped on the bevel gear dial take-off provides visual reference for corrections to outside dial hand position during freewheeling. Strike control is rack-and-snail, the brass snail being advanced by a 12-tooth star wheel turned by pins extending from the side of the time great wheel. Long vertical rods to the transmission and large fly, both mounted overhead, are driven by a contrate wheel and pinion located at the flatbed below. Winding jack reduction gearing is provided on the strike barrel arbor. Conventional motion work of 12-to-1 brass reduction gearing is mounted in a cast-iron bracket behind the dials. Half-round double yoke U-joints on the leading off rods are similar to those associated with most Howard tower clock models.

SH&D Figure 1. SH&D Model 1 tower clock overview, a near duplicate of the 1843 clock made by E. Howard for Bucksport, Maine. Elevating the transmission above the works permits driving four outside dials rather than the earlier limit of three. Note also the addition of a winding jack to the strike winding square at lower left.

Above, SH&D Figure 2. Overview of SH&D Model 2, strike on the left, time right. The entire frame, including the flatbed flora filigree, the two great wheels, plus the A-frame and bridge are cast-iron. The brass escape wheel has 150 iron pins which work on tempered steel pallets screwed to the end of a gooseneck brass pallet arm. **Below left**, SH&D Figure 3. Model 2 escapement and snail detail. The gooseneck pallet arm is signed and dated by the maker. Worn steel pallets are easily replaced. The snail's 12-tooth star wheel, at lower right, is advanced by four pins on the time great wheel which makes one revolution in four hours. **Below right**, SH&D Figure 4. Model 2 transmission/fly detail. The bevel gear transmission on stilts above the bridge drives the hands of four outside dials. A large fly with two adjustable vanes is driven by a rod connected to contrate wheel and pinion gearing below. It spins safely overhead, well above other operator interfaces with the clock.

1845 • ABEL STOWELL JR.

Abel Stowell Jr., born on February 14, 1789, was the second son of the seven children born to Abel and Relief (Jennison) Stowell, both lifelong natives of Worcester, Massachusetts. Abel Jr., and a younger brother, John J. Stowell, learned clockmaking and watch repair from their father, whose shop and home at the corner of Salem and Park Streets faced the Town Green. His father, known as "the old town clockmaker," was probably most famous for his Old South Church steeple clock, the earliest known in this country to use a wood beam flatbed frame with a deadbeat pinwheel escapement. One of several variations on the "new plan" by other makers was the town clock at Groton, Massachusetts, put up in 1809 by James Ridgway, who in 1802 married Faithy Stowell, Abel Jr.'s oldest sister. About 1815, Abel Jr. and John Stowell established their own shop near Boston in Medford. The following year, Abel Jr. returned to Worcester where he joined his father in the partnership of Abel Stowell & Son. They dealt in iron stoves, custom machines of iron and brass for the printing and wool-carding industries, and meeting house clocks made to order. Abel Stowell died intestate on August 3, 1818, with Abel Jr. being named an administrator. Probate records show an estate with assets drastically reduced by debts, including $1,200 owed his sons, Abel Jr. and John J. Stowell.

In 1820, Abel Jr. moved his family and "A. Stowell & Son" from Worcester to Charlestown, now part of Boston, where he established an upscale jewelry store. His brother John J., who died in 1837, joined him in the enterprise and is said to have been the more aggressive businessman. The store sold and repaired clocks and watches, and offered a stock of watch findings, bracelets, necklaces, studs, fans, eyeglasses, combs, needles, tea sets, and silverware of all sorts. They also made tower clocks and superb gilt bezel gallery clocks, signed "A. Stowell & Son, Charlestown, Mass." During this same period, Abel Jr. continued to make clocks in his own name, surviving examples being several signed shelf timepieces from the 1830s, and a tower clock installed in 1852 at Dorchester, Massachusetts, signed "Made by A. STOWELL, JUNr., Charlestown, Mass." A total of five tower clocks made by Abel Jr. have been identified. Two have survived, the one cited above at Dorchester, and another, ca. 1845, signed "Made by A. STOWELL & SON, CHARLESTOWN, MASS." owned by the Historical Society of Roxbury, Vermont. The Roxbury clock is in rough condition, but original except for a strike train retrofitted with a crane-striker mechanism by Geo. M. Stevens & Co. of Boston. Three other clocks have been identified but to date are missing: one formerly in the collection of Dr. Henry F. R. Watts of Boston dated 1845, another shown on an old photograph that has apparently disappeared into a private collection, and a third identified by Crossman was installed in the old Boston & Fitchburg Railroad Depot, demolished years ago.

In 1936, an inquiry of A. Stowell & Co., still in business on Winter Street in Boston, revealed that the original Stowell family had sold out years ago. A family by the name of Cook had owned and operated the enterprise for three generations. It appears that by 1855 Abel Jr. moved to Baltimore where he was listed in city directories until 1858 as a partner in Gould, Stowell, and Ward, jewelers, gunsmiths and purveyors of imported "fancy goods." Abel Jr. signed his last will and testament on January 18, 1860; it left $1 each to two married daughters and to sons Abel III and Alexander, the latter having established his own clock, watch, and jewelry store in Boston by 1849. The balance of the estate was divided between two spinster daughters. Apart from the value of a large and varied store inventory, the principle holding was real estate encumbered by mortgage liens in excess of its highest appraisal value. Abel Stowell Jr. died in 1861 in Baltimore at the home of Abel III.

Abel Stowell Jr. Tower Clocks

The tower clocks of Abel Stowell Jr. resemble those of his father made 30–40 years earlier only respecting their use of low horizontal flatbed frames. Otherwise, there are major differences. Most obvious is Abel Jr.'s shift from wood beams to cast iron, a strong versatile material widely used by most other makers after 1840. Both surviving clock frames are practically identical. The flatbed frame with ringed half-round legs is a cast-iron assembly, painted red, and measuring 55" wide by 22" deep by 21" high. At mid-frame, the front flatbed rail has an 18" by 4" recess where the setting dial and components associated with the rack-and-snail strike control are mounted. Above the recess, a truncated A-frame is topped by a bridge that provides for suspension and rating of a 1½-second pendulum. The arbors of a recoil escapement and a weighted fly on the end of the strike train are mounted in old style bearing blocks screwed to the A-frame. All wheels are brass with six spokes machined flush with their rims; they are mounted on steel arbors with cut leaf pinions. Hollow cast-iron winding barrels extend at opposite ends across the depth of the flatbed. Flat-spring Harrison maintaining power is supplied on the time great wheel, but there is no provision for winding jacks on either train. Abel Jr. was one of the few nineteenth century American tower clockmakers who favored the recoil escapement, in his case one with replaceable steel pallets. The dial hands are reset either by stopping the pendulum, or by freewheeling the time train under manual control. The Dorchester clock's four outside dials are driven by a bevel gear transmission screwed to the clock room floor below the flatbed. Conventional motion work is housed in sturdy cast-iron frames behind the outside dials. The Dorchester clock, a gift of chocolate magnate Walter Baker, was a top quality tower clock installation (now with electrical rewind) that struck on an 1816 Revere & Son bell.

Above, ASJr Figure 1. Rear view of the Roxbury clock signed A. Stowell & Son, Charlestown. The cast-iron frame and time train, plus the transmission and motion work displayed on the floor, are original. The strike side is a total retrofit of original parts by a chain driven crane-striker installed by Geo. M. Stevens & Co. of Boston. *Below*, ASJr Figure 2. Rear view of the 1852 Dorchester clock, time side perspective. Bevel gear transmission placement under the frame allows the use of iron leading-off rods to four outside dials. Note the distinctive universal joints; the yoke type on the right is an E. Howard replacement, probably made during the later installation of an illuminated front dial.

Above, *ASJr Figure 3. Dorchester front rail recess detail. At lower left is the rack and its tail which bears on a snail located behind the setting dial. The setting dial motion work, the snail, the strike trip lever, and bevel gear connections to the transmission are all driven by the arbor of the time second wheel. Note old style decorative bearing blocks on both the A-frame and flatbed rail.* ***Below***, *ASJr Figure 4. Dorchester escapement detail. The 7³/₄-inch brass escape wheel has 30 teeth. Held by screws in a brass anchor, tempered steel recoil pallets are easily replaced in the event of wear.*

1846 • CHARLES FRED JOHNSON

Charles F. Johnson, born in 1804 at Stratford, Connecticut, belonged to a prominent family whose ancestors included Robert Johnson, the founder of New Haven. His well-to-do family sent him to Union College, followed by three years of formal study in Europe. At the age of 33 he and his wife of two years, Sarah Dwight Woolsey Johnson, the daughter of a wealthy New York City merchant, moved to Tioga County in upstate New York, purchasing a large estate they called Meadow Bank Farm. Their homestead was located on the south side of the Susquehanna River, nearly opposite the village of Owego. It was here that Johnson lived for the next 39 years as a gentleman farmer and inventor involved in local organizations, societies, and the Episcopal Church. He is said to have invented the "atmospheric dock" for raising vessels, a circular tumbler combination lock, and several other items that came into general use after he abandoned them. A few years after his death, Johnson was described in *Our County and Its People* as "a scholar, linguist and litterateur...[who] possessed marked inventive powers, although he lacked the practical sagacity to render new ideas pecuniarily remunerative."

In the period between 1837 and 1846, Johnson collaborated with fellow inventor John J. Speed, a well-to-do farmer and merchant of Ithaca, New York. They developed an improved visual telegraph, using light signals to communicate, a system said to have been used afterwards by the Russians. They also devised a method for the "transmission of intelligence by electricity," but lost out to a more popular system promoted by Samuel F.B. Morse and his associates. Another Johnson/Speed collaboration is reflected in C.F. Johnson's U.S. Patent No. 4,662, dated July 28, 1846, covering a low-cost town or turret clock. A prototype made by the two men was put up in the Baptist Meeting House on Main Street in Owego. The town contract signed May 22, 1846, provided for a three-month trial after which it would be removed if it failed to keep good time, with all expenses paid by Johnson. One year later the village of Owego bought the clock for $200 on the condition that Johnson furnish a larger dial, painted black with gilt hands and numbers. The clock remained on the church for some years, the brunt of continuous fights between town officials and the church sexton as to who would wind it. The demolition of the church in 1856 to make room for a new edifice gave an easy excuse for the clock's removal. According to local history, it was taken to Mr. Johnson's house and never used again. As far as is known, this 1846 clock was the only one ever made, but Johnson continued to promote the virtues of his brainchild, offering to retrofit old clocks to his new system. As late as 1853 he advertised in *Scientific American*, "CHURCH CLOCKS,—on a new and improved principle, warranted perfect time keepers, and easily kept in repair. Old clocks regulated on a new principle & warranted to keep perfect time. CHAS. FRED JOHNSON, OWEGO, TIOGA CO., N.Y." Johnson remained in Owego until 1876, moving in his early 70's to Dorchester, Massachusetts, where he lived with a daughter until his death there on July 6, 1882.

Charles F. Johnson Tower Clock

Although no physical hardware has survived, the patent papers have and are of sufficient interest to illustrate Johnson's concept, which, it turns out, is not completely unique in American tower clock making. We find a similar principle—using an independent time regulator to advance the dial hands at intervals of a minute or more—used by Eli Terry in the 1830s and by the Turret & Marine Clock Co. and its successor, Geo. M. Stevens & Co., after 1858. Johnson's design consists of large cast-iron wheel time and strike trains set in motion by an independent "timepiece of the size and construction of those in ordinary use for household purposes" (such as a kitchen clock, for example). The pinwheel on the strike train of the independent time regulator lifts an arm that releases the pendulum of the main mechanism to swing, thereby advancing the hands of the outside dial. The strike is triggered at appropriate hours in a more or less conventional manner. Johnson's arrangement allows for eight-day running, using 12 pins on a wheel revolving once in 30 minutes. This means the hands advance once every $2\frac{1}{2}$ minutes, apparently a level of horological accuracy that Johnson was comfortable with. The patent also provides for a one-minute advance of the hands by the addition of more pins to the time regulator wheel. The use of a time regulator that cost only four or five dollars was the basis for Johnson's claim that he could manufacture such public clocks at less than one half their usual cost. However, the accuracy of the tower clock is no better than that of its cheap time regulator. (Russell Oechsle)

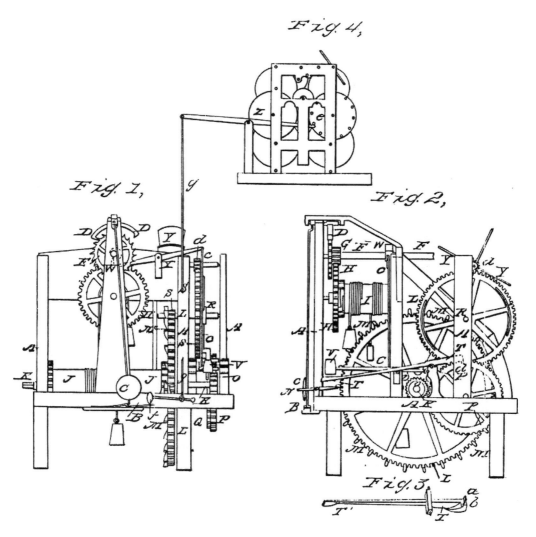

CFJ Figure 1. C.F. Johnson's drawing for a "Clock," U.S. Patent No. 4,662, dated July 28, 1846. Figure 4 delineates the low cost commercial time regulator.

1847 • JOHN DOUGLASS (DOUGLAS)

In 1890, Charles Crossman wrote in *The Jewelers Circular & Horological Review*, "John Douglass needs a passing word under the head of New England clockmakers, although he was not strictly such. He was a cabinet maker by trade, but he undertook to make clocks as well. He made one tower clock, which was a copy of Jocelin's and was placed in the old Chapel street depot, now the market." The job description is wrong, the Jocelin reference unverified, and the Chapel Street Depot long gone, but Crossman correctly identified Douglass as a tower clock maker. At least two examples of his work have survived in the New Haven area. His clock in the First Church of Milford, Connecticut, is signed "JOHN DOUGLAS/NEW

HAVEN/1849," and has run hand-wound, time and strike for 150 years. An earlier unsigned Douglass was installed in 1847 in the Fourth Meeting House of the Congregational Church of Durham, Connecticut. No longer operational and with some missing parts, the Durham clock, including its disparate wooden wheel motion work, is virtually identical to the one in Milford.

John Douglass was born in Connecticut in 1798 and worked in New Haven from 1840 to 1850, where he lived with his wife Anna and three children, a son, William K., born in 1827, and two daughters, Annella H. and Caroline, born in 1835 and 1840. He is first shown as a machinist and plumber living at 33 Hancock Avenue. Between 1841 and 1845 he worked at the same trade, with an address change to 196 State Street. From 1846 to 1850, his established clockmaking period, he listed himself as a machinist and brass founder at the same 196 State address. Douglass is shown in the 1850 U.S. Census as age 51, head of household of six people native to Connecticut, and a "Merchant" with $4,000 in real estate. He died on December 29, 1850, in New Haven, his wife shown in 1851 as Mrs. John Douglass at 196 State Street.

Where John Douglass learned clockmaking is not known, and his work, while not particularly elegant, is relatively unique. If he copied New Haven's preeminent old clockmaker, as Crossman suggests, Jocelin's clock in the tower of Yale's Lyceum on the New Haven Green would have served as a convenient model to follow, but that clock has disappeared and other examples thought to better reflect Jocelin's technical genius bear no resemblance to the Douglass clocks.

The Douglass installation at Milford in 1849 was the fourth clock put up in that church. It replaced an unsatisfactory wooden clock made by Barzillai Davison in 1825, that had replaced a "brazed wheel" clock put up by Ebenezer Parmelee in 1742, which, in turn, had replaced the first clock installed there in 1729, maker unknown. The Douglass clock would not win a beauty contest, but it cannot be faulted for durability as it has outlasted its predecessors by a wide margin.

John Douglass Tower Clock

The frame is an open rectangular flatbed of wooden planks partitioned across its depth into wide and narrow sections. It measures overall 43" wide by 29" deep by 9" high. Legless, it is raised to winding height on a wood beam base. Wooden barrels 18" long are mounted side by side in the wide section of the frame. They extend from their arbor winding squares at the front of the frame to cast-iron great wheels, where they engage the balance of the clockwork mounted in the narrow partition at the back of the frame. Wheel form varies in spoke shape and numbers. No provision is made for maintaining power, and only the Milford clock has a strike side winding jack. The trains are mounted both on the flatbed and also between two distinctive round top iron A-frames which extend above the back of the flatbed frame. The shorter of these two extensions supports a recoil escapement anchor and the pendulum. The larger of the round top A-frames extends 14" above the flatbed and is stamped "T. BANKSELLS," probably a blacksmith. It supports the iron strike control levers and the brass wheels of the strike train, which includes a deep-tooth count wheel. The third wheel of the strike train drives both the 78-tooth count wheel and the pinion of the fly arbor. The bell strike lever pivots on the frame, acted upon by nine pins on the side of the strike second wheel. The recoil escapement provides a high amplitude swing to a conventional pendulum rated at its bob end (in Milford, 1½-second beat, with wooden rod and lenticular bob; in Durham, a flat iron rod, lead lenticular bob, and 94" effective length). The time train take-off arbor also turns an edge-numbered setting dial plate against a fixed pointer. A stud on the side of the plate trips the hourly strike. Connected to the setting dial is a bevel gear dial take-off to a three-dial brass bevel gear transmission located on the floor under the clock mechanism. The setting dial is friction-mounted by flat springs, allowing it and all connections below it to the outside dial hands to be reset in either direction without stopping the clock. Iron leading-off rods from the transmission to the outside dials have universals with no provision for expansion or contraction. The dial motion work of both surviving clocks utilizes wooden wheels, possibly a safeguard against hand obstruction as easily repaired wooden teeth will break before major damage can be done to the clock movement itself. The bell strike lever pivots on the wooden frame, acted upon by nine pins on the strike train second wheel. The Milford installation has been converted to two-fall compounded wire rope that drops directly off the barrels, but part of the original hemp line remains on a barrel at Durham. Driving weights consist of fieldstone rubble boxes, which at Durham fall inside the hollow Greek Revival columns of the church portico.

***Above**, JD Figure 1. Back overview of the Milford clock. The first two wheels of the strike train, the time great wheel, and their pinions are cast iron with mixed spoking; other train wheels are brass with four webbed spokes, mounted on steel arbors with cut-leaf pinions. **Below**, JD Figure 2. End view of time take-off arbor. It drives a bevel wheel take-off connected to a three-dial transmission under the works, and also an edge-numbered spring-mounted setting dial which turns against a fixed pointer. A stud on the side of the setting dial triggers the U-shaped lever that sets off strike on the hour.*

Above, JD Figure 3. Milford escapement detail. A single strip of steel is shaped to form the pallet impulse planes, a precision version of the common kitchen clock verge. The escape wheel is expertly machined brass. Above to the left, note the lack of a rating adjustment on the pendulum's suspension end. *Below*, JD Figure 4. Front overview of the Milford clock. The unusual four-blade forged-iron fly has flared ends, and is driven by the same wheel that drives the count wheel. The strike winding jack bearing block and pinion are not original.

1847 • JEHIEL CLARK JR.

Connecticut-born Jehiel Clark migrated to upstate New York, where he became the first in a school of tower clockmakers in the village of Cazenovia, located about 25 miles southwest of Syracuse. He had three sons, Jehiel Jr., Nathan, and Ira, born in 1814, 1816 and 1820, respectively. Ira, the youngest son, was a farmer and heir to the family homestead on Pompey Hollow Road, four miles northwest of Cazenovia. Nathan was a blacksmith and farmer. Jehiel Jr., who learned the silversmith and clockmaking trade from his father, began making tower clocks in Cazenovia under his own name by 1846, when his father retired. This is supported by a surviving handbill dated February 5, 1847, reading, "**TOWN CLOCKS!**/MANUFACTURED BY/**JEHIEL CLARK, JUN.**/CAZENOVIA, N.Y." The document shows prices for various clocks and configurations, including eight-day running, striking the hour and showing the hours and minutes on up to four dials. Basic clocks with iron wheels cost $225, those with brass wheels $250. Added options "to strike in initiation of the ringing of the bell at 9 a.m, noon, and 9 p.m" cost $400 and $450. An option including all of the above plus "another part to ring and toll the bell at the usual Church hours on Sunday" cost $500 and $575, respectively. Clocks were furnished with one set of dial hands; additional hands cost $15 more per set. His clocks were "warranted for a term of five years to do the most satisfactory service." The handbill also carried the endorsement of 21 citizens of Cazenovia indicating that a Jehiel Clark Jr. clock installed "in our village...has kept most exact time since it was put up and many persons of mechanical genius who have examined it, assure us that the materials of which it is composed and its construction are of the very best kind and that it will continue to keep perfect time for a long series of years."

The above handbill was found in the records of the Delphi Falls Baptist Church, located about seven miles southwest of Cazenovia. It also served as a sales receipt, as on its bottom margin appears written in longhand, "Rec'd of G.W. Humphrey nine dollars in full for the amount of J. M. Taylor's subscription for a town clock, Delphi April 29, 1847." It is signed Jehiel Clark Jr., the total price having been $225. One of Jehiel Jr.'s earliest installations still in working order, the clock provides insight into what Cazenovia's old "iron town clock" made by Jehiel Clark Sr. probably looked like. One other Jehiel Jr. tower clock is known to have survived, plus a couple of "possibles." The former Presbyterian Church (now a Grange Hall) in Gilbertsville, Otsego County, New York, houses a Jehiel Jr. clock installed in the late 1840s. There are differences in the shape of the plate feet, the count-wheel spoking, and increased number of outside dials, but otherwise the mechanism is practically identical to the one at Delphi

Falls. Two additional possible clock sites are at nearby Morris and also in Hamilton, Madison County, New York, where the current clocks are "modern" replacements of earlier installations. In Morris, a town clock was purchased by public subscription in 1849; the old mechanism is gone, but its rubble box weights are configured like the aforementioned clock at Delphi Falls. The clock at Hamilton today is a late nineteenth century Howard, but old photographs clearly indicate the presence of an earlier clock, and in the late 1970s the escape wheel of a Jehiel Jr. clock was accidentally unearthed from the ditch running between the church and the house next door. Unfortunately, the homeowner has yet to be convinced that an archaeological dig of his front lawn would be a good idea.

By 1850, Jehiel Clark, Jr., gave up the town clock business, being described in the New York census as a goldsmith. In the same year, Austin Van Riper, the next leading figure in this school of Cazenovia tower clockmakers, took over the reins from Jehiel, Jr., probably buying out the business, patterns, castings, machinists and all. The seamless transition that followed is exemplified by a clock in Woodstock, New York; it is attributed to Van Riper, but to all intents and purposes it looks like one made by Jehiel Jr., except for a slight variation in plate feet. In addition, several other 1850 movements have the more highly figured plates typical of Van Riper, but retain many Jehiel Jr. clockwork features.

At or around the time of his father's death in 1852, Jehiel Jr. took his leave of Cazenovia, destination unknown. He does not turn up in subsequent New York State Census records.

Jehiel Clark Jr. Tower Clocks

The Delphi Falls clock is typical of all known Jehiel Jr. movements. The frame is of cast-iron triple plate-and-pillar construction. It measures 28¾" wide by 23¾" high. Overall depth is 32⅝", including the two back plates housing the clockwork trains and the extended wooden winding barrels supported on the winding square end by a front plate. Consistent with the maker's handbill, this $225 version of the eight-day clock utilizes all cast-iron gears with spiral spoking, except for the recoil escapement's brass wheel. Both the time and strike trains have five arbors pivoting in brass-bushed holes. The strike train is controlled by a notched flange count wheel (with straight spoking) mounted outside the back plate, along with the suspension of the clock's six-foot, lenticular bob pendulum. Clock weights are wooden boxes filled with rock rubble, originally designed for a 20-foot fall directly off the barrels. Damage to the plate supporting the winding square end of the barrels has been repaired and stamped "M.E.Card 1873." Card was a late partner with Stone & Marshall, successors twice removed from Jehiel Jr., demonstrating the chronological overlap of services provided by the Cazenovia School of Clockmakers. (Russell Oechsle)

JCJ Figure 1. Rear overview of Jehiel Clark Jr.'s 1847 town clock at Delphi Falls, New York. The cast-iron triple plate-and-pillar construction is typical of his tower clocks, and probably also those of his father, Clark Sr. The recoil escapement anchor is offset, engaging a brass escape wheel from the side. The five-wheel trains are cast iron with spiral spoking. Note straight spokes of the flange-type count wheel at lower right.

1847 • HOWARD & DAVIS

Edward Howard and David Porter Davis first met as apprentices to A. Willard Jr. from 1829 to 1834. Each were listed as independent clockmakers in Boston by 1842, prior to coming together again in 1844 as partners in Stephenson, Howard & Davis, balance and clockmakers. When Stephenson left three years later, the firm of Howard & Davis was born. Their share of former assets included the wooden factory building in the Highland section of Roxbury, to which they added a Boston sales office at 35 Water Street. In addition, from 1855 to 1858 they maintained an office in New York City at 17 Maiden Lane.

An early Howard & Davis advertisement showed their manufacture of a full line of scales, balances, and clocks. Clock types included those for gallery, office,

railroad, factory, watch, astronomical, regulator, ship, and car. They also offered at least three tower clock models: Stephenson, Howard, and Davis's modified version of **EH Model 1**, introduced by Edward Howard in 1843 (see page 113) plus two new models of radical design, **H&D Model 1** and **2**. **H&D Model 1** is a small, low cost, cast-iron flatbed sold in limited number. Examples survive from Arlington, Massachusetts, and Homer, New York, the latter signed and marked No. 8. On the other hand, the large, very popular **Model H&D No. 2** sold from Maine to Mississippi, its basic design being the precursor of later E. Howard & Co. flatbeds that found a huge market into the twentieth century. Both new models replaced the traditional winding barrel and weight line with space-saving sprockets and bicycle chain that stacked automatically under the flatbed.

Howard & Davis's precision scale and balance business was of high quality and very profitable. Highlights included a contract for the first postal scales in the United States, a $50,000 contract to supply standard weights and measures to every municipality in Massachusetts, and a federal government contract worth up to $100,000. At the same time, Edward Howard, whose drive and inventive genius was critical to the company's success, sought diversification, moving into manufacturing ventures that won a number of gold medals for fine work but also drained profits from clocks and scales, the financial backbone of the business. Among Howard & Davis speculations was the manufacture of patent sad-iron, leather splitting machines, locks, sewing machines, and fire engines. In the late 1840s, Howard even considered the large scale manufacture of steam locomotives, but was sidetracked by Aaron L. Dennison, a persuasive Boston watchmaker and dealer in tools and materials who intrigued him with the concept of mass produced pocket watches. Their first watch factory was built in 1850. What emerged several years and factories later was to revolutionize watch manufacturing around the world, the so-called "American System" of managing all phases of the watchmaking process under one roof. Howard became so totally engrossed in the project he appeared to have little or no spare time for the profitable business of making balances and clocks. This was left to Davis and his staff at Roxbury.

A few of the first watches were signed Dennison, Howard, & Davis, but otherwise Davis seems lost in the shuffle. His name is rarely mentioned or shows up as an officer in Howard's rapidly changing corporate structures. In 1860 their New York sales office reopened as "E. HOWARD & CO, Manufacturers of Fine watches and clocks, *Successors to Howard & Davis.*" Howard spent another 20 or more active years with the company, but Davis is said to have left by about 1865. By 1867, he and his son, David P. Davis Jr., are listed in the business of "Clocks" at 106 Water Street, Boston, at home in Roxbury.

Howard & Davis Tower Clocks

Except for the predominant use of cast iron, **H&D Model 1** is radically different from **SH&D Model 2** that immediately preceded it. H&D Model 1's flatbed frame is a flanged square-sided tub measuring 35" wide, 7" high, by 13" deep. Shoulder-to-shoulder depth is only 8¾", a payoff of sprocket chain drive. At Homer, New York, the legless flat-bed of clock No. 8 sits on an open-ended wooden box, a brass plate on its 18" high A-frame engraved "Made by Howard & Davis. Boston Mass." The A-frame bridge supports a four-dial bevel gear transmission on one end, and on the other end the suspension cock and rating nut of a 1½-second pendulum. A sculpted wood pendulum rod has an upper hole for access to the time winding square and a hole at the bottom end in which a cannonball bob is fixed. The time train's third wheel turns on a stud, and the deadbeat escapement on very short arbors is mounted *outside* the front A-frame plate. This provides unobstructed clearance for the time and strike chains which pass under the A-frame bridge to pulleys located above adjacent weight chutes. The escape wheel is spoked and brass; all others are spoke-less and cast iron, a low cost material also used for the clock's pinions, arbors, bearing blocks, and strike control components. The strike is tripped by a cam on the time second wheel arbor, which also drives the dial take-off and turns the pointer on a paper setting dial glued to a wood disk. Time and strike are wound by different cranks, a pinion on the strike crank meshing with the winding jack wheel. Alternating pins on both sides of the strike great wheel lift separate levers connected by iron rods to dual hammers that strike the bell. A large fly with two adjustable vanes is ratchet-driven on the back side of the clock. Strike control is by a slotted flange count wheel not seen on any other Howard tower clock.

As with H&D Model 1, the horizontal flatbed frame of the larger, higher quality **H&D Model 2** is a straight-sided cast-iron tub measuring 47½" wide by 10½" deep by about 38" high. Early frame legs are "factory ugly," but later models employ a sturdy cast iron under structure of improved design. Height is about 58" overall with "HOWARD & DAVIS, MAKERS, BOSTON MASS" cast in the lower portion of the time train A-frame. A large four-dial bevel gear transmission is mounted on the A-frame bridge, along with a cock for rating the 1½-second, wood rod, lenticular bob pendulum. Tangent thumb screws bearing on the crutch put the pendulum in beat. Both trains are driven by a bicycle chain over sprockets wound with the aid of winding jacks on the sprocket arbors. Maintaining power is provided by gravity lever. The dial take-off can be easily disconnected, allowing the hands to be reset in either direction without stopping the clock. A 60-minute setting dial is provided on a transmission bevel gear. Polished steel cut leaf pinions and arbors pivot in either Vuillamy bushings or brass bearing blocks screwed to the flatbed frame. Strike control is by rack-and-snail mounted on the back of the flatbed along with a ratchet-driven, adjustable two-blade fly. The strike lever is acted upon in one of three **H&D Model 2** variations: by roller pins in a split great wheel, by a two-lobe cam driven by the great wheel, or by a cam-tooth wheel attached to the great wheel. The generous use of high finish brass throughout the clockwork makes for a spectacular appearance. In addition, the frames are often brightly painted and decorated with detailing flourishes. This same basic model, with a change in maker name to E. Howard & Co. Boston about 1859, continued to be made until 1870, when it was replaced by an improved model of more sophisticated frame design.

Above, H&D Figure 1. Back overview of H&D Model 1. Traces remain of original paint and striping detail on the unrestored clock. The four-dial bevel gear transmission is missing from the cross end of the bridge. Note clearance under the bridge for unobstructed passage of the drive chains. *Right*, H&D Figure 2. H&D Model 1 deadbeat escapement detail. The 3⁷/₈" diameter escape wheel, mounted outside the A-frame, is the clock's only spoked brass wheel. The steel deadbeat pallets are replaceable. A long coiled wire spring attached at its upper end is manually hooked into the time third wheel teeth for maintaining power.

H&D Figure 3. H&D Model 1 count wheel detail. All components are cast iron. This is the only Howard model known to have a notched flange count wheel. At upper right, alternating pins on both sides of the strike great wheel lift twin levers connected by rods to the dual bell hammers overhead.

H&D Figure 4. Back overview of H&D Model 2. The time side on the left is generally similar to Model 1 except for its larger size, full length arbors pivoting in Vuillamy bushings, and strike control changes to the rack-and-snail, the rack employing Howard's distinctive horizontal tail. Note drive chain stacking box under the movement.

H&D Figure 5. H&D Model 2 time train detail. The pendulum rating nut and portions of a large four-dial transmission are shown on the A-frame bridge. At lower left, a weighted gravity lever provides maintaining power when hooked into the time second wheel teeth; it is automatically discharged. Train wheels are brass with five spokes machined flush with the outer rims.

1849 • JOSEPH R. BROWN

Joseph Rogers Brown, born January 26, 1810, in Warren, Rhode Island, was the first of five children of David and Patience (Rogers) Brown. From an early age he helped out at his father's clock and watch shop during off hours from the district school. Starting at age 17, he was employed at various Pawtucket machine shops, advancing quickly from rough work to finished machine parts, which paid about 88¢ a day. In the spring of 1828, his father moved from Warren to Pawtucket, Rhode Island, and enlisted his son's help in the manufacture of a tower clock installed in the town's Congregational Church. In 1830, they made a second town clock of the same type for the Trinitarian Church of Taunton, Massachusetts. After a brief stint on his own in 1831, Joseph rejoined his father at 60 North Main Street, Providence, Rhode Island, as partner in David Brown & Son, the nucleus of one of Rhode Island's major industries, the Brown & Sharpe Manufacturing Co.

In 1836, the father and son made a third town clock at a cost of $550 for New Bedford, Massachusetts. A year later, fire destroyed their shop. Undaunted and with $2,000 in insurance as capital, the Browns rebuilt the shop, rented additional space with a forge, and continued in business just up the street. The father retired in 1841 at age 60, and left Rhode Island in disgust over local politics, leaving Joseph Brown to carry on the business in his own name. During this period he made a town clock for his birthplace of Warren. The clock, signed, "JOSEPH R. BROWN No. 7 PROV. R.I. JAN 1849," has survived along with the rare "tumbling pallet" escapement invented by his father.

On September 12, 1848, Joseph Brown noted in his shop job book: "Lucian Sharpe came to work for me this day as an apprentice." Brown detested paperwork, preferring to work full-time on mechanical problems. On the other hand, Sharpe, while a competent machinist, thrived on administration and business management. This dovetail relationship culminated in Brown taking on Sharpe as a partner on March 1, 1853, before completion of his five-year apprenticeship. The date marked the start of continuous and rapid growth for the company renamed J.R. Brown & Sharpe. In the first year of their partnership they installed the last of their known town clocks high on the front wall of Newport's historic Old Colony House. Its expert workmanship shows the fine hand of Joseph Brown, but the clock is signed, "J.R.BROWN & SHARPE PROV. R.I. 1853 No. 8". Company emphasis on clocks, watches, and U.S. Standard rules was phased out as demand grew for new B&S products, although a line of watchman's clocks was continued for some time.

Liberated from business administration, Brown focused his attention on improving various measurement devices, a logical progression from his work with timekeepers. In 1852, he devised the earliest linear dividing engine put to use on this side of the Atlantic. The following year he perfected a vernier caliper that the ordinary machinist could afford. He introduced the American Standard Wire Gage, and later a full system of precision B&S Standards. In 1858, the company contracted to manufacture all Willcox & Gibbs sewing machines, producing over 400,000 units of all types. This turned Brown to the development of mass production machine tools for factory use, profits from which soon dominated all earlier production items. He invented or made decisive contributions to the development of the turret screw machine, the modern universal milling machine, the formed cutter, screw slotters, tapping machines, the friction clutch pulley, and the universal grinding machine. In 1868 the business incorporated as the Brown & Sharpe Manufacturing Company. Two years later all operations were consolidated in a modern fireproof facility on Promenade Street, overlooking Providence's Woonasquatucket River. The business depression of 1873 strained the company greatly, and took its toll on the aging Joseph Brown in spite of his reduced role in product development by this time.

He married Caroline B. Niles of Providence on September 18, 1837; they had two daughters. His first wife died in January 1851, and four months later he married Jane F. Mowry of Pawtucket. Joseph Rogers Brown died at age 66 of a massive heart attack on July 23, 1876, at Isle of Shoals, New Hampshire. He left his widow, a daughter, and major contributions to American manufacturing technology.

Joseph R. Brown Tower Clocks

Joseph Brown's unusually compact town clocks have survived as installed in Warren (No. 7) and Newport (No. 8), Rhode Island. Basically similar, there are significant differences.

SIMILARITIES: Their cast-iron frames consist of a horizontal flatbed stand with straight legs, measuring 34" wide by 23" deep by 24³/₄" high. Bearing blocks, bolted to the flatbed, support 11" diameter, grooved black walnut barrels with 16" diameter great wheels. Winding jacks are provided for both time and strike. Set back and bolted to the flatbed are twin 12" high A-frames, strike left, time right. Both pendulums are suspended by dual springs from a braced vertical extension on the time A-frame; their round wooden rods, painted black, have cast-iron cannonballs. Both have short 4" crutches with 4³/₈" forks spanning outrider extensions on the pendulum rod. The strike trains are conventional, with strike lever lifting pins on the second wheel, and a large two-blade ratchet-driven fly mounted above the extended winding barrels. Strike control is by rack-and-snail, with minor differences in lever design. The gear trains have six-spoke brass wheels with polished steel arbors and cut pinions. The time side of clock No. 8 is driven by a two-fall compounded 35-pound lead weight!

DIFFERENCES: Clock No. 7 at Warren uses the unique "tumbling pallet" escapement invented by Joseph's father. (See **1828 • David Brown**, page 75.) This complex arrangement is abandoned in clock No. 8 at Newport, giving way to a deadbeat escapement variation with its own critical parameters and multiple adjustments. The brass escape wheel has 20 short paddle-like teeth. Its brass anchor has replaceable steel deadbeat pallets and adjustable arbor pivot holes, because precise depthing is critical to keep the pallets from striking the rim of the escape wheel. Clock No. 7 has a 1½-second pendulum rated by an adjustable weight on a threaded rod extending above the escapement pallet arbor. The two-second pendulum of clock No. 8 oscillates in a small 4" arc and is rated by a brass napkin ring which can be moved up or down on the round rod to change its effective length. Clock No. 7's maintaining power is a manually-set spring-loaded plunger that engages a ratchet on the arbor of the time train second wheel, whereas clock No. 8 uses Harrison maintaining with small coiled springs. The hands of four outside dials on clock No. 7 are reset by freewheeling. Clock No. 8's dial take off is disengaged by a hand wheel on the center wheel arbor, allowing the dial hands to be reset in either direction without stopping the clock. The same center wheel arbor also serves to trip the strike, to advance the setting dial hands and the strike control snail, and to drive the dial take off with connections to the motion work of one large illuminated dial mounted outside the building.

JB Figure 1. Front overview of Joseph Brown's clock No. 7, strike to the left, time right. The matched set of A-frames set back on the flatbed table provides for short sturdy train arbors (8" shoulder-to-shoulder) while accommodating long wooden barrels mounted below. Note differences in winding jack tooth count.

JB Figure 2. Clock No. 7 time train detail. Pivoted assemblies with large roller pallets tumble in and out against upper and lower adjustable stops, imparting impulse to the pendulum with minimal friction. The clock's spring-loaded maintaining power plunger in the left foreground bears on a ratchet of the time second wheel arbor.

JB Figure 3. Front overview of clock No. 8, strike to the left, time right. Design symmetry is evident. Note the grooved wooden barrels and identical winding jacks. A vertical extension on the time A-frame provides for suspension of the two-second pendulum. New features include a multi-function center wheel, and a radical tooth-form variation on conventional deadbeat escape wheels (see JB Figure 4).

JB Figure 4. Joseph Brown's pendulum crutch detail. A widely spread fork on a short 4" long crutch bears on unusual outriders to impulse the pendulum rod. Just below (out of the picture) a brass napkin ring is moved up or down on the round rod to fine-rate the pendulum.

1850 • AUSTIN W. VAN RIPER

The village of Cazenovia, located on Lake Cazenovia about 20 miles southeast of Syracuse in upstate New York, was home to a school of five tower clockmakers whose collective work spanned 45 years. Austin W. Van Riper, the only one of the group born and working his entire short life in the village, was born in 1825 the son of Isaac Van Riper, a farmer and tanner. After limited formal schooling, young Van Riper learned the blacksmith, foundry and machinist trades, eventually operating his own machine shop adjacent to his father's tannery west of Chittenango Creek. Nearby was the Eagle Foundry, where Van Riper's predecessor, Jehiel Clark Jr., is thought to have made his tower clock castings.

Although undocumented, Van Riper probably took over Clark's tower clock business before the 1850 census, which shows Clark Jr. as "silversmith," and Van

Riper as "clockmaker." The transition was seamless, with clocks attributed to Van Riper in 1850 nearly duplicating a clock made as late as 1849 by Jehiel Clark Jr. In the nine years that followed, however, Van Riper made changes to nine or more new models of evolving sophistication and elegance. Undoubtedly he drew on the expertise of others around him, but Van Riper was the commanding genius, one of the country's most prolific tower clock designers of the period. He set up in business at Cazenovia's Empire Works (not purchased outright until 1855). The complex consisted of several acres of tillable land, a machine shop with an office, blacksmith shop, foundry, planing mill and woodworking shop, pattern rooms, chair and cabinet shop, and a lumber yard, all fully outfitted with a large inventory of machinist and woodworker tools driven by line shafting to permanent water power—a sizable undertaking for a man in his mid-20's.

Early on, he hired a retired farmer named Jonah Moor to do the sales roadwork. A good talker, it was claimed Moor got so many orders on a single sales foray it took the factory three years to complete delivery. Occasionally, Van Riper took to the road himself, leaving business affairs to Timothy Buell, and factory management to his lead mechanic Justice Marshall, who along with machinist John Stone later succeeded to the business. Most Van Riper clocks were sold in upstate New York, which enjoyed new levels of prosperity due to heavy commerce along the Erie Canal; however, sales were also reported in Pennsylvania, Virginia, Tennessee, Maryland, and as far away as Michigan and northern Alabama. *The Cazenovia Republican* claimed that by 1859, Van Riper town clocks could be found in almost every state in the Union.

Much of what is known about Van Riper's personal life comes from his correspondence with Edwin Meneely of the Meneely Bell Foundry in West Troy, New York. The two men enjoyed a close business relationship, swapping business referrals in the 1850s, with potential clock buyers passed on to Van Riper and bells buyers to Meneely. Toward the end, one letter mentioned that Van Riper had fallen ill on a trip south to Tennessee, followed by a bedridden period of several months. The sequence of events that followed is vague, but starting in April 1858, Stone & Marshall advertised regularly that they had purchased all of Van Riper's interest in making and selling town clocks. This included "Patterns, Drafts and Tools" used by the Empire Clock Works. Due to continuing bad heath, a month later Van Riper advertised "for sale the whole of the Empire Works...sold in parts or all together..." making no mention of the clockmaking business presumably sold to Stone & Marshall. Both announcements were premature as Van Riper recovered and returned to work, only to suffer a second attack the following year. He passed away on September 19, 1859, at the untimely age of 34, survived by his wife Mary. His estate probate listed household goods, over 30 debtors, and the full complement of land, buildings, tools and fittings associated with the Empire Works facility. Leonard White, a local entrepreneur, was the actual buyer of the factory complex in 1860, but Stone & Marshall continued to use the facility for clockmaking until moving operations to a vacant two-story mill directly across the Chittenango Creek early in 1865.

Austin W. Van Riper Tower Clocks

As mentioned above, an 1850 town clock attributed to Van Riper nearly duplicates an 1849 model made by his predecessor, Jehiel Clark Jr. Common features include the predominant use of cast-iron, five-wheel trains, brass-bushed pivot holes, recoil escapements with offset anchors, a notched-flange count wheel, and a cam tooth wheel acting on the bell strike lever. In general, Van Riper frames vary a great deal, but with evolutionary similarities identifiable as the work of one maker. All are of cast-iron, plate-and-pillar construction, with short arbor wheels in a shallow tall frame, with the barrels extending below, across the full depth of a long bottom frame. The time section of late model duplex frame clocks are better described as skeletonized chair-frames. Many of his surviving clocks retain their original fine paint job, considered a Van Riper hallmark. The plates of an 1850 model at Cooperstown, New York, are painted deep green with yellow lining and red highlights on plate edges and wheel spokes. Color combinations on later clocks include tan with red, reddish brown with yellow and black with silver. Van Riper redesigned his clocks at a startling rate, changing from five to four-wheel trains, from circular to spiral spoking, from recoil to deadbeat escapements, from short to 1½ or 2-second beat pendulums, and from external to internal notched flange count wheels, then to deep-tooth count wheels. In addition there are evolutionary changes in frame design, starting from Clark's curvilinear style, to straight line architectural and Gothic design, and finally, a change from integral time and strike frames to duplex frames of ever increasing sophistication and elegance. Van Riper's earliest known duplex frame clock was installed ca. 1854–1855 at Saratoga Springs, New York. About the same time, H. Sperry & Co. of New York City also introduced a successful duplex frame tower clock, although there is no known connection between the two makers. Van Riper's time and strike trains are mounted in separate side-by-side modules with a strike-tripping connection. His later duplex frame models make significant reductions in frame size; for example, Saratoga's early 41" high time module is reduced to 27" then 25" high, with corresponding reductions in strike module dimension. Two very fine clocks were made by lead machinist Justice Marshall for Van Riper in 1858–59. Their extraordinary features include cap jewels on the time train pivot holes and adjustable agate deadbeat pallets. All moving parts are brought to a high finish, including the paint job and a spiral-spoked bevel gear transmission high overhead. The clock's ornately curved skeletonized plates with fancy turned pillars and elegant spiral-spoked brass wheels create the pleasing spectacle of curves turning against curves, accompanied by the leisurely beat of a two-second pendulum. The first of these exceptional clocks was installed in 1860 at a cost of $2,000 (four times the usual price) at Nashville, Tennessee, but has since disappeared. Fortunately, a counterpart has survived in the town where it was made. First offered by Van Riper to Cazenovia as a town clock, after much haggling it was sold as such in 1862 by Stone & Marshall, then relocated by them in 1874 to the towering steeple of Cazenovia's Methodist Episcopal Church. Here it remains today in running condition, one of America's most beautiful town clocks. (Russell Oechsle) (See **1859 • Stone & Marshall**, page 158.)

Above, AVR Figure 1. A very early Van Riper, ca. 1850. It retains Clark's curvilinear frame with extended wooden barrels, five-wheel trains, offset anchor recoil escapement, and flange count wheel mounted outside the frame. Note winding jack on the strike barrel arbor, and wheel circular spoking. *Below*, AVR Figure 2. Van Riper ca. 1852. The architectural style frame is a significant change to a more simplified plate casting. While most clock features remain unchanged, time and strike trains are reduced to four wheels, and the escapement to an offset anchor deadbeat.

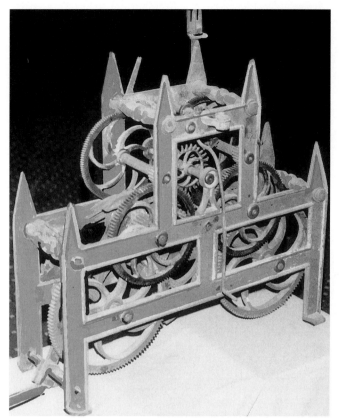

AVR Figure 3. This 1853 Gothic frame clock followed an 1852 transition model of the same style but different shape. It introduces spiral spoking used in all subsequent models. Changes include a count wheel mounted inside the frame, and replaceable deadbeat pallets on a stylized anchor centered above the escape wheel.

AVR Figure 4. Van Riper duplex frame clock ca. 1854–1855. A sophisticated clock designed for superior timekeeping, time is on the left, strike on the right. The unusual hammer-head strike-tripping connection is simplified in later models to levers connected by a chain. Note use of larger wheels and the deep tooth count wheel mounted outside the strike frame to the right.

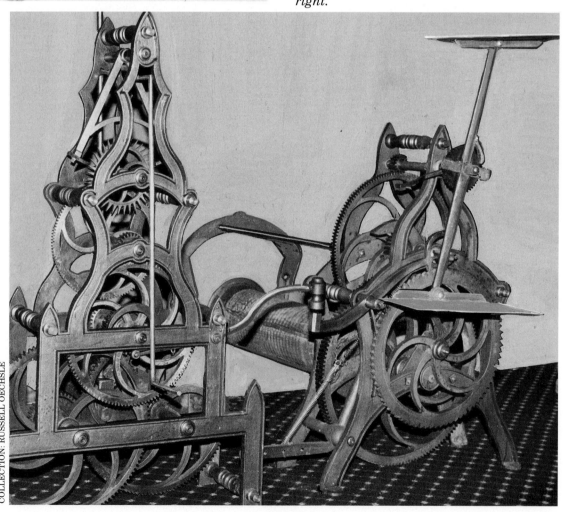

Jehiel Clark, Jr.
1847

Jehiel Clark, Jr
1849

Austin Van Riper
1850

Austin Van Riper
1850

Austin Van Riper
1852

Austin Van Riper
1853-54

Austin Van Riper
1854-55

Austin Van Riper
1856

Van Riper/Stone & Marshall
1862

Stone & Marshall
1871

AVR Figure 5. Cazenovia tower clock frame chronology.

1851 • REEVE & CO.

Reeve & Co. is something of a mystery. The town clocks of Joseph and Thomas Reeve, presumably brothers, were of a mature, distinctive design, very well executed and sold over a wide geographical area. Yet little is documented about the personal life of the Reeves, whether or not they were brothers, where they learned clockmaking, or the extent of their facilities. Distinctive features found in their clocks also appeared in the work of what may be called the "New York City School." The school also included Smith's Clock Establishment, H. Sperry & Co., Alonzo Taylor, and A.S. Hotchkiss & Co., all tower clockmakers in the city between 1845 and 1872.

The Reeve brothers and their company first appeared in the 1850 New York City directory as clockmakers at 87 Elizabeth Street in lower Manhattan. They lived across the East River at 209 Pearl Street, Brooklyn. In 1852 the company moved to 167 Centre Street. Rode's *Partnership Directory* shows the following names as associated with Reeve & Co.: Joseph Reeve, Thomas Reeve, Augustus LaFeuer and Sydney Taylor. Taylor's role in the operation is unknown, but from 1856 to 1858 LaFeuer was listed in the city as a machinist at "LaFeuer & Beary, Town Clocks & Machines, White & Elm," apparently a short-lived spin-off of Reeve & Co. From 1852 to 1859 Reeve & Co. is shown on the corner of Centre and Canal Streets along with the usual separate listings for Joseph and Thomas Reeve, both still domiciled at 209 Pearl Street, Brooklyn. In New York City both men are usually shown as machinists, but in 1854–55, Joseph Reeve's occupation is shown as "town clocks" and Thomas' as "machinist," suggesting different areas of expertise. In 1854, they furnished technical specifications to the U.S. Lighthouse Bureau for a light rotating machine; the $800 cost of the prototype was reduced to $700 for subsequent orders. This diversification shows up in their directory listing as makers of "Town Clocks and Fine Machines." By 1859–60, Reeve & Co. appears to have abandoned the town clock business, with both principals shown simply as machinists at 169 Centre Street. They are unlisted in New York City during the early Civil War years, only to have "Joseph Reeve, machinist" and "Reeve & Co., machinists" reappear in 1863–64. A final listing in 1865–67 shows "Reeve, Thomas, machines, 536 Bdwy, h Bklyn."

Surviving Reeve clocks from installations in Morristown, New Jersey (1852) and Marietta, Pennsylvania (1853) have "REEVE & CO. NEW YORK" cast into the front plate, and are also signed by S. Penfield on the setting dial. For some years it has been assumed that Penfield, who was listed in New York City directories as Sylvester Penfield, a clockmaker at 205 9th Avenue,

merely supplied the setting dial mechanisms. This notion was corrected by the discovery of a transaction in February 1852 at Reading, Pennsylvania. The county commissioners of Berks County awarded S. Penfield of New York a contract to install a new town clock and bell in their courthouse. With Penfield acting as agent, the bell was made by Meneely Foundries and the clock was probably supplied by Reeve & Co. Having made the sale, Penfield put his name on the setting dial, a common practice at the time. The same scenario would have applied to Reeve clocks installed in Morristown and Marietta, mentioned earlier, which are both signed by Penfield and Reeve. The A-frame tower clocks made by Reeve & Co. after 1850 and those made by Smith's Clock Establishment in the 1840s were almost identical. In fact, S. Penfield was first employed as "the agent for Smith's Tower Clocks," before dealing with Reeve after 1850 when Smith's quit the tower clock business. This suggests that Reeve & Co. was the successor to Smith's Clock Establishment, or that the Reeve brothers may have worked as machinists for Smith's during the early development of the A-frame tower clock design. (See **1842 • Smith's Clock Establishment**, page 109.)

Based on surviving examples, Reeve & Co. made just one model tower clock, set apart by its free-standing A-frame signed "REEVE & CO. NEW YORK" cast in the bottom cross piece of the front plate. Reeve & Co. clocks have been identified at the following locations: Reading and Marietta, Pennsylvania; Morristown, New Jersey; Essex, Connecticut; Jonesboro, Tennessee; Fayetteville, North Carolina; South Bend, Indiana; Fredericksburg, Virginia; and Ottawa, Canada. Strangely enough, there are no known New York City Reeve installations, and some of the above may have been Smith's clocks as all reputed sites have not been positively verified.

Reeve & Co. Tower Clocks

Reeve cast-iron frames consist of two A-frame plates, spaced by shaped pillars, held together with hex nuts, and secured to a floor platform with screws. Parallel barrels extend outboard from journals on the arbors of the great wheels and are supported on their free end by a cast-iron stand attached to the main frame by a single threaded rod. The A-frame measures 24" at its base by 9½" deep by 37" high. Its closely spaced plates, which support all core clockwork, measure about 8" shoulder-to-shoulder. Reeve's precisely cast plates have beaded edges, as distinguished from Smith's plates which are flawed flat castings without beading. Train wheels are brass; arbors and cut leaf pinions are steel. Bullseye brass bushings are force fit into plate pivot holes. Coiled spring maintaining power is provided on the time side, along with an integral winding jack on the strike second wheel arbor. The one-second pendulum is suspended and rated by an elongated nut at the apex of the front plate. Its wooden rod has a brass-lined crutch slot and an 11-inch cast-iron lenticular bob. The very long crutch is unusual: in addition to imparting motion to the pendulum at its pin end, on its upper end it supports replaceable deadbeat jeweled pallets impulsed directly by an offset pinwheel. A bevel gear take-off outside the back plate of the A-frame is connected by a vertical rod to a four-dial transmission located above the movement. The setting dial, consisting of a glass-covered brass pill box with a two-hand dial painted white, is mounted outside the front plate and is driven by motion work connected to the time second wheel arbor. Distinctive Reeve features also appearing in other New York City School clocks include: decoratively cut spoke corners; deep-tooth count wheel; strike side winding jack via the second wheel arbor; offset escape pinwheel with agate deadbeat pallets; elongated pendulum rating nut; and a ring-type cast-iron frame on the transmission.

R&C Figure 1. Reeve & Co. Marietta town clock front overview, strike to the left, time to the right. The strike second wheel arbor also carries a winding jack pinion, the winding ratchet, and the deep-tooth count wheel. In addition to the maker identification on the front plate, the dial of the pill box setting dial is signed by S. Penfield.

Above, R&C Figure 3. Harrison maintaining power detail. The heavy coiled spring on a rounded core is a rarely seen type of maintaining power. **Below**, R&C Figure 4. Overview of the Morristown, New Jersey, Reeve tower clock package showing relative size of the rubble weight boxes. Note large fly and 21" outboard barrels (strike diameter 10", time 6").

R&C Figure 2. Deadbeat pinwheel escapement detail. The offset pinwheel measures 7³/₄ inches across with 26 D-shaped pins. The agate pallets are screwed to a round platform integral to the crutch which also impulses the pendulum at its bottom end. Note decorative spoke corners typical of New York City School.

1851 • H. SPERRY & CO.

Julius Henry Sperry, a small town boy with a big city future, was the most successful of six brothers associated with the sale of clocks in New York City. Born about 1812, Henry was the oldest of eight children of Sheldon and Desdemona (Stillman) Sperry of Burlington, Connecticut, a town set off from Bristol in 1806. The hilly, thinly populated area depended on agriculture, but surprisingly produced two major tower clock makers and Hotchkiss & Fields, a shelf clock factory employing 30 to 50 people. Sperry may have been one of the ambitious young men the factory sent out to peddle clocks in affluent markets to the south; if so, he would have been drawn by the financial opportunities that moved him, a younger brother, and his widowed mother to New York City by 1834.

Henry Sperry's first clock establishment was a store at 204 Bowery. He added mirrors to the line and moved several times in the decade that followed. In 1844 he and George L. Shaw formed the partnership of Sperry & Shaw on Cortlandt Street. They advertised themselves as "Agents for all the Principle Manufacturers in the United States" and sold a wide range of clocks made mostly by factories in Connecticut, but also the one-year clocks of A.D. Crane. Sperry & Shaw followed the trail made by Chauncey Jerome, overcoming restrictive English trade barriers to export over 40,000 cheap American mantel clocks in a single year. The operation was highly successful until 1849 when a consortium of Connecticut clock manufacturers set up their own outlet, the American Clock Co., located a few doors away from Sperry & Shaw on Cortlandt Street. Cut off from its main source of supply, the partnership dissolved. Sperry bounced back with his usual resilience by 1851, selling clocks and looking glasses as H. Sperry & Co. at 18 Maiden Lane and at 153, 157, and 159 Broadway. He featured the "CELEBRATED DOLLAR CLOCKS," and ventured into the manufacture of tower clocks. In November 1850 the trustees of Rutgers Street Church (now St. Teresa's) accepted a parishioner's gift of a steeple clock made by H. Sperry & Co. Today it continues to serve the same Lower East Side neighborhood, the city's oldest tower clock running eight days, hand-wound, time and strike.

From 1853 to 1858 Henry Sperry consolidated sales and manufacturing operations in a six-story building at 338 Broadway. Bold lettering on five levels identified the establishment as "H. Sperry & Co's Empire Manufacture of Tower Clocks." A public clock dial, with the legend "TIME WORKS WONDERS," was suspended from the third floor over the sidewalk. It told local time on two dials, along with a third dial on the second floor which showed London time. A large tower clock movement was displayed behind a storefront window at street level, and the wind direction displayed on the building's top floor. New York's 1855 Industrial Census assessed Sperry's worth at $45,000 in real estate, $10,000 in tools and steam-powered machinery, $40,000 in brass clocks, and 8,000 pounds of brass stock. Feature articles in *Frank Leslie's Illustrated Newspaper* in 1858 indicated that Sperry employed fifty of the "best operatives in the Union." His tower clock designer and superintendent of construction was A.S. Hotchkiss, like Sperry, a native of Burlington, Connecticut. Reporters wrote that the great reputation of Sperry's manufacture brought him orders from all parts of the United States. Local installations included tower clocks at the Rutgers Street Church, Brooklyn City Hall (1851), St. George's on Stuyvesant Square (1857—$1,800), and the "Brick Church" on Murray Hill (1859—$1,500). Plans were underway on a clock of huge proportions for New York's new city hall. It was to be placed on a stone foundation in a lower level of the building, and show the time in every room as well as on its cupola. The great wheels alone would be five feet in diameter! It was proposed to wind this truly marvelous clock by water power from the Croton Reservoir, eliminating the need for a custodian.

In 1859, H. Sperry & Co. moved to 487 Broadway and challenged the world to compete with what he advertised as the largest and most varied stock in the United States. Public clocks for churches and municipal buildings were also offered nationwide, finished to order and warranted to run with perfect accuracy. Unfortunately, Henry Sperry never saw the fruition of his ambitious plans as he died in 1859 at age 47 (will proven May 4). For several years thereafter, younger brothers William and Timothy Sperry ran the business at the same address. For a time they sold the same tower clocks models under the name of Sperry & Co., but lacked Henry's entrepreneurial drive and turned to other pursuits by 1865.

Henry Sperry Tower Clocks

At least three models were made, all running eight days, time and strike. Frame styles vary, but all models share some features with the work of other clockmakers included in the New York City School. (See **1851 • Reeve & Co.** page 140.) **HS Model 1.** The cast-iron plate-and-pillar frame of the 1851 Rutgers Street Church clock is held together by hex nuts and measures 31" wide by 18$\frac{1}{6}$" deep by 37$\frac{1}{2}$" high. Both trains, including the 17" great wheels and their inboard barrels, are mounted in unbushed pivot holes. The wheels are bronze with machined teeth. Arbors and cut pinions are steel. A fly with large adjustable vanes and the bevel gear dial take-off are mounted outside the back plate. The 1$\frac{1}{2}$-second pendulum, suspended and rated from a cock on the front plate, has a round wooden rod and cannonball bob. Strike control is by rack-and-snail, the snail turning with a time great wheel having Harrison maintaining power. The deadbeat pinwheel escapement has replaceable agate pallets. The strike winding square is on the end of the second wheel arbor, which also serves as a winding jack. The time second wheel arbor trips the strike and drives the setting dial plus a bevel gear take-off connected by a vertical rod to a New York type transmission well above the mechanism.

HS Model 2. An old engraving is all that remains of a spectacular Sperry tower clock with eight outside dials that was lost in a catastrophic 1865 fire. The cast-iron frame of Sperry's clock for St. George's in New York consists of a large flatbed on turned legs, having a skeletonized A-frame superstructure with acorn finials. It shares mechanical features with HS Model 1. Differences include: 28-inch diameter great wheels

that pivot in flatbed bearing blocks; a 21-foot long compensated pendulum; escape wheel pins shaped to retain lubricant; a spring pin clutch to reset the dial hands without interrupting clock operation; winding jacks on both time and strike; an odd overhead governor/fly; and a strike great wheel having a secondary wheel with cam-shaped teeth lifting a bell strike lever capable of delivering full tone on a 10-ton bell.

HS Model 3. An example, installed about 1855, survives in Tarrytown, New York. The time and strike trains are located side-by-side in separate, distinctly shaped plate-and-pillar frames with a strike trip connection. After Henry Sperry's death, this duplex model continued to be made and sold by the company successors, Sperry & Co. and Alonzo Taylor. (See **1864 • Alonzo Taylor**, page 165.)

Left, *Figure 1. HSC Model 1, installed in a church on Rutgers Street in 1851, is New York City's oldest hand-wound clock still in operation. The curvilinear plates, offset pinwheel escapement, and many other features are typical of clocks designed by A.S. Hotchkiss later in the century. **Right**, Figure 2. HSC Model 1 escapement detail. The offset pinwheel enables use of a perpendicular hammerhead arm to support replaceable deadbeat agate pallets. The arm can be slid back on its arbor, disengaging the escapement to reset the hands by free-wheeling.*

Above, Figure 3. HSC Model 1 time train detail. The setting dial position and style is typical of the New York City School of tower clockmakers, as are the decoratively cut spoke corners on all train wheels. Note the elaborate crutch fork and the round pendulum rod. **Below**, Figure 4. Engraving of the spectacular 1857 HSC Model 2 lost in an 1865 fire. It was designed for Sperry by A.S. Hotchkiss, who, when in business for himself, made a similar clock that has survived at the Rock Island (IL) Arsenal.

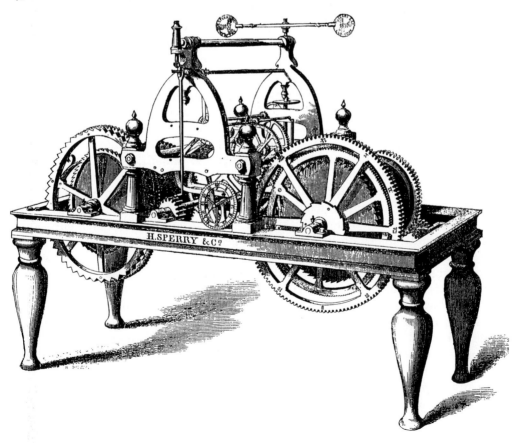

Figure 5. An example of H. Sperry & Co.'s Model 3 duplex frame tower clock installed in the 1850s survives at Tarrytown, New York. Severely damaged during a hurricane, it was repaired by Seth Thomas Clock Co., who replaced the original time frame and installed a Graham deadbeat escapement in place of the original pinwheel (see p. 166, Figure 1).

1852 • DAVID M. ANDERSON

David M. Anderson was born ca. 1792 in Lebanon, Pennsylvania, 20 miles east of Harrisburg, where he was raised and served a clock and watchmaking apprenticeship. In his early 20s, he moved about 25 miles southeast to Waynesburg (now Honey Brook), where he worked and lived until his death in 1862 at about age 70. He was active in town affairs, serving as postmaster for several terms. In 1829 he set up a small shop on Main Street and hung out his shingle "D.M. ANDERSON/Clock and Watchmaker," later adorned with a miniature tower clock. In addition to the usual repair work, he made sturdy tall case clocks with painted iron dial plates, some with moon phase; he also made musical clocks. Over the years he trained a number of apprentices, but his only son never learned the trade.

In 1835, Anderson and Isaiah Lukens of Philadelphia submitted bids to make a large town clock for the Chester County Courthouse at West Chester, Pennsyl-

vania. Anderson was favored by the common folk as being a home county clockmaker who submitted the lower bid. Regardless, the local gentry, although small in number, had contributed the bulk of the money and supported Lukens, whose 1828 clock for Philadelphia's State House (Independence Hall) had been widely acclaimed. It was no contest—Lukens got the contract. Anderson waited another 15 years to earn the title of Chester County's first and only known tower clock maker. About 1850, Anderson began construction of a town clock to be placed in the tower of the Presbyterian Church just up Main Street from his workshop. The costs were paid for by small contributions ranging from 10¢ to $15, totaling in all $128.50. A family located to the north refused to contribute and were accordingly denied a dial on their side of the church until 75 years later. Local history has it that Anderson "carved" the clock patterns in his shop, and the iron castings were made by Ephraim Stauffer at the forge next to "The Mill" at Cupola. Clearly, Anderson's design was modeled almost part-for-part on the distinctive work of Jacob Custer (1805–1871), the "Wizard of Norristown," whose many installations in southeastern Pennsylvania included tower clocks at nearby Coatesville and Phoenixville. Anderson's clock was put up in the church tower by 1852, and it was he who wound it and serviced it for the remaining 10 years of his life. Unfortunately, the church tower was inclined to sway in strong winds, a recurring problem that threw the pendulum out of beat. After several decades, the clock became irregular and eventually stopped. It was restored by local mechanics in 1925 and in 1979, but now stands silent where originally installed in the tower of the Honey Brook (Waynesburg) Presbyterian church.

David M. Anderson Tower Clock

Anderson's tower clock has more similarities to Custer's than differences. Similarities include: the clock mechanism installed *above* the bell; the predominant use of cast iron throughout the mechanism; the rectangular plate-and-pillar frame held together by tapered pins; the same type deadbeat escapement; maintaining power consisting of a wire spring wound on the third wheel arbor; the notched flange count

wheel mounted outside the frame; and a two-second pendulum with similar suspension and a lenticular bob rated by an adjustable wood rod assembly. Most obvious is Anderson's replication of Custer's unique concentric bevel gear motion work. As with Custer, it is driven by similar duplex gearing, is mounted on the frame, and drives radiating leading-off rods inside tubes connected to the hands of four outside dials. Differences are minimal. For example, the time and strike sides are reversed and the winding squares extend through what is the back plate in Custer's clocks. This has the advantage of putting the operator on the same side as most components requiring adjustment. A small four-blade fan is exposed outside the frame. Anderson's clock is 10 inches shorter than Custer's, measuring 31" wide by 22" deep by 41" high, a difference mostly attributed to Anderson's smaller great wheels. Other differences include: unsigned frame plates with decorative pillars and five-spoke wheels vs. Custer's six. Finally, all Anderson's pivot holes are brass bushed, with angled oil sinks, probably an "improvement" imposed during one of the clock's two major restorations. (See **1836 · Jacob Custer**, page 91.)

DA Figure 1. Clock front (winding side) overview. Its many similarities to Custer are obvious. Note switched trains and extension of the winding squares through what is the back of Custer's clocks. Twin wheel rollers support the dial end of the leading-off rods.

DA Figure 2. Anderson strike control detail. He moves the notched flange count wheel to the strike side on the left. The use of counterbalance weights and changes in strike control levers differs from Custer. Dial hands are reset by a friction-mounted pinion to the right of the vertical rod take-off.

DA Figure 3. Anderson deadbeat escapement detail. Although following Custer's wheel tooth count and one-piece deadbeat anchor, Anderson's escapement is less refined and more closely coupled.

1855 • JOHN STOKELL

In 1855, a superb four-dial clock was installed high in the 200-foot steeple of the newly constructed Marble Collegiate Church at 23rd Street and 5th Avenue, New York City. After a century of good service, the clock became irregular, and its dials electrified. The mechanism survived as disassembled loose parts stacked in a kitchen closet until 1994, when they were carried up seven long flights of stairs piece-by-piece and reassembled for display where originally located in the tower, an arduous project taking several weeks to complete. The clock's setting dial, which would identify the name of its maker, is missing, but a search of *The New York Times* of December 27, 1957, just after the clock had been retired, indicates that it "was made in Manhattan by John Stokell in 1855." It is more likely, however, that Stokell actually imported the clock or assembled it from imported parts, as it is of classic English "four poster" design.

The same year the clock was installed, New York City's Industrial Census listed John Stokell at 26 Platt Street, a clockmaker, having machinery valued at $800, a brass inventory worth $1,000, and a clock inventory valued at $300. Little else is known about the man. Charles S. Crossman wrote in the December 1890 *Jewelers Circular and Horological Review*, "John Stokel [sic] of New York City, was a maker of regulators with Graham escapements and second pendulums which were really quite fine in finish. He commenced in 1820 and continued until 1843 when he died of a paralytic stroke while in the shop. His business was continued by his son for a short time." Crossman's could be in error about Stokell's death in 1843, or a son of the same name may have replaced him as the account indicates; the fact is that only one clockmaker by the name of John Stokell was listed in New York City directories from 1825 through 1858. He worked in 1825–1831 at 40 and 59 Elm Street, in 1832 at 157 Broadway, in 1833–1840 at 4 Centre Street, in 1840–1843 back to 59 Elm, in 1843–1848 at 6 Little Green, and in 1848–1851 at 26 Platt Street. Throughout this period his home address was shown as 130 Leonard Street, New York City. Between 1852 and early 1858, his occupation was shown as "Clock maker" or "clocks," working at 26 Platt Street, New York, and as living in Brooklyn for a couple years before returning to Manhattan toward the end of his life. Stokell died in late 1857 or early 1858, leaving "Stokell, Cynthia A, wid John, clocks, 26 Platt h. 105 Ludlow."

John Stokell Tower Clock

Stokell's clock is a typical "four-poster," dating in England from about 1800 when improved smelting techniques enabled large clock frame components and parts to be made of cast iron. The strong heavy frame, a logical successor to the earlier forged-iron cage, consists of one-piece end sections with decorative finial corner posts plus vertical and horizontal cast-iron bars, assembled and held together by washer-headed machine screws. Overall, the cast-iron frame measures 62" wide by 27" deep by 45" high. The wheels are brass with six spokes, time train to the left and strike to the right, pivoting in Vuillamy bushings screwed to the vertical risers. The second wheel of the time train turns an idle wheel connected by a friction plate to a center wheel arbor located between the time and strike trains. The center wheel, a typical English feature, is rarely seen in American clocks. The center wheel arbor is multi-functioned: it carries a cam that trips the strike; it drives a bevel gear take-off connected by a vertical rod to a large wheel transmission mounted above the frame; and it turns the strike control snail and the two hands of the setting dial via associated motion work. A winding square on the front end of the friction-mounted center wheel arbor allows the resetting of all dial hands and associated components while the mechanism continues running. Iron leading-off rods with fork universal joints radiate from the transmission to conventional motion work behind four outside dials. The clock's Graham deadbeat escapement has replaceable steel pallets and a 30-tooth escape wheel measuring 9" in diameter. Bolt-and-shutter maintaining power is hooked into the time second wheel teeth prior to winding by lifting a weighted shutter covering the time winding square. Both winding barrels are of wood, the strike side measuring 13" in diameter by 20" in length with a 23" diameter great wheel. A removable winding jack is provided. Strike control is by rack-and-snail. The two-second pendulum, with a 100-pound cast-iron bob, provides rating adjustments at both ends. Its long tapered wooden rod is slotted to take the crutch pin, and has thumb screws to set the beat. All wheels, including bevel gears and other components, are easily removed from their arbors, being held by screws to their collets. The entire clock, although in rough unrestored condition, is well conceived and beautifully made, well up to Stokell's reported high standards.

Above, *JS Figure 1. Front overview, time to the left, strike to the right. Note the classic "four poster" frame, bolt-and-shutter maintaining power, and Vuillamy bushings—all characteristic of English clocks after about 1800. Missing from extended center wheel arbor is the two-hand setting dial.*
Below, *JS Figure 2. Back overview, strike to the left, time right. The English style center wheel is driven by a time train wheel of the same size. The two-second pendulum, overhead transmission, ratchet-driven fly, and pendulum are mounted outside the frame. Roller pins on the strike second wheel lift the strike lever to sound the bell.*

JS Figure 3. Center wheel detail. A friction plate bearing on the center wheel to the right allows resetting the dial hands without stopping the clock. A roller-ended rod riding on the snail trips the strike. The bevel gear take-off drives the transmission located above. The large lantern pinion above consists of leaf-shaped steel trundles inset into brass collars, invented by Henry Hindley of Yorkshire, England.

JS Figure 4. Detail of the Graham escapement with removable steel pallets. Note the escape wheel and the pallet anchor attached to arbor collets by screws for easy removal, a technique duplicated throughout the clockwork. At lower left is one of two hand knobs to put the pendulum in beat.

1858 • AARON DODD CRANE

Aaron Dodd Crane was born on May 8, 1804, in Caldwell, New Jersey. He attended local schools, living and working on his father's farm into his late 20's. Isolated as he was from the mainstream of American clockmaking, Crane was a self-taught genius who came up with unique alternatives to established horological solutions. In 1829, at the age of 25, he received a United States Patent for a three-wheel clock that struck on cat gut strings. A year later he produced a tower clock model of revolutionary design, described in a Burlington, Vermont, *Free Press* editorial as having a very short pendulum that moved very slowly, calculated to run a year on one winding with a weight fall of only 25 feet. The forerunner of over 50 tower clocks made after 1858 by the Turret & Marine Clock Co., almost every wheel had its own escapement, and the strike train required less weight to give a heavier blow, while dispensing with the usual fly. Throughout his lifetime Crane had a number of patents in several categories. Unlike most inventors, he always found eager backers, but no great fortunes were made.

On January 12, 1831, Crane married Sarah Ann Campbell of Verona, New Jersey. They had five children, including Moses and Augustus Crane, trained by their father and skilled clockmakers, machinists, and inventors in their own time. From 1835 to 1841, Crane lived and worked in Newark, New Jersey, toward the end of the period developing a unique torsion pendulum year mantel clock. His sale of the patent led to the manufacture of several torsion pendulum models in nearby Belleville, where Crane lived for a while. A torsion pendulum mantel clock sales office opened in New York City, operating as J.R. Mills & Co. and later as the Year Clock Company. Crane's continuing interest in tower clocks shows up in an 1845 J.R. Mills & Co. handbill offering to manufacture "Turret, Steeple, or Town Clocks, running from one month to a year." None have survived. The Year Clock Co. failed in 1848, with Crane's promised one-third of the profits coming to naught. He returned to Newark, where he gained control of the patent rights and is shown as a one-year clockmaker until about 1855. Meanwhile, promising connections in Boston resulted in his move to nearby Roxbury. Operating under the name of the Boston Clock Co., he made a series of spectacular one-year skeleton astronomical timepieces, and perfected the invention of his improved tower clock. On February 16, 1858, after months of haggling with Washington bureaucrats, Crane was awarded U.S. Patent No. 19,351, variously designated in patent papers as Church Clock, Public Clock, and, finally, Escapements. It represented a lifetime of thought, experimentation and compromise on a tower clock of radically different design. The only surviving tower clock hardware made by Aaron Crane is his 1858 patent model, but tangible evidence of his innovations exist in surviving examples of over 50 clocks made under licensing agreement by the Turret & Marine Clock Co., and in the later clocks of its successor, Geo. M. Stevens & Co. Not the least of these improvements was the crane-striker, a heavy duty one-wheel, two-pawl ratchet escapement with a deep tooth count wheel on the same arbor, but no fly. The system was so widely used that it passed into manufacturing language as the *crane-striker*, and was employed in alarm apparatus into the mid-twentieth century. On the other hand, variations on the torsion pendulum mantel clock have survived to this day. Both of these breakthroughs outlived their inventor, Aaron Crane, who died of tuberculosis at age 56 on March 10, 1860, in the home of his son Moses Crane, at Roxbury where he was buried. (See **1858 • Turret & Marine Clock Co.**, page 155, and **1864 • Geo. M. Stevens**, page 162.)

Aaron Crane Tower Clocks

AC Patent Model. It took four times longer than usual to patent Crane's tower clock as the Patent Office balked at his total redesign of all parts in such a general category as town clocks. Claims for an automatic reset of obstructed hands and a low inertia floating hammer were disallowed but remain on the model. The patent administrator also faulted the drawings for not showing hands, pendulum, or crutch, etc., to explain to the eye immediately that it was a clock. Crane's lawyer made word changes, and the patent was awarded on February 16, 1858, a full year after it had been submitted. The works are driven by three weights wound on barrels with separate walking escapements on all three primary wheels. Only the strike barrel is wound manually, lever action during strike serving to wind the time and pendulum-drive components automatically. The outside dial hands advance at full minute intervals, with the hour hand turned by unique "daisy cam" motion work. The overall patent model design is not reflected in the **T&M Model 2** flatbed illustrated in Boston directories in 1860. However, **T&M Model 1** is represented by two identical clocks originally installed at Windham, New York, and Stow, Massachusetts, which closely resemble Crane's patent model. The Windham clock is signed by Geo. M. Stevens & Co. along with Crane's 1858 patent date. One explanation is that these two clocks represent an early model, part of a leftover inventory sold by Stevens as successor to the Turret & Marine Clock Co. Both are of cast-iron plate-and-pillar construction, measuring only 17" wide by 12" deep by 26½" high. Outboard winding barrels awkwardly added outside the frame appear as afterthoughts, but the design, physical layout and component details of the Stevens clock and Crane's patent model are very close—including use of a free pendulum, weight line (rather than the sprocket drive of later Turret & Marine clocks) walking escapements on all three principal wheels, and a dumbbell counterpoise to rewind the pendulum-drive remontoire. Differences from the model include use of conventional dial motion works, the lack of automatic rewind, the addition of a winding jack, and use of a coiled spring remontoire on the pendulum drive escapement—all changes consistent with those made to Turret & Marine flatbeds by Stevens & Co. after their succession to the business.

ADC Figure 1. The Crane patent model overview. A coin is added for relative size, model height being 11³/4 inches. Almost every wheel has a distinctive tooth form suited to its specialized function: for example, the daisy cam motion work, the strike great wheel, and the automatic dial reset device at the upper right, and the three escapement ratchets.

ADC Figure 2. Back view of the clock from Stow, Massachusetts. A winding jack, deep-tooth count wheel, strike great wheel and winding ratchet all share a common arbor, not requiring a fly. The time and strike barrels, both mounted outboard of the frame, appear to be modifications improvised by Stevens.

ADC Figure 3. Stow clock with plate removed. At the upper right is the time escape wheel, its rim perforated to allow clutch resetting of the hands without stopping the clock. The dumbbell counterpoise drops to wind the pendulum drive remontoire at upper left. At bottom left is the strike great wheel, with a sturdy walking pawl escapement to drive the bell hammer both back and forth.

154

1858 • TURRET & MARINE CLOCK CO.

Aaron Crane (1804–1860) and his older son, Moses Crane, established the Turret & Marine Clock Co. (T&M) in Boston in 1858. The senior Crane's torsion pendulum year clocks sold well in Boston, and he reasoned that New England offered a more enlightened market for the tower clocks they proposed to make on a radical new plan. By about 1856, they moved from Newark, New Jersey, to Roxbury, Massachusetts, a Boston suburb, and the following year Aaron Crane submitted his tower clock patent application to Washington, D.C. On February 16, 1858, after a year of bickering, he received U.S. Patent No. 19,351. Crane, who was in the terminal stages of tuberculosis, licensed use of this patent to the T&M. The 25-year-old Moses Crane, a skilled and inventive machinist who had worked at his father's side, was superintendent of manufacturing operations and contributed to product development. An 1858 T&M advertisement shows the company's small beginning at 5½ Water Street, Boston. In 1859, Moses was joined by George A. Walker as General Agent, and Collins Stevens, a middle-aged Boston manufacturer of shoe lasts having little or no experience with tower clocks. The capital probably infused by these new partners allowed the company's expansion to both 5 and 13 Water Street, their base of operations for about three years.

T&M tower clocks introduced radical features never seen before, and many not seen since. The company advertised a patent escapement fire alarm, an improved fog-bell striker, and "THE PATENT UNIVERSAL CLOCK, Indicating time on any number of dials throughout a building." They also offered church bells, and a variety of mantel, office and marine clocks. During its short life, the T&M did very well for itself, selling over 50 tower clocks in five states for about $400 each. The following installation sites are known: Acton, Centerville, Hudson, and Lee, Massachusetts; Kennebunk and Saco, Maine; Manchester, Connecticut; Phenix [sic], Rhode Island; and Milton, Vermont. Six clocks have survived, two retrofitted by Stevens & Co. to conventional time trains with Graham deadbeat escapements.

In 1859, Moses Crane married Collins Stevens' cousin, and following his father's death in 1860, inherited the patent rights on which the T&M operated. In 1861, Collins Stevens brought into the business his oldest son George, a well-educated young bookkeeper. Moses Crane apparently took exception to the arrangement, as he left the partnership by late 1861, taking with him the patent rights on which the company operated. He continued to advertise tower clocks, but went

on to make a fortune as a prolific inventor and principal supplier of equipment to the Gamewell Fire Alarm Co. Walker and Stephens remained at 5 Water Street, in business briefly as the Turret Clock Co. Spurred by national prosperity after the Civil War, Geo. M. Stevens & Co. sold hundreds of tower clocks into the twentieth century, their horological roots in the innovations of the Turret & Marine Clock Co.

Turret & Marine Clock Co. Tower Clocks

Aaron Crane's model for Patent 19,351 provides for both time and strike using only three ratchet-type wheels. Each employs a "walking" escapement, consisting of two reciprocal pawls directed by cams into frictionless engagement with the escape wheel. This type escapement, in various sizes, can handle a variety of workloads, from the slight power needed to keep a pendulum in motion, to the great power needed to swing a heavy hammer back and forth against a large bell. The escapement wheel impulsing the pendulum is the only wheel in constant motion; all others only move when triggered to strike or to advance the minute hand at one-minute intervals (simultaneously rewinding the pendulum drive remontoire spring). The strike walking escapement, pumping a lever with a solid rod connection to the bell hammer, requires no fly, only a deep-tooth count wheel. The automatic fail-safe protection in the event of hand obstruction, its "daisy cam" motion work, and "floating" hammer suspension are all unique.

T&M Model 1. Two identical production clocks have survived that closely resemble salient features of Crane's patent model; one is signed by Geo. M. Stevens & Co., Boston, along with Crane's 1858 tower clock patent date. It seems likely that both clocks were preempted and modified by Stevens from the leftover inventory of an early production model after the Turret & Marine Clock Co. was disbanded. (See **1858 • Aaron Dodd Crane**, page 152.)

T&M Model 2. The public first saw Model 2 as a full-page, engraved illustration in the 1860 Boston Directory. This tower clock incorporates many innovations in Crane's patent model, redesigned for greater compactness, site versatility, and ease of maintenance.

The cast-iron flatbed frame, with out-curving cast-iron legs, measures 32" wide by 12" deep by 36" high. This small mechanism and its free pendulum accommodate a variety of cramped tower environments. It can be wound from either side of the frame, with the strike winding jack shifted to either side. The 1½-second free pendulum is connected to its driving escapement by a fine wire, and with correct vertical alignment can be suspended at any angle or level above or below the mechanism. It is temperature compensated and precisely rated by a calibrated thumb nut under its cast-iron lenticular bob. The pendulum drive spring remontoire, rewound at regular intervals, in effect provides one-minute maintaining power. Power is conveyed by a conventional bevel gear transmission to the unique "daisy cam" motion work of four outside dials. Outside dial hands, which advance at one-minute intervals, can be reset without stopping the clock via a hand clutch that engages 1 of 60 holes around the rim of the minute wheel. A simple 60-minute setting dial is provided on the clock. If the hands become obstructed, the leading-off rod disconnects without stopping the clock, then automatically reconnects *on time* after 12 hours,

following removal of the obstruction. Power is delivered to both the retract and strike side of the bell hammer by a solid rod connection. The weight line on both time and strike consists of bicycle-chain engaging sprockets on the great wheel arbors. The chain automatically stacks itself in narrow boxes under the mechanism (a system introduced by Howard & Davis as early as 1851). The elimination of winding barrels results in an inner frame depth of only eight inches shoulder-to-shoulder.

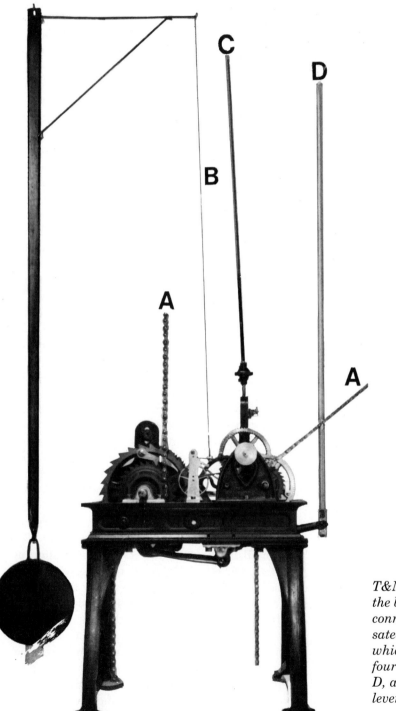

T&M Figure 2. Model 1 dial reset. If the hands are obstructed, this spring-loaded device on rod C disconnects the dials from the works, which continues to run. Obstruction removed, a 12-tooth Geneva cam automatically reconnects the hands on time after 12 hours.

T&M Figure 1. Model 2 clock overview. At A are the bicycle chain weight lines; at B, the light wire connection to a $1^1/2$-second temperature compensated pendulum; at C, the time leading-off rod, which extends power through a transmission to four dials with daisy cam motion work; and at D, a solid rod delivers power to the bell hammer lever during the entire retract/strike cycle.

T&M Figure 3. Model 2 clockwork detail. Note the "workbench" mounting arrangement and ease of access to all components. At A is the strike module; at B, the pendulum drive/beat count module; and at C, the time module. Each module has its own walking escapement and can be easily removed for cleaning or maintenance.

T&M Figure 4. Model 2 dial motion work detail, planetary gearing reduced to its bare essentials. An 11-tooth "daisy" cam wheel, less subject to obstruction than conventional gears, is given an eccentric motion by an off-center plug on the minute-hand rod. This motion is conveyed to the pins of a spider on the cannon pipe, turning the hour hand at the required rate.

1859 • STONE & MARSHALL

Stone & Marshall were successors to Austin Van Riper's successful Empire Works tower clock business, located on Chittenango Creek in upstate Cazenovia, New York. Falling ill on a sales foray to Tennessee in 1858, Van Riper was bedridden for several months, during which period his chief mechanics, John Stone and Justice Marshall, advertised they would "carry on the business...having been in the employ of Mr. Van Riper for several years past and become thoroughly posted in this branch of business...." Van Riper's subsequent recovery and return to work delayed transfer of the business to Stone & Marshall until after his death in September 1959. The two partners continued to conduct their operation at the Empire Works, actually owned by local entrepreneur Leonard White who had purchased half-interest on the day of Van Riper's death and taken over full ownership in January 1960 for $1,000 plus assumption of the property's $2,500 mortgage. White's direct involvement in the clock business is shown in his November 1859 letter to the Meneelys, inquiring if he could expect continuation of the reciprocal exchange of sales leads as "our clocks will be manufactured at the same place, and by the same workmen." By early 1865, Stone & Marshall moved to a two-story former oil mill directly across the Chittenango Creek.

Information about the personal life of the partners is limited. Justice W. Marshall was born about 1828, coming at age 16 to Cazenovia where he mastered his trade at Shapely's Machine Shop, one of several local foundries. In 1850, he quit Shapley's to cast his lot with Van Riper's fledgling town clock operation. Both men gained, as Marshall set the groundwork for eventual ownership, and his employer gained a talented mechanic who contributed to the proliferation of tower clock models produced during the Van Riper era. Marshall and his wife Geraldine had two children, Fred A. and Jessie, and descendants still live in Cazenovia. Marshall died on September 5, 1905, at age 77. John J. Stone was born in 1836, reportedly the son of a "traveling trader." Abandoned at the age of 4, he was adopted by Mary Kelly of Cazenovia with whom he lived most of his life. Stone never married and died on October 11, 1882; his estate went to the sister of his deceased adoptive mother. Milton Card also figures into the Stone & Marshall operation. A self-styled "engineer" and the son of a prosperous Cazenovia farmer, he bought land south of the village in 1864 and was probably first employed by Stone & Marshall about that time. In 1870, Stone & Marshall sold Card a one-third share in the business for $1,000. The firm, now called Stone, Marshall & Card, offered town clocks in at least two models that replicated late model Van

Riper duplex frame clocks. Later, demand slackened with the loss of a major customer, Thomas I. Bailey of Nashville, Tennessee, who switched to A.S. Hotchkiss & Co. and its successor Seth Thomas as his source of town clocks. Times were changing nationwide, and like other small shops challenged by the coming of factory competition, they sought relief in diversification. In 1868, Stone, Marshall and Card were joined by a Cazenovia newcomer, inventor Philo Felter. They set up and operated the American Lock Company in the old mill building, producing a variety of high quality locks. Felter's invention of a sidebar lock was particularly successful, resulting in the takeover of the promising venture by the Yale Lock Co. in 1878. Rumor had it that Felter took off in the night without dividing the profits with his partners, leaving all worldly goods behind including "the supper dishes in the sink." Town clock production apparently ceased in the mid-1870s. A final mention of the remaining partners in 1879 describes Marshall and Card as at work in the old factory making slings for clay pigeons called "spring traps." After Stone's death in 1882, Card purchased the deceased partner's share of what remained of the company's assets for $375, implying that the company was still in existence and of some value. Marshall and Card retained ownership of the factory property until 1903, when the site was sold to the Village of Cazenovia. Later in life Card held a number of responsible civic positions, including that of town clock custodian for 30 years.

With the demise of Stone & Marshall, the distinguished succession of Cazenovia town clock makers came to an end. It spanned 45 years, starting about 1830 with the senior Jehiel Clark, followed by his son, Jehiel Jr., Austin W. Van Riper, then finally by the Stone & Marshall partnerships—a distinguished line of small shop craftsmen passed over with the advent of highly-financed well-engineered factory clocks of Howard and Seth Thomas. (Russell Oechsle)

Stone and Marshall Tower Clocks

S&M Model 1. This magnificent tower clock, made for Van Riper before his death, was the work of his skilled machinist Justice W. Marshall, hence the Stone & Marshall attribution. The earliest example, now lost, was sold in Nashville, Tennessee, for $1,500. A second example of the same model, sold after much bickering for $500 as Cazenovia's town clock, still survives where installed in 1874. As with the Van Riper duplex models that preceded it, separate time and strike movements with skeletonized cast-iron plate-and-pillar frames are mounted side-by-side with a strike tripping connection. The ornately curved frames and the polished spiral spoking of the wheels create a pleasing spectacle of curves turning against curves, an elegant design. Most wheels are brass with six spiral spokes

158

polished to a high finish, including the bevel gears of a spectacular transmission mounted high overhead. The chair-frame time unit consists of an extended base to accommodate the barrel, and a tall A-frame (measuring 9" shoulder-to-shoulder) that supports the pendulum and the rest of the time train. Time train pivot holes have jeweled end caps and jeweled deadbeat pallets on its ornate brass anchor. Dial hands are set by freewheeling. Arbors and cut-leaf pinions are of highly-polished steel, and the cast-iron frame pillars decoratively turned. The strike is tripped by a cam on the time second wheel arbor, which also drives the dial take-off and a setting dial (now missing). The two-second pendulum, fine-rated at its suspension end, has a tapered wooden rod and a 14" lenticular bob. Overall, the time frame measures about 24" wide by 26" deep by 44" high. The strike frame is larger, measuring about 36" wide by 35" deep by 50" high. It has a notched

flange count wheel and a large-vane, ratchet-driven fly, both mounted outside the frame. The strike control levers and the bell strike cam wheel are generally similar to earlier Van Riper models. The clock frames are painted a warm brown with fine yellow striping. The smaller **S&M Model 2** time frame measures 16½" wide by 19" deep by 33" high, its strike frame 25" wide by 22⅝" high. Changes include minor variations in frame design, no jewel fittings, and a one-piece iron recoil escapement. Two of several known examples of this model survive in Peterboro, New York, near Cazenovia. The first, installed in 1871, failed in the early 1930s and was replaced by a duplicate model clock found by chance in its original crates long overlooked in the attic of the old clock factory. Both the old clock and its replacement are virtually identical, differing only in the color of their paint.

Left, *S&M Figure 1. This magnificent Model 1 town clock was moved to its present location in 1874. A duplex frame with lever connections to trip the strike, the time unit is elevated to allow for the long two-second pendulum which just clears the floor of the room below. **Right**, S&M Figure 2. Model 1 escapement detail. The impulse faces of a showy cast brass anchor have replaceable jeweled pallet slips. Time train pivot holes have jeweled end caps in threaded brass collars. Note above, the decoratively turned frame pillars and the hand nut for fine rating the pendulum.*

Left, S&M Figure 3. Model 1 time module. Made in two highly decorative cast-iron sections bolted together, the resulting chair-frame provides flatbed support for the long barrel and a shallow plate-and-pillar section, which provides for short sturdy time train arbors. **Right**, S&M Figure 4. Model 1 strike module. Three decorative plates are spaced apart over a large winding barrel and its great wheel. A 10'' shoulder-to-shoulder front section supports the strike train, plus a large two-blade fly and a notched flange count wheel, both mounted outside the frame. Note at upper left the lever and chain connection to the time unit that trips the strike.

160

S&M Figure 5. Stone & Marshall Model 2 time module, a scaled down version of Model 1 with a fixed pallet anchor recoil escapement. One advantage of the duplex frame arrangement is that the time module can stand alone, ready-made for time-only applications.

1864 • GEO. M. STEVENS & CO.

George Milton Stevens was born in Boston in 1838, the oldest of three sons of Collins and Nancy (Geyer) Stevens. He graduated from the prestigious English High School in 1856 and worked briefly as a bookkeeper before joining as a clerk with the Turret & Marine Clock Company (T&M) on Water Street, Boston, where his father was a partner. It is safe to say that Collins and George Stevens learned everything they knew about tower clocks from Moses Crane, the new firm's highly-skilled superintendent and son of Aaron Crane, a horological genius on whose patents the T&M operated. By late 1861, a dispute resulted in Moses Crane leaving the firm and taking with him the patent rights inherited from his father. Collins and George Stevens exercised damage control in 1862 by patenting their own version of a remontoire escapement, reducing operating space to 5 Water Street, and renaming themselves the Turret Clock Company. Two years later they reorganized once more as Geo. M. Stevens & Co. at 52 Sudbury Street, Boston.

The new company rode the wave of prosperity that followed the Civil War, selling at least 22 "Stevens Detached Remontoire" time and strike tower clocks by 1868. Their early clocks used a number of T&M's features in modified form, a major difference being Stevens' use of wire rope on cast-iron barrels, rather than T&M's chain-and-sprocket winding system. Moses Crane never sued for patent infringement, but he had little use for Stevens the rest of his life.

By 1868, Geo. M. Stevens & Co. abandoned use of the remontoire escapement, switching to a conventional Graham deadbeat with undercut teeth, a four-wheel time train, and a crutch-driven pendulum. Retained were the T&M hand-setting clutch and the crane-striker, features used in some Stevens models until 1900 or later. Tower clocks were priced from $350 to $600, depending on the model and what the market would bear. Glass dials imported from France and Germany were offered at added cost. In 1868, Stevens advertised, "Cog-wheels of all sizes, constantly on hand or made to order," suggesting some in-house manufacturing capability. In 1869 the company moved to 90 Sudbury Street, Boston, where, at the behest of the U.S. Lighthouse Service, they developed and produced lighthouse fog alarms. Their alarms, patented in 1873, made use of the tried-and-true crane-striker and also Crane's patented "floating" hammer, representing significant improvement over former government approved lighthouse alarms made by Jacob Custer of Pennsylvania.

Geo. Stevens & Co. remained active well beyond the 1870 cut-off limitations of this work, but a short summary follows. Stevens clock models varied in size and style after 1870. Collins Stevens died in 1873, and a corporate structure evolved thereafter. The company met in head-to-head competition with E. Howard & Co. and often won the sale, particularly in small New England towns. Eventually, almost all trace of earlier T&M features disappeared as Stevens moved to compete with standardized "factory clocks" that dominated the market after 1872. The Stevens' line grew to include electrical work and fire alarm systems, three-legged gravity escapements, chiming clocks, and time and strike post clocks. In all, probably over 450 tower clocks were sold, many of which are still running hand-wound and giving good service. George Stevens retired in 1905 and in 1909 the company moved to smaller quarters at 53 Franklin Street. It is unlisted in Boston directories after 1916.

Stevens was a rarity among clockmakers; he died rich. In a long successful business career, he sold hundreds of well made tower clocks that were largely derivative of the work of other clockmakers, and by prudent investment left a sizable fortune. He and his wife of 42 years, Addie Holden Stevens, lived in a fine home on Massachusetts Avenue in Cambridge, with a farm retreat at Swampscott. The couple was childless, but had a life filled with relatives and friends, including the offspring of his two brothers. Stevens' only known outside affiliation was with the Charity Lodge of Masons. After his wife's death in 1908, Estelle Rogers, a cousin related to Moses Crane's wife, took care of the household. A victim of diabetes for several years, George Stevens died in February 1917 after an illness of two months. His estate was valued at about $270,000—millions in today's dollars. Apart from bequests to relatives, he intended that the bulk of the money go in small amounts to local charities. As it turned out, most went to estate trustees, lawyers, and taxes, until its depletion in 1989, 70 years after Stevens' passing.

Geo. M. Stevens & Co. Tower Clocks

GMS Model 1 (1864–1868). Of the 22 clocks made, only three have survived (two with missing parts) from their original installations in Keene, New Hampshire, and in Oxford and Wenham, Massachusetts. In addition, an installation at Poughkeepsie, New York, was sufficiently flawed for George Stevens to travel from Boston to check it out. The cast-iron frame measures 47" high, by 34" wide by 16" deep overall. All parts are stamped with the clock serial number. GMS Model 1 descends directly from clocks made by the Turret & Marine Clock Co.: it has a similar flanged square-sided flatbed with bowed legs, strike crank winding jack, deep-tooth count wheel strike control, fly-less crane-striker, hand-setting clutch on the minute wheel, and a 1½-second free pendulum. The time side uses a larger Crane walking escapement, a different tripping system to rewind the remontoire spring, and an outboard fly to cushion the advance of the dial hands at one-minute intervals. Other differences include a four-wheel time train in brass bushings press fit into free-form A-frame plates, and the use of steel weight line and cast-iron barrels. The time barrel is mounted within the A-frame, but the longer strike barrel requires a frame offset and uses two clicks on its ratchet. The clock runs eight days on a winding and drives up to four outside dials. Its frame is painted black with red wheel spokes, signed by the maker with the Stevens patent date, and filigreed with blue, red, and gilt detailing.

GMS Model 2 (1868–1872). The cast-iron frame design and crane-striker is unchanged, but major changes to the time side include a four-wheel time train, having Vuillamy bushings, mounted vertically in a 26" high cast-iron A-frame. The A-frame is topped by a bridge from which is suspended a conventional crutch-driven 1½-second pendulum with a compensated bi-metal cylindrical bob. Other changes include use of a signed and numbered deadbeat escapement with replaceable steel pallets and Harrison maintaining power. A large cam on the minute wheel arbor trips the strike and doubles as a 60-minute setting dial. The only holdover on the time side is the minute wheel clutch for resetting the dial hands without stopping the clock. GMS Model 2 is more modestly painted, typically in brown or green, with black or white trim, and signed by the maker on the flatbed.

GMS Figure 1. GMS Model 1 front overview, time left, strike right. Note the time free-form A-frame, its inset setting dial, and the escapement remontoire fly. The crane-striker ratchet and associated wheels are on a single arbor wound with winding jack aid, its wheel seen at bottom right.

GMS Figure 2. The Stevens "detached remontoire" escapement. Although larger and with a different triggering system, it is modeled after the Turret & Marine walking escapement. A remontoire spring in the escape wheel hub is automatically rewound at one-minute intervals. The vertical wire at top right conveys impulses from a falling 1 oz. weight to a free pendulum identical to T&M. (See T&M, Figure 1, p. 156.)

GMS *Figure 3. Model 2 overview. The crane-strik-*
er with a winding jack has been retained but its
steel weight line winding barrel requires a
Stevens hallmark, the frame offset. The time train
is a complete redesign, including its cast-iron A-
frame with Vuillamy bushings, Harrison main-
taining, and a four-wheel train with Graham
deadbeat escapement. Precision pendulum rating
and beat adjustments are provided.

GMS *Figure 4. Crane's "floating hammer" pro-*
vides added bell power in Stevens' tower clocks,
and also in Stevens' fire and fog alarm applica-
tions. It operates on the principle of a battering
ram, swinging the bell hammer in both directions
by a solid rod connection to the strike train below,
while "floating" pendulum-like from overhead
suspension.

1864 • ALONZO TAYLOR

Little is known about Alonzo Taylor apart from his surviving tower clocks. They mark him along with Smith's Clock Establishment, H. Sperry & Co., Reeve & Co., and A.S. Hotchkiss & Co. as belonging to the New York City School of tower clockmakers at work between 1850 and 1870. New York City Directories first listed Taylor as a "machinist" at 68 Duane Street. His occupation was more explicitly identified by an 1855 industrial census that showed Taylor as being in the sewing machine business with assets of $600 in tools, 7.800 pounds of iron castings, and 208 [sewing] machines valued at $15,600. Apparently it was a labor intensive operation requiring some skill as he had 12 employees paid an above-scale wage of $48 per month. Remaining in the same business at least through to 1863, he moved to 107 Elm Street in 1857, and moved again in 1859 to 487 Broadway, the same address of H. Sperry & Co., a major dealer, exporter, and manufacturer of clocks. In the same year of 1859, H. Sperry died. His firm was taken over by younger brothers who continued operations as Sperry & Co., which is unlisted after 1863. Meanwhile, Alonzo Taylor remained at the same 487 Broadway address, and starting about 1864 sold at least three well-made tower clocks which have survived. One, installed in Farmington, Connecticut, and signed "A. Taylor New York," was similar to duplex model clocks sold earlier by the Sperrys. Two other Taylor clocks, installed about 1865 in western New York State, integrate time and strike in one distinctive frame utilizing many features of the duplex frame model. Taylor's listing in the 1865–66 city directory clarified what had transpired. It reads: "Taylor, Alonzo, 487 Bdwy & machinist 3rd Ave n 33d, h. 903 39th. ALONZO TAYLOR (Successor to Sperry & Co) manufacturers of TOWER CLOCKS AND REGULATORS." Taylor seems to have continued making sewing machines, while taking on Sperry's tower clock business as well. In 1866–67, he remained listed as successor to Sperry & Co., manufacturer of tower clocks and regulators, but with operations consolidated at 188 E. 33rd Street. The following year Taylor was unlisted altogether. In 1868–69 he is listed simply as "Taylor, Alonzo, machines, 205 E 23d, 112 E 27th," an occupation he pursued with some address changes until about 1875. During the next several years he remained in the city with an intriguing occupation change to "liquors" at 97 Spring Street. Presumably a restaurateur by 1880, he ran an "eating h[ouse]" at 56 E. 12th, shown at home in New Jersey.

Alonzo Taylor Tower Clocks

Taylor's three surviving clocks represent two models designated here as **AT Model 1** and **AT Model 2**. All are signed "A. Taylor, New York" and share the following New York City School distinctive features: decorative spoke corners; an offset escapement pinwheel with deadbeat pallets; Harrison maintaining power; deep-tooth count wheel strike control; elongated pendulum rating nut; two-hand setting dial; strike side winding jack; and a New York type transmission located above the movement. There are also model differences.

AT Model 1, installed at Farmington, Connecticut, has in recent years been retrofitted for electrical rewind, but is otherwise complete, original and restored to immaculate condition. The clock is similar to duplex frame clocks installed earlier by the Sperrys. Separate frames for time and strike are anchored to the floor side-by-side, with a connection to trip the strike. Each frame consists of cast-iron skeletonized plates spaced by plain round pillars and held together by hex nuts. The time frame is a concave-sided A-frame measuring 23½" wide at its base by 18" deep by 34" high. The beehive-shaped strike frame measures 26" wide by 24" deep by 28" high. Flanged-end plates of both wooden barrels are of cast iron as are both great wheels, all other wheels being brass. Steel wheel arbors with cut-leaf pinions originally pivoted in unbushed holes (now brass bushed). A 1½-second pendulum, with a round wooden rod and cannonball bob, is suspended and fine-rated from a cock at the apex of the time back plate. The escapement has an offset 22-pin pinwheel with deadbeat agate pallets mounted on a brass hammer-head arm. The arm can be disengaged from the escape wheel to reset the dial hands by freewheeling. The time second wheel arbor trips the strike and drives the two-hand setting dial motion work and a bevel gear take-off outside the front plate. The take-off is connected by a vertical rod to a four-dial transmission located above the mechanism. Replaceable pins, around the side of the strike second wheel, lift the bell strike lever. A two-vane adjustable fly mounted behind the frame is ratchet-driven. The strike barrel is wound via reduction gearing on the strike second wheel winding square.

AT Model 2. Examples have survived in western New York State in hand-wound running condition at Pike (recently restored) and at Warsaw, the latter installed in 1865 at a cost of $700. AT Model 2 is more compact than Model 1, supporting both time and strike in a single frame measuring 25" wide by 24" deep by 28" high. The cast-iron frame consists of two skeletonized pagoda-shaped plates spaced apart by plain round pillars and held together with hex nuts. The pendulum is suspended and fine-rated from a cock extending from the front plate. The deadbeat pinwheel escapement arrangement is the same as AT Model 1, and allows for freewheeling in the same manner; however, the pallets are polished steel, not agate. Barrels, ratchets and great wheels are cast iron; all other wheels are brass with machine-cut teeth. Arbors and cut-leaf pinions are steel. The time train second wheel arbor also trips the strike and drives a two-hand setting dial on the front of the clock and a bevel gear take-off mounted inside the frame back plate. A ratchet-driven fly with two large adjustable blades is mounted outboard of the back plate.

AT Figure 1. AT Model 1 front overview, strike left, time right. Strike trip levers are the sole connection between separate strike and time units. Large sprocket wheels seen on each barrel are part of the recently installed electrical rewind system that otherwise does not impact the original mechanism in any way.

Left, AT Figure 2. AT Model 1 time module detail, front view. Frame shape provides support for an offset pinwheel escapement. Thumb screws and the square pallet arbor allow disengagement of the pallets for freewheeling while maintaining their alignment for re-engagement. The time module is also suitable for time-only applications. **Right**, AT Figure 3. AT Model 2, front overview. Clockwork features of Model 1 are incorporated into one small frame, elevated here on a wooden box for comfortable winding height. The scalloped frame corners are reminiscent of "pagoda-style" turret clocks popular in England in the last half of the eighteenth century (see JE Figure 4, p. 13).

AT Figure 4. AT Model 2 barrel detail. Both time and strike great wheels and barrels are cast iron, the strike barrel diameter being 9½", almost twice that of the time side. The time great wheel has Harrison maintaining power, and the strike train has a winding jack on the second wheel winding square arbor. Note the deep-tooth 78-tooth count wheel and the limited use of Vuillamy bushings.

1867 • ANDREW S. HOTCHKISS

Andrew Stephen Hotchkiss, the second of six children of Stephen and Patty (Wiard) Hotchkiss, was born December 14, 1814, in Burlington, Connecticut, a hilly, sparsely populated town recently separated from Bristol to the south. Details of his early life and where he learned tower clockmaking are unknown. The shelf clock manufactory of a distant relative, Elisha Hotchkiss Jr., offered local employment, but Hotchkiss, like other native sons of Burlington, left town early to make his mark elsewhere. In January 1846, he married Adelia C. Pond of Burlington. The following year he was listed in New York City directories as a clockmaker, originally at 98 First, and in 1851 at 15 E. 13th. The latter date probably coincided with the start of his employment by Henry Sperry, another Burlington native son who succeeded in the big city. In 1857, *Frank Leslie's Illustrated Newspaper* reported that Hotchkiss was on the staff of H. Sperry & Co. as a tower clock "designer and superintendent of construction." At least five H. Sperry & Co. tower clocks dating from 1851 have distinctive Hotchkiss features. New York City installations included clocks at Brooklyn City Hall, Rutgers Street Church, St. George's Episcopal Church, Brick Church at Murray Hill, plus a tower clock displayed in the street level window of Sperry's Empire Tower Clock Manufactory at 338 Broadway.

After the untimely death of Henry Sperry in early 1859, his younger brothers continued to offer Hotchkiss-designed tower clocks under the name of Sperry & Co. before selling out to Alonzo Taylor about 1864. Again, directory listings for Hotchkiss leave unexplained gaps. In 1863 he was shown in the Williamsburg section of Brooklyn, as "clockmaker h. Quincy n 12th." He next surfaced in December 1867 at the U.S. Army Arsenal at Rock Island, Illinois, where he was hailed as a "nationally known clock maker." On this occasion, he brought the parts for a $5,000 tower clock which he personally assembled and adjusted to show apparent time, then 20 days later returned to his shop in Williamsburg (Brooklyn). In 1868, "Hotchkiss, Andrew H. clocks" appeared in New York City directories at 18 Cortlandt Street, a few doors away from the American Clock Co. At the same time or possibly earlier, Hotchkiss shared the workshop of William S. Hill, a "clock manufacturer" across the East River at 1st and 11th in Brooklyn. They had a puzzling relationship, a legally drawn "co-partnership" to conduct business as independent entities. Surviving Hill invoices detail typical transactions, which included Hill being paid by Hotchkiss for dial making, motion work, grooved barrels, escapements, iron stock, bolts, bevel gears, weights, dial hands, boxing, painting, cartage, tower clock installation (@ 50¢ to 60¢ an hour) and even supplying complete tower clocks. The co-partnership agreement was renewed as late as 1870. At some point, Hotchkiss introduced a general purpose, lower cost model that sold very well over a wide area, a precursor of the "factory clocks" to come. Examples survive from Saugerties and Babylon, New York, to Bolivar, Tennessee, and Holly Springs, Mississippi. Originally signed "A.S. Hotchkiss New York," later versions added "& Co.," presumably to reflect support by the American Clock Co. Representation by this New York sales agent by late 1871 put Hotchkiss in the company of Connecticut's leading clock manufacturers, one being Seth Thomas & Co. This old line firm sought entry into the tower clock business then entering a post-war boom dominated by E. Howard & Co. Hotchkiss represented that foothold and sold out to Seth Thomas about 1872; the exact date is uncertain. Hotchkiss tower clock manufacture shifted immediately to the Thomas movement shop at Thomaston, Connecticut. For many years Seth Thomas wisely traded on the A.S. Hotchkiss national reputation. Early Seth Thomas tower clocks retained many Hotchkiss design features, their setting dials being signed by both principals. Early Hotchkiss clock installations appeared as the work of Seth Thomas in their 1874 catalog, and A.S. Hotchkiss Tower Clocks got separate listing in city directories until 1877. After the takeover, Hotchkiss actively participated during the transition period and remained a Seth Thomas consultant long after his retirement. A.S. Hotchkiss died at home at Brooklyn at age 86 on September 13, 1901.

A.S. Hotchkiss Tower Clocks

Three models probably designed by A.S. Hotchkiss date from about 1850–1859 when he supervised production at H. Sperry & Co. They include **HS Model 1**, **HS Model 2**, and **AT Model 1** (see **1851 • H. Sperry & Co.** pages 143-146, and **1864 • Alonzo Taylor**, page 165). In business for himself after Sperry's death, A.S. Hotchkiss installed huge cast-iron flatbeds, designated here as **ASH Model 1**, but probably similar in design to Sperry's **HS Model 2**. Hotchkiss clocks for Manhattan's St. George's Episcopal Church (ca. 1859) and New York City Hall (ca. 1860–61), have not survived, but a comparable flatbed signed "A.S. Hotchkiss New York 1867" has survived at the U.S. Army Arsenal at Rock Island, Illinois.

ASH Model 1. The base of the Rock Island cast-iron frame is a highly finished flatbed on decoratively turned legs, measuring 93" wide, by 36" deep, by 35½" high. Overall height is 89"—including the curvilinear A-frame bridge on turned pillars with acorn finials. Three six-spoke bronze wheels on polished steel arbors with cut pinions make up each train, running in bearing blocks and Vuillamy bushings. On the time side the 3-foot diameter great wheel and 27" second wheel are marked with the hours and minutes, respectively, and move against fixed pointers, acting as a setting dial. Both trains have integral cast-iron winding jacks, with Harrison maintaining on the time side. The strike side has an adjustable two-blade ratchet-driven fly, and a great wheel with 32 steel roller pins that activate the bell strike lever. The escapement has an offset pinwheel with 30 oil-retaining pins, polished agate deadbeat pallets, and provides for freewheeling disengagement via a thumb nut on the pallet arbor. The distinctive closed-bow crutch and pallet arms, Hotchkiss hallmarks, are also found on ASH Model 2 and on early Seth Thomas tower clocks. A 32-foot long three-second pendulum is fine-rated at its suspension end, its shaped wooden rod supporting a 350-pound cannonball bob. Power delivered to a transmission centered in the clock room is conveyed via long leading-off rods, roller wheel supported, to the motion work of four 12-foot dials of unique porthole design.

ASH Model 2. The cast-iron curvilinear frame of this lower cost, general purpose model is of plate-and-pillar construction. It measures 29$\frac{1}{2}$" wide by 26$\frac{1}{2}$" deep by 33" high. Time and strike wheel trains pivot in Vuillamy bushings. A strike side winding jack is provided, along with Harrison maintaining on the time side. The barrels are hollow cast iron. Most wheels are brass with machined teeth and rims, the spoking left as-cast. The offset deadbeat pinwheel escapement is a smaller version of the one in ASH Model 1. The strike is tripped, the 60-minute setting dial pointer turned, and the bevel gear take-off driven by connections to the time second wheel arbor. The 1$\frac{1}{2}$-second pendulum has a shaped wooden rod and a cast-iron lenticular bob, rated by a typical Hotchkiss elongated hand nut on its suspension end. At least three versions of ASH Model 2 were produced. The earliest is signed "A.S. Hotchkiss, New York," and is distinguished by its three-wheel time train, high tooth count great wheels, deep-tooth count wheel mounted on a frame out-rider, and the strike pinwheel. A later version, probably dating from 1870–1872, is signed "A.S. Hotchkiss & Co., New York." Its time train has four smaller wheels, an integral deep-tooth count wheel, and a Grimthorpe type cam tooth wheel to lift the bell strike lever. An optional skeletonized base, mating with the lines of the movement, measures 17" high by 39" wide by 35" deep, raising the movement to a comfortable winding height. A third ASH Model 2 variation, found at Cumberland, Maryland, adds a second frame that strikes the quarters.

ASH Figure 1. ASH Model I at Rock Island, IL. This heroic clock has been skillfully retrofitted for electrical rewind, maintaining the integrity of all downstream parts. A portion of one of its four unusual porthole dials is visible behind the clock. Note the closed-bow arms of the crutch and escapement pallet arbor.

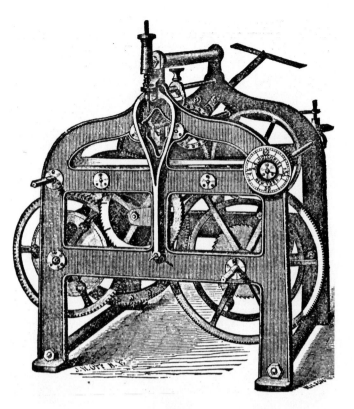

Left, ASH Figure 2. *Handbill engraving of ASH Model 2, probably pre-1870. The model is distinguished from later versions by differences in the maker's signature, large three-wheel trains, a conventional strike pin-wheel, and a frame outrider supporting the deep-tooth count wheel.* **Below left**, ASH Figure 3. *Post-1870 version of ASH Model 2. Signed "A.S. Hotchkiss & Co." Compare differences from Model 1, particularly in wheel size and number, and integral count wheel placement.* **Below right**, ASH Figure 4. *Post-1870 ASH Model 2 with front plate removed. Frame plates are spaced apart by three plain round posts. Note four-wheel time train, offset escapement pinwheel, and replacement of strike great wheel lifting pins with a cam tooth wheel.*

EARLY AMERICAN TOWER CLOCKS

END OF PART ONE

Haverhill, Massachusetts

Warren, Rhode Island

Haverhill, New Hampshire

Hatboro, Pennsylvania

New York, New York

Burlington, New Jersey

Rochester, Minnesota

174

Clockmakers and others associated with American tower clocks from 1668 to 1998

• Tower Clocks Survive

• Tower clocks survive

ADAMS, ELMER W.: Seneca Falls, New York, 1833-1842. Adams was one of a number of Connecticut clockmakers in the early 1800s who sought their fortunes in central and upper New York State, a gateway to the west. A native of Canton, Connecticut, near Bristol where he probably was trained, Adams first appears at Seneca Falls in 1832-1833 when he joined Chauncey Marshall, a local entrepreneur, in the partnership of Marshall & Adams. Marshall was the financier and Adams the horologist who managed their factory located near the confluence of the Seneca River and the Erie Canal. They made unique eight-day strap brass movements and imported Connecticut wooden works which were installed in a variety of plain and empire style cases. It was a highly successful enterprise for several years, enabling Adams to buy out Marshall's share of the partnership in 1836. His timing was poor as the country was heading into a major financial depression. Adams filed for bankruptcy on October 12, 1837, in debt to over 20 creditors for $12,851. He sold a portion of his clock inventory in Chillicothe, Ohio, and what remained upon his return to Seneca Falls. Changes in company name and location are reflected in his clocks by over-paste labels, one reading, "E.W. Adams /Horologist/Manufacturer of /TOWN CLOCKS, TIMEPIECES/ and/ REGULATORS/ Seneca Falls, /New York." These labels appear to have been used after 1837 and before 1847 when Adams left Seneca Falls for good. There is no evidence that actual town clocks were ever produced. NTCS. (Russell Oechsle)

ALLEN, ALEXANDER: at work in Rochester, New York, from 1845-1865. After many years in the watch, jewelry, and repairing business, declining health forced his retirement, at which time he established a machine shop. The 1860 Rochester Directory shows him on 1 Buffalo Street, offering small machinery, town clocks, patent models and watchmaker's regulators made to order and warranted. Allen spent his last years about 30 miles east of Pittsburgh in Saltsburg, located on the Western Division of the Pennsylvania Canal, and named for its salt resources. *The Saltsburg Press* of March 17, 1886, printed a long account of Allen's professional life. According to the article, while still living in Rochester, Allen "remodeled" an 1801 English clock, made by John Thwaites of Clerkenwell, which had

been moved in 1858 to the Cathedral of the Immaculate Conception at Albany, New York. He claimed to have added a mechanism that chimed the quarter hours on nine bells. Both the clock and chiming mechanism are inoperative today but have survived in the Cathedral tower. The mechanism is signed "Alex. Allen, Rochester" but has only three levers, incapable of striking on nine bells. Its cast-iron frame appears identical to tower clock frames used by Ephraim Byram of Sag Harbor, with whom Allen probably had earlier dealings. In April 1862 Allen claimed to have "completed" a $2,000 Rochester clock that sounds suspiciously like a highly acclaimed clock installed by Byram in Rochester's Plymouth Church about the same time. According to the *Mount Morris Union* of October 11, 1862, Allen was hired by this Upstate New York village to repair their town clock, making "such alterations...*as to permanently secure us correct time.*" [ital. added.] Apparently he accomplished this miracle by simply lowering the clock movement 33 feet below the dials, and reducing the driving weight by one-half! The Mount Morris clock, maker unknown, was purchased with public funds in 1835 and destroyed along with the old Town Building in 1955. In 1865, while Allen was still located in Rochester, flood waters of the Genessee River carried away the contents of the building where he was located, a loss Allen estimated at $3,000. According to the Saltsburg article, Allen had invented an automatic fire alarm which he sold along with his machine shop to parties in Letonia, Ohio, who later employed him as their factory foreman. The company then consolidated with a Cleveland house which put him in charge of manufacturing telegraphic and complicated electrical instruments. When the business failed, about 1872-74, the resilient Mr. Allen "embarked on the jewelry business in Letonia, Ohio," where he remained until his removal to Saltsburg in the 1880s. He was known in Saltsburg for his fair dealing and courteous manners, being regarded as "a skilled workman, enterprising businessman and honorable citizen." He advertised the repair of clocks and watches, with particular attention paid to English and French chronometers, and the conversion of key-wound watches to stem winders. It was also claimed that he repaired organs with no less skill than he repaired watches. Given Allen's relatively unknown status and extravagant claims, it is difficult to separate fact from fancy in this account of his accomplishments. (Alton A. DuBois, Phillip J. Zorich)

ALLEN, WILLIAM: an emigrant from Birmingham, England, William Allen arrived in America by December 1772, when he joined Charles Jacob and Abraham Claude, watchmakers of London, in their recently established shop on West Street, Annapolis, Maryland. Allen advertised himself as a clockmaker "who makes and repairs all Sorts of musical, Chime, Town, and plain clocks after the best manner...also repairs Gentlemens [sic] Fire-arms and most Kinds of Metal and Hardware work...." NTCS.

AMERICAN CLOCK COMPANY: 1850-1880, New York City. A major clock dealer, wholesaler and sales agent. It was successor to the Connecticut Protective Clock Co., a consortium of major clock manufacturers in that state. In 1850, it first opened offices in New York City at 44 Cortlandt Street, then moved in 1851-52 to 3 Cortlandt, where it remained until moving again in 1873 to 381 Broadway. Membership changed over the years. In December 1864, Ethel Hine and Seth E. Thomas signed as co-partners in a takeover of the American Clock Co., described as New York agents marketing clocks made by the New Haven Clock Co., E.N. Welch Mfg. Co. and Seth Thomas Clock Co. A.S. Hotchkiss & Co., a Brooklyn tower clock maker with a growing national reputation, was added to the list in 1871. In 1872 A.S. Hotchkiss sold out to Seth Thomas, and for several years thereafter was directly involved in setting up their tower clock division. An 1874 catalog featured "A.S. Hotchkiss Tower Clocks, Manufactured by Seth Thomas Clock Co., Thomaston Conn." The American Clock Co. was shown in the catalog as the sales agent at 581 Broadway, with branches in Chicago and San Francisco. Eight tower clock models were illustrated with prices ranging from $125 to $1,925. The catalog also listed as credentials about 50 representative Seth Thomas installations, many of which were actually put up by A.S. Hotchkiss & Co. in the 1860s, years before the Seth Thomas takeover. Surviving examples of transition tower clocks are signed by both Seth Thomas and A.S. Hotchkiss. There are no known tower clocks signed by the American Clock Co., which is unlisted in New York City Directories after 1879.

ANDERSON, DAVID M.: b. ca. 1782, Lebanon, Pennsylvania; d.1862, Waynesburg, (now Honey Brook) Pennsylvania. At work as Waynesburg's clock and watch maker 1829-1862. In 1850-52, he made the Town Clock, a modified version of the large cast-iron clocks produced in good number by Jacob

Custer of Norristown, Pennsylvania. (See **1852 • David M. Anderson**, page 146.)

ANSONIA CLOCK COMPANY: 1858-1878, Ansonia, Connecticut; 1879-1929, Brooklyn, New York. Founded in Derby, Connecticut, both the company and its Ansonia location were named after Anson Phelps, an importer of brass and copper who went into clockmaking to increase the use of brass from his rolling mills. The company was a major producer of small, novelty, and French-derivative house clocks. After moving to Brooklyn in 1879, the firm added two and four-dial street clocks and timepiece and striker turret clocks to its line. The latter were cast-iron flatbeds with A-frames and cabriole legs, the clockwork appearing to be of conventional "factory clock" design typical of the period. The A-frame castings were signed "Ansonia Clock Company, Brooklyn, NY., U.S.A." By 1929, the company sold most of its timekeeping machinery and some of its dies to the Russian Government, ceasing operations altogether by 1930. NTCS.

BAGNALL, BENJAMIN: b. 1689, England; d. July 1773, Boston, Massachusetts. While still young, he immigrated to America. Some claim he first arrived in Philadelphia, a Quaker enclave, where he could have learned clockmaking from Peter Stretch or others. By 1710-1712 he was of Boston, said to have been New England's first clockmaker. He first married Elizabeth Shove in 1712; they had seven children, including Benjamin Jr. and Samuel, who also became clockmakers. His second wife was Sarah (1703-1791), the daughter of Abraham Redwood of Newport, Rhode Island. In 1717-18, Bagnall made a public clock for Boston's Brick Meeting House, located at that portion of Boston's Washington Street known then as Cornhill. The clock was installed in the cupola of a three-story building having a roof that sloped toward Washington Street. As first made, the clock was wound daily, but he later modified it to run a week on a winding, and, in 1735, was paid £10 for keeping it in good repair for one year. By 1767, it was thought the clock was beyond repair, but Gawen Brown came to its rescue and agreed "to rectify the Hand of the Dyal [sic]...and to clean said Clock for Forty Shillings lawful money." In 1839, Bagnall's old clock, although still going strong, was sold at auction. An entry in Charlestown's Treasurer's Book shows Bagnall to have been paid on August 22, 1724, for cleaning that town's public clock. Included in his goods offered for auction after his death at age 84 was, "A New handsome Clock for a Church." The Quakers were barely tolerated in Boston, but Bagnall appears to have met with instant success, not only as a businessman but in social circles. He was described in his obituary as a "Watch-Maker of this town...one of the people called

Quakers...He was a good Husband and a tender Parent; honest and upright in his Dealings; sincere and stedfast [sic] in his Friendship; liberal to the Poor, and a good Citizen; he acquired the Regard and Esteem of all who had the Pleasure of his Acquaintance." His residence was shown as "in Cornhill [now 209 Washington Street], Boston, well situated for Trade." NTCS.

BAILEY, THOMAS I: ca. 1854-1876, Nashville, Tennessee. Bailey was an independent agent who acquired town clocks manufactured in the north, which he sold and installed in a half-dozen southern states. An 1859 Nashville advertisement read, "The subscriber is connected with one of the best manufacturers of Turret Clocks in the United States, and will undertake to plan, arrange and set up such Clocks in any desired location. The Clocks of these makers are *guaranteed to be first-rate time Keepers*. They are strong and durable, and warranted for two years. They are constructed so as to strike regularly the hours, may also be arranged so as to chime quarter or half hours, of any interval of time for regulation of SCHOOLS, COLLEGES OR FACTORIES and upon any number of Bells from which they are made capable of giving their full tones...THOMAS I. BAILEY, Agent. At the office of I.M. SINGER & CO., 45 North College St. Attention given to repairing and improving Turret Clocks in any part of the State. Address Box 535, Nashville, Tenn." A letter to the Meneely bell foundry revealed one of Bailey's early connections to be Austin Van Riper of Cazenovia, New York, who had supplied an extraordinarily fine tower clock for Nashville's new County Courthouse at a cost of $2,500. In the letter, Bailey asked Meneely for a discount on an 800-pound bell so that he might be compensated for "the responsibility & trouble" of hanging it up. There is evidence that Bailey also installed a Van Riper tower clock in the old Howard School at Nashville as early as 1854. In the late 1860s and 1870s, Bailey turned to A.S. Hotchkiss & Co. and its successor, Seth Thomas Clock Co., as his principal tower clock suppliers. Bailey wrote in an 1876 Seth Thomas catalog, "It affords me pleasure to give my testimony in favor of the A.S. Hotchkiss Tower Clock manufactured by the Seth Thomas Co., of which I have bought several within a few years." Most of these Bailey installations are gone, but some remain, including Hotchkiss clocks at Bolivar, Tennessee, and Holly Springs, Mississippi. At some locations, Bailey replaced the manufacturer's setting dial with one of his own, boldly signed "THOS. I. BAILEY, NASHVILLE TENN." (Russell Oechsle/ Lloyd Larish)

BALCH, DANIEL: b. 1734, Bradford, Massachusetts, the son of Rev. William Balch; d. 1790, Newbury-

port, Massachusetts. Probably apprenticed to clockmaker Samuel Mulliken of Bradford. Balch set up shop in Newburyport, Massachusetts, ca. 1756, where he made tall case clocks and instructed his two sons in the trade. He was designated custodian of the Newburyport town clocks from 1781 to 1783. NTCS.

BALDWIN, ASA: Fair Haven, Connecticut, ca. 1820. Charles Crossman wrote in an 1890 *Jewelers Circular and Horological Review* that Baldwin "never served a regular apprenticeship, and did not style himself a regular clock maker. He made a tower clock which was placed in the Centre Street Church, the drawings for which were made by a Mr. Olmstead, of New Haven, who made a few clocks in that city shortly after 1800." Nathaniel Olmstead was at work ca. 1820 at 117 Chapel Street, New Haven, Connecticut. Several early clocks are said to have been put up in New Haven's Center Church on the Green, none well documented before Eli Terry's installation in 1825. Conceivably, Baldwin made an unidentified clock installed in neighboring East Haven's famous "Old Stone Church" in 1798. It was a wooden works clock reported to have been an excellent timekeeper until it collapsed at last from neglect, being replaced in 1915 by a Howard round-top. NTCS.

BALZER, THE FAMILY: Freeport, Maine, "Clockmakers to the City of Portland, Maine." First established in 1970, Rick and Linda Balzer and now their two sons have dedicated themselves to the restoration of disabled antique tower clocks, large and small, an outstanding example of their work being the mammoth Howard with four 22.5-foot dials at the old Ayer Mill in Lawrence, Massachusetts. In 1994, they ventured into the manufacture and sale of weight-driven time, strike, and chime tower clocks of their own design. These twentieth century clocks use a traditional flatbed with A-frame, standing on cabriole legs. Their advanced technology features include automatic electrical rewind, jeweled double three-legged gravity escapement, hi-tech pendulum, and programmable chime and strike cams. TCS post 1870 (Donn Haven Lathrop)

BARBORKA, JOSEPH: b. September 2, 1839, Bohemia; d. November 30, 1921, Iowa City, Iowa. While still in his homeland, this son of a blacksmith was apprenticed to a Prague jeweler, and in 1863 married Lydia Dusanek; they had six children. The family immigrated to the U.S. in 1874, living briefly in Chicago before settling down in Iowa City by 1876. Barborka opened a jewelry store at 21 Dubuque Street, offering watch, clock, and silversmith repair, plus pianos and organs. Between 1890 and 1905 or later, he manufactured about 30 tower clocks under the trade name of The Western Clock Manufactory. Over half of his installations have been identified, including timepieces, strikers, and at least one three-train chiming clock. They are found mostly in the mid-west, some representing the lowest bid on U.S. government contracts made in competition with E. Howard & Co., Seth Thomas & Co., or Nels Johnson. Several examples of Barborka's fine, colorfully painted clocks have survived, some in running condition. The frames are cast-iron cyma curved flatbeds on cabriole legs, surmounted by A-frames, employing gunmetal wheels and steel cut pinions. Barborka offered either Graham deadbeat escapements with undercut escape wheel teeth or a modified gravity escapement with a 15-tooth escape wheel making one revolution per minute. Pendulums are either one or two-second beat, the latter featuring Harrison gridiron compensation. He sub-contracted all foundry and heavy machine work to outside sources. After Barborka's death at age 83, the maintenance of his local tower clock installations was continued by his son Augustus. TCS post-1870.

BARWELL, BARTHOLOMEW: from Bath, England; at work in New York City 1749-1762, located at "Smith's Fly, near the Fly-Market." On December 25, 1752 he made a public protest, "Whereas its has been falsely reported that I...am entrusted with the Care of the Clock belonging to the New Dutch Church of this City, greatly to my Hurt and Prejudice: This is therefore to acquaint the Publick, that I am not in the least concerned with the Care of it, otherwise than when employed to clean it, as it is now, and for many years past has been, under the care of Mr. Isaac Vanhook...." The maker of the clock in contention is unknown, but in 1803 representatives of the Dutch Church proposed that they loan the clock and use of their steeple to the City of New York on the condition that the City would keep the clock in good repair and well-regulated. The City Common Council accepted the offer on the condition that Trinity Church and the First Presbyterian Church would entrust the regulation of their clocks to the City as well. As an act of good faith, the City fired their apparently incompetent superintendent of public clocks, authorizing the comptroller to employ a "more suitable person in that office, his duties being to regulate...church clocks" (see **DEMILT,** page 186). This represented the first concerted effort to display uniform public time throughout the City of New York. NTCS.

BASSETT, NEHEMIAH B.: clock and watch maker at work in Albany, New York 1798-1819. An *Albany Gazette* advertisement of December 6, 1798, read: "NEHEMIAH B. BASSETT, Watch Maker, State-street, near the Dutch Church, Has Just Received, A handsome Assortment of Warranted Watches...He makes, and has likewise for Sale, Warranted Brass Clocks, in Mahogany Cases...N.B. Watches, Church or House Clocks, repaired in the best manner...and on the most reasonable Terms." NTCS.

BEALS, J.J., CLOCK ESTABLISHMENT: Boston, Massachusetts, 1841-1869. A dealer of a variety of house clocks, including Willard-type timepieces. Two large public clocks were displayed on the exterior of the company's "circular building" at the junction of Blackstone and Union Streets in Boston. They advertised themselves as wholesale and retail dealers in American and foreign clocks and clock materials. An 1840 Beals clock label shows the company as located at the corner of Hanover and Blackstone Streets, Boston, offering "Church, Gallery and Hall Clocks." NTCS.

BISBEE, J.: at work as a clockmaker in Brunswick, Maine, ca. 1798-1825. Bisbee was best known for his animated public clockmaker's sign. Its strike arrangement consisted of the figure of a young Negro with a whip in hand mounted on a horse. The hour was announced by the boy striking the horse, which kicked the hour on the bell with its heels. Bisbee gave up clockmaking about 1825. NTCS. (Donn Haven Lathrop)

BLAKESLEE (BLAKSLEE), ZIBA: b. July 9, 1768, Plymouth, Connecticut; d. November 9, 1834, Newtown, Connecticut. The son of Abner and Thankfull (Peeter) Blakeslee, he married Mehitable Botsford of Newtown on May 3, 1792. A clockmaker, jeweler, foundry man, and wood joiner, he advertised in the April 16, 1792, *Farmer's Journal*, "ZEBA BLAKSLEE...carries on, at his shop at the head of the street in Newtown, the Goldsmith's business in all its branches: Casts Bells for Churches.—Makes and repairs Surveyor's Instruments,—Church Clocks, Clocks and Watches of all kinds—where orders will be punctually attended...." His son William was taken into partnership after 1820. NTCS.

BOSTON, EARLY TOWN CLOCKS OF: References to "town clock" were made in Boston records before 1700, but chances are they were small portable timepieces used by the town crier to call out or strike a bell on the hour. In 1668, **Richard Taylor** was allowed 30 shillings for repairing the town clock which guided him in striking the bell, and later paid £5 per year to keep a clock and to repair it. He died in 1673 and was replaced by **Thomas Matson Sr.,** who died in 1677. From 1673 to 1680, **Giles Dyer** was hired to "keepe the Clocke," and was paid in 1680 for "setting up ye Clock at ye North Meeting House." In 1684-1687, care of the town clock was entrusted to **William Sumner**, a blacksmith born in 1656 in Boston. He was paid "to keepe the clocke at ye North end of Boston," plus 14 shillings for work done in the past, before he removed to Middletown, Connecticut, in 1687 where he died in 1703. In 1689, **Robert Williams** was ordered to "carfullie looke after and keepe the Towne Clocke in the old Meeting House." NTCS.

BROWN, DAVID: b. April 17, 1781, Attleboro, Massachusetts; d. September 8, 1868, Pawtucket, Rhode Island. Apprenticed to Nehemiah Dodge and Payton Dana, both of Providence. A jeweler, and maker of clocks, watches and instruments, David Brown worked from 1802 to 1867, first in Attleboro, Massachusetts, then in Warren and Providence, Rhode Island. He was the father of Joseph R. Brown, the founder of Brown & Sharpe Mfg. Co., and is best known for his unique "tumbling pallet" escapements. NTCS. (See **1828 • David Brown**, page 75.)

BROWN (BROWNE), GAWEN: b. 1719, England; d. 1801, Boston, Massachusetts. Emigrated from London in 1748, arriving in Boston where he stayed the rest of his life. A prosperous clock and watch maker, he dealt mostly in imported English goods. About 1769, he put up a Town Clock which still displays the time from the steeple of Boston's Old South Church. (See **1769 • Gawen Brown**, page 16.)

BROWN, JOSEPH ROGERS: b. January 26, 1810, Warren, Rhode Island; d. July 23, 1876, Isle of Shoals, New Hampshire. Joseph Brown was a clock, watch and instrument maker, a master machinist and inventor. From 1831 to 1874 he was associated in Pawtucket and Providence, Rhode Island, with David Brown & Son, Joseph R. Brown, J.R. Brown and Sharpe, and Brown & Sharpe Mfg. Co. (See **1849 • Joseph R. Brown**, page 132.)

BURNAP, DANIEL: b. November 1, 1759, Coventry, Connecticut; d. September 26, 1838, Coventry, Connecticut. Reportedly an early apprentice and journeyman of Thomas Harland, he became master to Eli Terry and many other clockmakers at his shop in East Windsor (now South Windsor, Connecticut). About 1805, he retired to his birthplace as a well-to-do highly respected landowner active in town affairs. (See **1791 • Daniel Burnap**, page 25.)

BYRAM, EPHRAIM NILES: b. November 25, 1809, Sag Harbor, New York; d. June 27, 1881, Sag Harbor, New York. A self-taught, highly-skilled village mechanic, astronomer and tower clock maker, in 1836 he received the American Institute's Gold Medal for his clockwork planetarium. From 1850 to 1854 he was a partner in Sherry & Byram, Sag Harbor clockmakers. (See **1838 • Ephraim Niles Byram**, page 98.)

CARD, MILTON. (See **1859 • Stone & Marshall**, page 158.)

CENTURY TOWER CLOCK, THE: 1886-1915 Milwaukee, Wisconsin. (See **Johnson, Nels,** page 197.)

CHASE, TIMOTHY: b. 1793, Charlton, Massachusetts; d. 1875, Belfast, Maine. He learned his trade in a clock factory near Boston. In 1818, his family moved to Head of Tide, Maine, where he set up as a clockmaker, moving to Belfast in 1829 where he established a jewelry store. In 1836, he and Phineas Quimby made the Belfast Town Clock. (See **1836 • Chase & Quimby**, page 95.)

CLAGGETT, WILLIAM: b. 1696, Wales or England; d. 1749, Newport, Rhode Island. He emigrated to Boston with his parents, Caleb and Ann Claggett, at the age of 14. Well-educated for his day, young Claggett was apprenticed to Benjamin Bagnall of Boston, and later, was master to his son, Thomas, and to his son-in-law, James Wady, both Newport clockmakers. In 1715, at the age of 19, Claggett married Mary Armstrong, and the same year set up a shop in Boston as a "Clock-Maker near the Town-House." In 1716, they moved to Newport, where he repaired and also made clocks, watches, compasses, and at least one pipe organ. He was also known as a writer, political activist, engraver, printer, notary public, and a friend of Benjamin Franklin, with whom he shared electrical experiments. Best known for his imposing brass-movement tall case clocks, he also made two large gallery clocks for Newport churches, and *The Annals of Trinity Church* (Newport, Rhode Island) documents that he repaired their tower clock, which he, himself, made (long since replaced except for its outside dial). NTCS.

CLARK, JEHIEL: b. 1781, Plymouth, Connecticut; d. 1852, Pompey, New York. Clark was the first of the 12 children of Jehiel (Sr.) and Patience (Sanford) Clark. The family's 11 sons included a number of well-known clockmakers, the most famous being Heman Clark, who remained in Plymouth, served an apprenticeship with Eli Terry, and later joined him in a partnership. Jehiel Clark, the oldest son, migrated to the upstate New York Finger Lake frontier, seeking cheap land and business opportunity. He was first reported in 1808 as a silversmith in Pompey, New York, a small village which adjoins the town of Cazenovia, about 20 miles southeast of what is now Syracuse. Early land deeds show his purchase in 1814 of about 28 acres of land suitable for farming. He built his center-chimney homestead (still standing) on Pompey Hollow Road, about five miles from Cazenovia proper. Later he acquired additional parcels of land in Cazenovia, including a 70 by 40-foot commercial property just off the main street, probably the site of his gold and silversmith shop. He then added clockwork to his line, about 1830 making at least one documented town clock for

Cazenovia, and probably others. The clock was short-lived, as noted in November 1862 by the *Cazenovia Republican*, "The old town clock, which for so many years has graced the spire of the Methodist Church, is a wreck. It is so badly damaged that repairs are impossible...The old clock is the first iron town clock (and the only one of that pattern) built by Mr. Jehiel Clark. It was never a very good one, but by the expenditure of a good deal of money and trouble it has been made to do useful life for about 20 years." As flawed as it was, Clark's pioneering effort marked the start of a school of Cazenovia tower clockmakers that included his son, Jehiel Jr., followed by Austin Van Riper, and Stone & Marshall—an industry that endured for over 45 years and sold many fine clock models as far away as Michigan and Tennessee. None of the senior Clark's tower clocks are known to have survived, but undoubtedly they were similar to surviving cast-iron clocks made by his son who worked with him a few years before his retirement in 1846. The same year, Jehiel Clark transferred the farm to his youngest son, Ira, subject to his lifetime use of the homestead, and also transferred his commercial property in Cazenovia to Jehiel Jr., who manufactured tower clocks there under his own name until 1850. The old man died in 1852 at the age of 80 and was buried in a cemetery at Oran a few miles from his homestead. NTCS. (Russell Oechsle)

CLARK, JEHIEL Jr.: b. 1814, Pompey, New York; d. date and place unknown. The first of three sons of Jehiel Clark, he was trained by his father as a silversmith, goldsmith, and town clock maker. After his father's retirement in 1846, Jehiel Clark Jr., made predominantly cast-iron tower clocks in Cazenovia under his own name until about 1849. (See **1847 • Jehiel Clark Jr.**, page 127.)

CLIFFORD, ALFRED D.: b. April 3, 1854, Phillipston, Massachusetts; d.—. A commercial vegetable farmer, Clifford had a working knowledge of mathematics and astronomy. In 1880, he designed and built the world's largest wooden tower clock for the Congregational Church of Phillipston, Massachusetts (established 1785). He used only hand tools and worked in the dark attic of the church by the light of a lantern. The huge frame alone measured four feet wide by eight feet high by 14 inches deep, not including its winding barrels and large winding jacks which were mounted outboard of the frame. In all, the mechanism contained 29 wheels, the great wheels being made up of laminated planks bolted together and measuring 36 inches in diameter by 2½ inches thick. The cogs were individually carved and driven into holes pre-drilled by Parker's Chair Shop of Goulding Village. The wheel arbors pivoted in hardwood bearing blocks, at first lubricated with

pork lard, later with Vaseline. The hand-filed escape wheel and the forged deadbeat pallet anchor were of metal, connected by a short crutch to the wooden rod of a two-second pendulum. The pendulum bob was a 417-pound boulder hand-drilled to take the rod, and rated by the addition or removal of small stones to its top surface. The driving weights were also raw boulders, weighing 500 pounds on the time side and half a ton on the strike. As planned, the clock was to have both time and strike, but construction of the dial portion was prevented by lack of funds. The massive wooden works only struck the hours on the steeple bell, a task now taken over by an electric timer and solenoid. TCS post 1870.

CONVERSE & CRANE: 1865-1870, Boston, Massachusetts. Moses Crane, a former partner in the Turret & Marine Clock Co., joined Converse & Co., 130 Washington Street (upstairs), Boston, in 1864. The following year he became a partner, and by 1870 its sole proprietor. Their 1868 advertisement indicated a small job shop operation: "...Manufacturers (to order) of all kinds of Small Machinery and Turret or Town Clocks. Also Manufacturers of MODELS of New Inventions for obtaining Patents, TELEGRAPHIC AND MAGNETIC MACHINERY and INSTRUMENTS....Small Geer-Cutting and Jobbing done in a superior manner." NTCS.

CRANE, AARON DODD: b. May 8, 1804, Caldwell, New Jersey; d. March 10, 1860, Roxbury, Massachusetts. A horological genius, this self-taught one-year clockmaker invented the torsion pendulum, the "walking escapement" and many other unique clock features. He also invented a double remontoire, free pendulum tower clock made by the Turret & Marine Clock Co. Many U.S. Patents. (See **1858 • Aaron Dodd Crane**, page 152.)

CRANE, MOSES GRIFFIN: b. August 19, 1833, Newark, New Jersey; d. July 7, 1898 (suicide), Newton Highlands, Massachusetts. He was the oldest son of the five children of Aaron Dodd and Sarah Ann (Harrison) Crane. Moses worked for his clothes as a boy, and learned the clockmaking and machinist trades from his father. Moses moved to Boston ca. 1856, prior to the establishment of the Turret & Marine Clock Company at 5 and 13 Water Street, Boston. Founded in 1858, the company's principals were Collins Stevens, George F. Walker, agent, and Moses Crane, superintendent of production. They sold over 50 clocks in about three years based on a licensing agreement on Aaron Crane's U.S. Patent Number 19,351. In 1859, Moses married Collins Stevens' cousin, Emaline Rogers; they had seven children, including Newton Crane, who later worked with his father and held over 28 U.S. Patents in his own name. Moses broke off from his partners in late

1861. He worked for a small Boston job shop briefly before establishing the firm under his own name in 1870-79. Along with machinist services offered during this period, he continuously advertised the manufacture of tower clocks in local directories, but none signed by him are known to have survived. Meanwhile, he shifted his time and interest to the invention and manufacture of electromechanical fire alarm equipment. In this capacity, he held over 30 U.S. Patents and became the principal supplier of equipment to the Gamewell Fire Alarm Co. of New York City. In 1873, Moses and his family moved to Newton Highlands, a suburb of Boston, where he built a large home on Crystal Lake and speculated in real estate. He also converted a former schoolhouse into a fire alarm equipment factory, eventually selling out in 1886 to the Gamewell Company for $47,000. In spite of previous agreements to the contrary, Moses continued to compete in the alarm business and, accordingly, was sued by Gamewell for breach of contract. In his last years, he lived in relative luxury, attending of his extensive real estate holdings. At age 64, depressed by lawsuits and his fruitless rivalry with Gamewell, Moses Crane ended his life with a gunshot to the head. (See **1858 • Turret & Marine Clock Co.,** page 155.)

CURRIER, EDMOND (JR.): b. May 4, 1793, Hopkinton, New Hampshire; d. May 17, 1853, Salem, Massachusetts. Although his father practiced medicine in Hopkinton, Currier had limited formal schooling. Starting at the age of 14 he served four years as a saddler's apprentice, followed by an apprenticeship with an unidentified watchmaker. He also worked several years for a master clockmaker in Concord, New Hampshire, before setting up on his own in Hopkinton where he offered a variety of goods, including tools and machines of his own design and clocks. An inventive and industrious man, his account book lists 448 customers in 15 New Hampshire towns. After marrying Laura Jones, he moved to Salem, Massachusetts, in 1825, where he set up business on Essex Street just west of Court. The *Salem Gazette* for February 1, 1828, indicated a relocation to 7 Derby Square, Salem, where in addition to the usual variety of jeweler's goods and clock repair he offered "gallery and turret clocks made to order." He is not known to have made any, but in 1827 received high commendation for services rendered as Salem custodian: "For the first time, within our recollection, our Town Clocks have been made to run and strike in Harmony...thanks to Mr. Currier, through whose skills this harmony has been produced." NTCS (David Proper)

CURTIS, JOEL: b. October 1786, Wolcott, Connecticut; d. August 20, 1844, Cairo, New York. The early training of Curtis is not documented, but it appears

likely he worked for Eli Terry considering his proximity to Plymouth and the similarity of his hang-up wood movements to those mass-produced by Terry during the "Porter Contract." Curtis was awarded three patents (including one for a gear-cutting machine) in 1814, and moved the same year from Connecticut to Cairo, New York. Located on a cross-state turnpike near the Hudson River, 30 miles southwest of Albany and the Erie Canal, Cairo offered ready access to emerging Upper New York State markets as well as ample water power to run his machines. Joel Curtis and his brother Isaac established their factory in what had been a former mill in the Forge section of town (now called Purling). By 1825, the brothers were joined by Benjamin Bement, a local entrepreneur whose added capital probably accounts for the name change to "Joel Curtis & Co." They were very prolific, with few Connecticut contemporaries matching their manufacturing longevity of 30-hour, pull-up wooden movements in the Eli Terry tradition. Curtis developed at least two other time, strike, and alarm models. Their clock factory was described as thriving, with goods shipped to all parts of the country. The same source documents that a wooden town clock made in the Curtis clock factory was put up in the steeple of Cairo's Presbyterian Church and even after losing its minute hand continued its daily rounds at least through 1884. It probably remained in the tower until 1952, when all church contents were sold at auction, including the clock for $35! A witness described it as resembling "an oversized grandfather's clock." Frequently nineteenth century clock installations in Upstate New York are referred to as having replaced earlier unidentified wooden movements at the same site. Wooden tower clocks were rarely signed, but given the existence of the Cairo clock and the factory's production capability, Curtis & Co. was a viable source for some of these earlier installations. NTCS. (Russell Oechsle)

CUSTER, JACOB DETWEILER: b. March 5, 1805, Worcester Township, Pennsylvania; d. September 30, 1871, Norristown, Pennsylvania. A self-educated, self-taught clock and watchmaker, inventor, and master mechanic whose restless genius led him in many directions, he held several U.S. Patents. It was said he could simplify the mechanics of anything he touched. (See **1836 • Jacob Custer,** page 91.)

DAVIES, H.J.: ca. 1873, New York City. An over paste label on a Jerome & Co. octagon marine clock reads, "H.J. DAVIES, Successor to GEO. A. JONES & CO., Manufacturers of TOWER CLOCKS, Fine REGULATORS and American clocks Clocks...SALESROOM, 5 CORTLAND [sic] STREET, Near Broadway, NEW YORK." George A. Jones & Co., was of Bristol, Connecticut, and 6 Cortlandt Street, New York City in 1870. An advertisement in the August 1873 *Watchmaker and Jeweler* shows Davies to have been the former superintendent of George A. Jones & Co., and Davies & Hodgens to be the actual successors to the company. Both of these companies were probably recruited as agents by Geo. M. Stevens & Co., Boston tower clockmakers who had a sales office in New York City at the same 6 Cortlandt Street address in 1872. (See **Jones, George & Co.,** page 199.) NTCS.

DAVIS, DAVID PORTER: b. 1814, Westford, Massachusetts; d. ———, Roxbury, Massachusetts. An apprentice to Aaron Willard Jr. He first worked alone as a Boston clockmaker in 1842, by 1843 becoming a partner in Stephenson, Howard & Davis, and then with its successor company, Howard & Davis. By 1860 he broke with Howard, working alone at 15 Washington Street, Boston, followed by several years after 1867 at 106 Water Street with his son in the business of "clocks." (See **1844 • Stephenson Howard & Davis**, page 116, and **1847 • Howard & Davis,** page 128.)

DAVIS, JOHN: Of unknown origin, probably an apprentice to John Whitear of Fairfield, Connecticut. An early drawing of Christ's Church in nearby Stratford shows a steeple clock with a single diamond-shaped dial board having two hands on a three-foot diameter chapter ring. The church was demolished in 1858. Its records read, "An agreement made this 25th day of February, 1750-51, between the Church Wardens...and John Davis, clock maker, a stranger, and is as followeth: That the said Davis is to keep the clock of said church in good repair for two years from the date hereof and to have for his labor £5 for each year, provided the said clock goes well the said time; if not, he is to have nothing for his labor...the Church Wardens are not to be put to more trouble about paying the money than to pay it either in Stratford or Fairfield; and to be paid in old tenor money." John Whitear probably made the bell, and the clock as well. NTCS.

DAVISON (DAVIDSON), BARZILLAI: Of Norwich, Connecticut, in 1775 a jeweler in gold and silver, offering fine timekeepers. By 1795, of Norwich Landing where he advertised for a "smart likely Boy" to apprentice in the clock and watchmaking business. In 1800 he advertised in Chelsea's *Connecticut Courier*, "BARZILLAI DAVISON, Having for some years, been almost out of his business in the Watch Way, is now determined to set down to that business and attend to little else." In 1825, the First Church Congregational of Milford, Connecticut, commissioned Davison (or possibly his son) to make a wooden tower clock at a cost of $260. He

allowed $40 credit toward what was due for their "old brazed wheel clock" (made by Ebenezer Parmelee of Guilford), and then, reportedly, sold the old clock in New York for $600. Davison's clock proved an unsatisfactory timekeeper by 1838. In 1849, the church replaced it with a metal tower clock made by John Douglass of New Haven, which still runs hand-wound, time and strike. NTCS.

DEMILT, SAMUEL & BENJAMIN: 1795-1840, located at 139 Pearl Street, New York City. Early marine chronometer importers catering to the whaling industry; also tool and parts suppliers to the watchmaker trade. Accurate time was essential to marine navigation, and, lacking a reliable government meteorological service, the Demilts erected their own observatory as a courtesy to their customers. Included was the City of New York to which Benjamin Demilt submitted at least two invoices between 1807 and 1810: one debit being $100 for "regulating Public Clocks" and another of $300 for regulating three clocks. In 1828, the Common Council voted to place a clock or chronometer in the city hall to establish a reliable standard for all city public clocks. They allocated a sum not to exceed $1,500 for a transit telescope, astronomical regulator, and turret clock to be placed in the city hall cupola. In 1830, the city allocated an additional $3,000 for a bell, bell-striking machinery, glass dials, and "contingencies." On May 2, 1831, the Demilts received $1,500 for "the public clock now nearly completed." Benjamin Demilt died in 1835 and his brother Samuel in 1845. They were succeeded in business by a former employee, German-born Dominick Eggert, who had learned the trade in Bristol, England, before coming to New York in 1818. It is not specified who made the Demilt City Hall clock, but it proved unsatisfactory after only 20 years, being replaced in 1852 by one made by Sherry & Byram of Sag Harbor, Long Island. The Byram clock also had a short life, being destroyed in an 1858 City Hall fire. H. Sperry & Co. of New York offered to make a new city hall clock of "immense proportions." The mechanism was to be displayed on a lower floor, its great wheels measuring five feet in diameter, driven by reservoir water power, and running slave clock dials throughout the building. The grandiose plans were interrupted by Henry Sperry's death in 1859, and the job went to A.S. Hotchkiss, Sperry's former tower clock designer. NTCS.

DENNISON, AARON L.: b. March 6, 1812, Topsham Village, Maine; d. January 9, 1895, Handsworth, Birmingham, England. A Boston specialist in watch repair, tools and materials, his name appears on the setting dial of at least one well-made tower clock installed in 1842. In 1850, he and Edward Howard pioneered the development of the American plan of systematized watch manufacture. (See **1842 • Aaron L. Dennison**, page 104.)

DEUBLE, GEORGE MICHAEL: b. 1798, Baden, Germany; d. 1860, Canton, Ohio. Deuble served apprenticeships as a weaver and a clock and watchmaker in Germany before immigrating to America in 1825 with his wife Susannah (Schmitt) and son Martin. After a brief stay in Philadelphia, they moved to Mahanoy City, Pennsylvania, about 30 miles northwest of Allentown, where he began making clocks. Betrayed by three partners in succession, he walked cross country to Canton, Ohio, seeking the counsel of a brother and sister who had settled there in 1830. He survived the long walk, subsisting largely on apples taken from orchards along the roadside. Arriving at his destination, he saw his future in Canton, which had as large a population as Cleveland but no resident clock and watchmaker. He returned to Mahanoy City, packed up his family and their belongings in a one-horse wagon and made the journey back to Ohio, tying sapling trees to the back of the vehicle to serve as brakes while climbing steep mountain grades. At first Deuble eked out a living working on farms or doing odd jobs. It was hard-going, occasionally forcing the family to cook pig-ear weeds for food. A second son, George, was born in 1832. Eventually Deuble's mechanical skills, reliability, and honesty prevailed. He fitted up a shop in his house and in 1833 became Canton's first resident clockmaker and watch repairer, building a reputation as an excellent jeweler. He also made a four-dial town clock for the cupola of the second Canton Courthouse built in 1868. It was his only known venture in this direction, although on July 25, 1854, he had received U.S. Patent No. 11,362, for an improvement in the "Striking part of Tower Clocks," which suggests earlier tower clock activity. He trained his sons in all aspects of the jeweler's trade, then brought them into the business, since conducted by several generations of Deubles still active in Canton today. NTCS.

DEWEY , HIRAM TODD: b. July 13, 1816, Poultney, Vermont; d ———-. The second son of Orinda (Todd) and Jeremiah Dewey, Hiram was a jeweler, clock and watchmaker and inventor. He worked in his father's clock shop in Chelsea, Vermont, from an early age, his apprenticeship running from 1829 to 1836, when he was given his time and left home to seek his fortune. He moved to Sandusky, Ohio, then to Indiana, where he was in the jewelry business for several years. Later he returned to Sandusky, and began manufacturing town clocks, improved by the use of fewer wheels in the movement. A tower clock of this description has survived in Lebanon, Ohio. It is unsigned but attributed to Dewey because the entire strike train is replaced by a single 78-tooth escape wheel of extra large proportions, which strikes the bell by its action on a simple recoil anchor. The clock's conventional four-wheel time train also employs a recoil anchor with a crutch connection to a 48½" pendulum. The flatbed frame, with New Hampshire-type bumper ends and a large A-frame, is constructed of joined wooden beams. Dewey continued in the jewelry business until 1857, when he purchased a farm near Sandusky and spent the balance of his life in the grape and wine business. H.T. Dewey & Sons are listed in 1898 as wine merchants at 138 Fulton Street, New York City. (Donn Haven Lathrop)

DODGE, EZRA: b. 1766, Pomfret, Connecticut; d. August 29, 1798, New London, Connecticut. The brother of Seril Dodge, both served as apprentices to Thomas Harland of Norwich, Connecticut. Ezra worked in New London from 1787 to 1798, marrying Elizabeth Hempstead in 1790. His first shop was located on the main street where he made and sold "all sorts of Clocks and Watches, viz. Church clocks with one, two or three dials, chiming, repeating and plain eight day clocks exhibiting the moon's age, day of the month and seconds; also Watches, horizontal, repeating or skeleton with day of month or seconds from centre...." Dodge often changed his New London shop location, and advertised frequently for apprentices and experienced journeymen clockmakers. By the year of his death at age 32, he had increased his stock in trade to include a general assortment of groceries, rum, brandy and gin. One of the first struck down by the 1798 yellow fever epidemic in New London, Dodge left an insolvent estate administered by his wife, Elizabeth. NTCS.

DODGE, SERIL: b. ———, Pomfret, Connecticut; d. April 22, 1802, Pomfret. The brother of Ezra Dodge and also an apprentice to Thomas Harland of Norwich, he worked in Providence, Rhode Island, from 1784 to about 1800. On August 13, 1784, he advertised in the *Providence Gazette*, "SERIL DODGE, Clock and Watch-Maker...hath just opened a Shop, opposite Messieurs Clark and Nightingale's Store, North of the Great Bridge, in Providence, where he manufactures and sells all sorts of Clocks and Watches, viz. Church clocks...that wind up by the Influence of the Air; Organ, chiming repeating and plain Clocks, exhibiting the Moon's age, Day of the month and Seconds; Perpetual Air Time-Pieces, either plain or Skeleton, that shew the Operation of the Air on the Movements, constructed so small as to stand on Desks or other convenient Places, and take up but little Room; Spring Table-Clocks, chiming, repeating or plain, &c. &c. &c. Watches, horizontal, repeating and Skeleton, with the day of the Month from the Centre, suitable for Physicians." Both Seril Dodge and Benjamin Hanks of Connecticut advertised church clocks wound up by air currents at about the same time. There is no known connection between the two clockmakers other than both served as apprentices to Thomas Harland. Examples of air clocks have not survived from either maker. In 1788, Seril Dodge, watchmaker, moved his shop two doors north of the Baptist Meeting House in Providence. He moved again in 1793 to a shop opposite the market, where, in addition to being a clock and watchmaker, he offered the usual variety of goldsmith and jewelry ware. By 1796, he returned to Pomfret, where he died in 1802 of the same yellow fever scourge that had taken his brother Ezra a few years earlier. NTCS.

DOUGLASS (DOUGLAS), JOHN: b. 1798, Connecticut; d. December 29, 1850, New Haven, Connecticut. At work from 1840 to 1850 in New Haven where his occupation is variously shown as a machinist, plumber, brass foundryman and merchant. At least two of his unusual church clocks survive, one running hand-wound since 1849. (See **1847 • John Douglass**, page 123.)

DOW, WILLIAM: a clock and watchmaker at work in Washington, D.C. ca. 1819-1820. His specific origins are unknown, but he claimed to have been brought up in the business and to have practiced the trade for 20 years with the most eminent workmen in Europe. Originally with Keyworth & Dow of Washington, he withdrew by November 24, 1819, when he established a store of his own on Pennsylvania Avenue. On April 6, 1820, he advertised in the *Washington Gazette*, "WILLIAM DOW, Clock and Watchmaker...continues to manufacture steeple, turret, church, bank, office, and chamber clocks, of every description made to go with weights carrying any number of dials, extending the hands, warranted to move without friction to the works...." He also offered to make and repair a wide variety of very complex regulators intended for watchmakers, and to repair "Harrison Chronometers for ascertaining longitude." NTCS.

DUDLEY, BENJAMIN: b. ——England; d. ———. He emigrated from England to Savannah, Georgia, in 1768, and removed to Newport, Rhode Island, by 1785. A silversmith and clock and watchmaker, he made a single dial time and strike public clock for Newport's Colony House in 1786. (See **1786 • Benjamin Dudley**, page 23.)

DUFFIELD, EDWARD: b. 1720, West Whiteland Township, Philadelphia County, Pennsylvania; d. ca. 1803, Lower Dublin, Philadelphia County, Pennsylvania. A watch, clock, and instrument maker, Duffield hung a two-dial public clock outside the second story window of his shop at Second and Arch Streets, Philadelphia. From 1762 to 1785 he took care of Peter Stretch's clock in the State House (now Independence Hall). He was the friend of Benjamin Franklin and executor of his estate. Duffield moved to Lower Dublin and continued clockmaking until past the age of 80; his public clock made for the local academy became the village standard, replacing many house sundials customarily serving that purpose. NTCS.

DUNGAN, ELMER ELLSWORTH: b. December 25, 1861, Flourtown, Pennsylvania; d. December 10, 1930, Fort Washington, Pennsylvania. An ambitious and energetic businessman of diverse interests and talents, Dungan's only financial failure came with the manufacture of the novelty Dickory Dickory Dock mouse clock. In addition to his furniture, jewelry, publishing, and bowling businesses, he was an avid clock collector. He designed the works for a four-foot diameter illuminated dial installed on the highest gable of his home. The clock mechanism featured a large setting dial with two hands, a three-legged gravity escapement with maintaining power, and a nine-foot pendulum. It was built in 1919 by his friend D. Brooke Johnson, an expert machinist living in nearby Ambler, Pennsylvania.

DUNSTER (DEMPSTER), CHARLES: b. 1815, —; d. 1890, Leesville, Ohio. Little is known about the personal life of Dunster other than his description as an old German living in Leesville, Carroll County, Ohio. By trade a country blacksmith, he was celebrated locally as a genius and self-taught clockmaker who used common shop tools to built a weight-driven clock with eight or more dials showing the time in principal cities around the world. Based on this accomplishment, he was commissioned to build a tower clock for the first building (Chapman Hall, 1865) constructed at Mount Union College in Alliance, Ohio. The clock was of unusual construction, having three outboard barrels and three wheel trains in two cast-iron frames mounted side by side on a wood beam table. The frames were of curvilinear plate-and-pillar construction, originally painted white with red gears. All parts except the escapement were cast-iron, including the wheel trains, which pivoted in unbushed holes and showed no appreciable wear after 100 years of operation. The time train had two barrels and two wheel trains, one regulating the time and the other advancing the hands of the outside dials. The deadbeat escapement had a 60-tooth brass escape wheel and open-caliper brass arms supporting adjustable steel pallets. The one-second pendulum had a 68-pound lenticular bob. Mounted outside the frame plates were two large wheels about 30 inches in diameter with removable pins around their full perimeter. The large pinwheel, connected to the strike train, allowed correction or variation in the strike sequence (including quarter strike). The large pinwheel connected to the time train provided for corrections to the strike trip mechanism. The Dunster clock was replaced in 1935 by an electrical arrangement. The old movement, now restored, is in the collection of McKinley Museum at Canton, Ohio. (Harold Sloan)

EBERHARDT, JOHANN LUDWIG: b. May 17, 1758, Alm, Thuringia south-eastern Germany; d. April 10, 1839, Salem, North Carolina. A European-trained clock and watchmaker and silversmith, he immigrated to America in 1799, and worked at his trade in the Moravian Community of Old Salem, North Carolina. He made tall case clocks and attended to the care and enhancement of several local tower clocks. (See **1766 • Johann Eberhardt**, page 10.)

EBERMAN, JOHN JR.: b. 1749, Lancaster, Pennsylvania; d. 1835, Lancaster, Pennsylvania. The older son of a German immigrant, he was probably an apprentice to Rudy Stoner, Lancaster's first clockmaker. From 1785-1812 he had a shop in Lancaster Borough. Primarily known for tall case clocks, he also made at least four distinctive tower clocks, one striking the hour and the quarters. (See **1785 • John Eberman Jr.**, page 19.)

ELLIOTT, LUTHER: b. February 1794, —-; d. April 1, 1876, Amherst, New Hampshire. A machinist in the employ of Thomas Woolson Jr., it is claimed he made the Amherst, New Hampshire, town clock, designed by Woolson and installed about 1813-15. By 1818, Elliott removed to Reading, Massachusetts, where he married Esther Damon. In 1846, the family returned to Amherst, where Elliott eventually died of old age at 82. (See **1815 • Thomas Woolson Jr.**, page 58.)

EMRICH, EDWARD: ca. 1870-1890, Rochester, New York. A French emigrant, Emrich is thought to have been the apprentice to an M. Schwilgue, who was commissioned by the French Government to repair the Apostolic Clock in the Church at Strasbourg. After Emrich's immigration to the U.S., he engaged in the manufacture of tower clocks at a factory he established at Rochester, New York. Examples are not known to have survived. In 1877 he began work on a replica of the Strasbourg clock, the traveling exhibition of monumental clocks being in vogue toward the end of the century. On March 25, 1881, he completed the work which is said to have been sold to a San Francisco promoter. Later, while visiting relatives in France, Emrich's uninsured factory was totally destroyed by fire, a disaster from which he never recovered. NTCS.

ESSEX, JOSEPH: an emigrant from Great Britain, at work in Boston from 1712-1715. His notice in the *Boston News-Letter* of November 10, 1712, reads, "JOSEPH ESSEX...now keeps Shop in Bittler's Buildings, in King Street [now State], Boston, and performs all sorts of New Clocks and Watch works; viz. 30 hour Clocks, Week Clocks, Month Clocks, Spring Table Clocks, Chime Clocks, quarter Clocks, quarter Chime Clocks, Church Clocks, Terret [sic] Clocks, and new Pocket Watches, new Repeating Watches...These articles to be performed by...Joseph Essex and Thomas Badley." The partnership was a flash in the pan: Essex, described as a jack-maker and trader, was bankrupt by January 1715 and Badley was declared insolvent by 1720. NTCS.

EVANS, DAVID: b. Philadelphia, Pennsylvania. Reputed to be the nephew of David Rittenhouse, Evans was a clock and watchmaker on Gay Street in Baltimore, Maryland, by 1773. He served briefly in the Maryland Militia, his shop being "much neglected during his absence in camp." In 1779, his shop on Gay Street offered clock and watchmaker supplies, and the services of "two excellent Workmen, regularly bred to the business in Europe." By 1785, he had increased his inventory of tools and supplies, and also offered a musical clock that played seven tunes, including George Washington's March. By 1788, however, he sought relief as an insolvent debtor, putting to auction his good brick house and kitchen with a back shop for casting and forging metals. Early in 1790, Evans proposed erecting a town clock on the Baltimore Court House to be paid for by public lottery. It was to have a 700-pound bell, with added provisions for fire alarm and call-to-court features. Sufficient funds were raised by September 1790 for Evans to make and erect a fire alarm which met with the approval of a committee of Baltimore clock and watchmakers. Apparently, the balance of the project was abandoned. NTCS.

FASOLDT, CHARLES: b. February 23, 1819, near Dresden, Germany; d. May 13, 1889 (Bright's disease), Albany, New York. He learned clock and watchmaking, and married Augusta Drexel while still in Germany; they had six children. Due to long service in the Saxony army, Fasoldt was appointed a captain with the German rebellion forces. When the revolt failed, he was sentenced to death, but escaped with his family to New York City. On his way to the west coast, he visited a brother in Rome, New York, where he settled as a clock and watchmaker in a jewelry store. He prospered over time, taking on from 10 to 15 employees and branching into the manufacture of clock and watchmaking machinery. In 1851, he advertised clocks, watches, surgical mechanical instruments, and chronometers, the latter costing from $150 to $300. About 1861, he moved to Albany, New York, where he set up a factory at 643 Broadway that eventually employed 50 workers. Fasoldt precision machines and special tools, many developed by himself, produced the American Patent Pocket Chronometer, astronomical regulators, tower clocks, and improved microscopes and illuminators. His micro-metric rulings ran from 5,000 up to 1,000,000 lines per inch on a glass eyepiece. Fasoldt held many U.S. patents, and at one point sued E. Howard & Co. for patent infringement. Patents dating from 1873, 1875, and 1884 provided for improvements to his tower clocks, made in a limited number. While installing one at Newburgh, New York, in 1872, he contracted a severe cold that seriously impaired his eyesight, later restored to normal. Fasoldt's tower clocks were of unconventional design, small in size, highly finished and made with great precision; he claimed an error rate not exceeding 10 seconds a year. Separate time, hand-drive and strike units were designed to prevent damage to the works if the exposed hands became obstructed by ice or snow, a common event in upstate New York. Grooved winding barrels were mounted outboard of all three clockwork trains, each driven by separate weights. A free pendulum, suspended above or to one side of the movement, was mercury-compensated and kept swinging by Fasoldt's unique jeweled escapement. The dial hands advanced at leisurely one-minute intervals, slowed by a planetary gear governor with a small ratchet-driven fly. A larger fly on the independent strike module controlled strike interval. Fasoldt's most notable tower clock won the "World's Grand Prize Award" at the 1876 Centennial Exposition in Philadelphia. The mechanism has survived along with at least five other known examples of his tower clock work. TCS post-1870.

FENTON, GAMALIEL: Of Mansfield, Connecticut, Gamaliel was the oldest of 12 children of Jonathan and Mary (Webber Cary) Fenton. He probably learned his trade at Hanks' Mansfield foundry, moving to Walpole, New Hampshire, just before the turn of the century. First shown as "potter," on February 24, 1798, he advertised, "...now carrying on the Bell Foundry in Walpole, where Bells of any weight may be had, on as reasonable terms, and on as short a notice, as any foundry in the United States...Town Clocks also manufactured, by said Fenton...." He also offered for sale the family farm, consisting of 36 acres with a new 40-foot house, another small house, together with a "good Barn, and a Shop for a mechanic, or Trader, lying one mile and a half from the Meeting House." Local legend has it that he bought the farm for $2,000, and sold it the same year to a Walpole native for $700. Nathan Fenton of West Hartford, a possible relative of Gamaliel, was co-partner of the New Haven bell foundry of Fenton & Cochran in 1800. NTCS.

FLOYD, THOMAS: Charlestown, South Carolina. On June 15, 1767, he advertised in the *South-Carolina Gazette*, "THOMAS FLOYD, late of Mr. Smith's, Clock-Maker in Upper-Moor-Fields, formerly belonging to his Majesty's Royal Office of Ordnance, begs leave to acquaint the nobility, gentry and others, that he lives in the corner house on Mr. Burn's Wharf; and in person, performs the following articles in trade, viz: makes, repairs and cleans church and turret clocks, spring, and common house ditto, and attends them by the year, if required: Likewise gun-work in general, at the most reasonable terms.—Ores and mines assay'd by the said Thomas Floyd." In August the following year, he advertised, "THOMAS FLOYD...has opened Shop in Church-street, formerly the sign of General Wolfe, where he performs the following articles of his business himself, viz: Making, cleaning and repairing Church and Turret Clocks, also musical, astronomical, and common ditto— Jack-work in all its branches. Common foundry, mill and bell brasses, Gate, bar and chamber bells cast, and bell hanging in general.—Gunsmith's work, &c..." NTCS.

FOSTER, NATHANIEL: Newburyport, Massachusetts, 1797-1893. The custodian of Newburyport town clocks from April 1818 to 1828, he was at work until age 89. NTCS.

FOURNIER, STANISLAUS: b. November 23, 1814, *St. Albin de Cauf, department de la Siene Inferieur*, France; d. March 25, 1883, New Orleans, Louisianna. A few years after completing his apprenticeship with the celebrated Lepaute firm of Paris, Fournier was sent to New Orleans in 1841 to install one of their tower clocks in the newly-constructed St. Louis Hotel. Fournier, a bachelor with no serious home ties, became so enamored with New Orleans that he remained there the rest of his life, conducting a clock and watch business at 60 Royal Street for over 30 years. He achieved premier status at his trade, repairing watches and making large wall and standing clocks, placing his name on dials fitted with regulator movements imported from France. He is not known to have made any large tower clocks himself, but he did handle their maintenance and repair. For example, in the early 1850s he removed and "entirely transformed" the St. Louis Cathedral tower clock, imported from France in 1819 by J. Delachaux at a cost of $2,900. Fournier's work included the illumination of two large outside dials separated by as much as 176 feet, their slender iron drive rods requiring "metallic expanders" to allow for variations in temperature and settling of the building walls. He added a third illuminated dial in the choir loft. As described in *The Picayune* of February 24, 1858, "...its bells, striking the quarters and hours in different tones in harmony, were novelties for the region. The white, gold-edged hands and figures of the transparent Chartres and Royal dials stood out by day against a black background created by velvet-lined 'dark chambers.' By night they were given a clear, reddish tinge, against black, by gasburner reflectors set in the chambers, operating at a record height for New Orleans, and cut off by prearrangement of the clockwork....The main weight and wheel had no direct action on the escapement or regulator of movements, but periodically imparted power to a small brass piece for constant, even, direct action and measurement of time." The brass wheel clockwork, with what appears to have been a remontoire escapement, was glass-encased, and employed a gridiron-type compensated pendulum. Fournier made periodic repairs to the clock for a number of years, a responsibility passed on to his successors in business at 60-Royal Street, E. Barbier and Thournot. Described as a "clever horologist," Fournier had an inventive turn of mind. He pioneered the early development of electric clocks, invented a stopwatch timing the minutes, seconds, and quarter-seconds of the first four places in a horse race, and patented a "tell-tale" register, an early time clock allowing establishments to check on the vigilance of their night watchmen. Fournier advertised his business location and signaled the public to check their timepieces at the noon hour with the firing of a small cannon set off by the public clock mounted outside his shop. Failing mentally and going blind by the 1870s, Fournier smashed the contents of his clock and watch shop. He was committed to the Louisiana Retreat for the Insane (now De Paul Hospital), where he died at age 68 in 1883. (J.M. Kinabrew Jr.)

FRARY, OBADIAH: b. May 20, 1717, Deerfield, Massachusetts; d. August 20, 1804, Southampton, Massachusetts. A skilled cabinetmaker, he also made a few good brass clocks for families and meeting houses between 1745 and 1775. (See **1768 • Obadiah Frary**, page 13.)

GEIRING, FLORIA: ca. 1874-79, Bethlehem, Pennsylvania. A local watchmaker, Geiring's major additions to Augustine Neisser's 1747 tower clock at the Central Moravian Church of Bethlehem extended its running time from 30 hours to eight days. Changes included the addition of long outboard winding barrels supported by large brass-bushed bearing blocks, new great wheels and pinions, time maintaining power, plus the curved iron bar outriders that secured the old iron cage frame to a massive iron flatbed. Geiring got the job on the condition that he wind and maintain the clock for five years. Thereafter, it was hand-wound by a succession of custodians until 1946, when the old works was electrified. (See **1747 • Augustine Neisser**, page 7.)

GRIFFITH, NATHANIEL SHEAFF: At work in New Hampshire at the Sign of the Clock, in Hampton 1767-1768, and later in Portsmouth, 1769-1796. This dubious character was a watch repairer, clockmaker and dealer in miscellaneous goods. While in Hampton, he was accused anonymously of "bedaubing the Linings and Cushions of a certain Gentleman's pew" with human excrement. In a long and extravagantly stated newspaper reply, he denied the charge, but it had the effect of driving him out of town. In 1769, he set up near the Parade in Portsmouth, New Hampshire, as a watch repairer and clockmaker, who would "undertake to make Clocks for Meeting-Houses of any size." At the same time, his advertisements cast doubt on the credentials of a town competitor, John Simnet, who claimed to have had 25 years experience as a London watchmaker. Simnet responded, calling Griffith "A Tinker or Smith, near where I dwell, intending to fleece the Ignorant...a Watch Butcher...a disgrace to the Art, and an Impostor on the Public." It was the opening salvo in a war of words over a two-year period, ending when Simnet departed to set up a shop in New York City. Griffith remained in Portsmouth, bedeviled by customer complaints and suspicious robberies, accompanied by "cruel insinuations...that I was knowing of the pretended losses, and that I was even the incendiary." In 1791, he moved his shop to Daniel Street, near the State House. His career ended five years later with the sale of his "mansion" in Portsmouth, with its commanding view of the sea, the harbor, and part of the town. NTCS. (See **John Simnet,** page 207.)

HAMLEN, NATHANIEL: b. November 29, 1741, Lebanon, Connecticut; d. January 19, 1834, Augusta, Maine. He married Sarah Baker of Wellfleet, Massachusetts, in 1763, and they produced eight children. Hamlen first came to Augusta, Maine, in 1784. He settled there in 1785, a successful house carpenter who also made spinning wheels and wooden clocks. He advertised the latter trade with a large public clock that he maintained on the gable of his house. It became the town's time standard at the corner of Winthrop and State Streets. Hamlen died at the age of 92. NTCS (Donn Haven Lathrop).

HANKS, BENJAMIN: b. October 29, 1755, Mansfield, Connecticut; d. December 17, 1824, West Troy, New York. He was the first of 10 children of Uriah and Irene (Case) Hanks. Benjamin's father was described as farmer, carpenter, blacksmith, gunsmith and clockmaker, who also made gun locks during the Revolution, and invented a wire-drawing machine that he put to practical use. Young Benjamin is said to have learned silver smithing and clockmaking after 1773 as an apprentice to Thomas Harland of Norwich; if so, it was a short service as he married Alice Hovey in 1775. They had eight children, including Truman, Julius, and Horatio who were instructed by their father and worked in related trades. Hanks was described as a commanding presence, with bright dark eyes, about six feet tall with broad shoulders, a natural candidate for the state militia in which he served during the Lexington Alarm as a drummer boy, advancing in later years to the rank of Lieutenant Colonel. An energetic, inventive, and enterprising businessman, at various times he worked as a clockmaker, a repairer of clocks and watches, a gold and silversmith, a farmer, the owner of a grist mill, a loom maker, a wool and silk processor, and the owner of two foundries manufacturing large church bells, tower clocks, bronze cannons, and surveying instruments. He first set up shop about 1777 in Windham, Connecticut, before settling in Litchfield ca. 1778. In 1785 or later, he returned to his birthplace on Hank's Hill in Mansfield, where he farmed his father's gift of 100 acres of land, ran a saw and grist mill, and established a brass foundry and instrument-making business. In 1808, he sought a livelier business site, leaving the Mansfield operation to family members, and traveling west with his son Julius to the Gibbonsville section of Washington, New York (later West Troy, now Watervliet). The town was located on the west bank of the heavily traveled Hudson River, across from prosperous Troy, just north of the state capital at Albany, and a few 100 yards from the eastern terminus of the Erie Canal, then under construction. In this propitious location Hanks established Benjamin Hanks & Son. Julius ran routine foundry operations, freeing his father to establish Troy's first iron foundry, to patent an improved method for molding and casting church bells, and to see after his interests in a woolen mill and the foundry at Mansfield. In the course of covering all bases, he lived at various times in Albany, on the family farm in Mansfield, and in Gibbonsville.

In December 1783, it was reported in a Richmond, Virginia, newspaper that, "An ingenious mechanic in the state of Connecticut, has invented and executed a clock which winds itself up by the effect of air, without any other assistance, and without putting a stop to its mechanical operation." In May 1784, President Ezra Stiles of Yale College examined Hanks air clock and wrote in his diary that it "...has a Ventilator similar that of a smoke jack, which moves with every breeze of wind; Two hours ordinary breeze will wind up the whole eight days. A clock of six months going has seldom its weights depressed two Inches, & ordinarily it is closely wound up. Hence I think it is perpetual tho' not equable motion." Flattered by the college president's attention, Hanks sent him a description and draw-

ing of his invention. Stiles wrote in his diary on July 1 that Hanks thought of it in this way: his new house in Litchfield smoked, and "to relieve this he took a sqr of Glass out of a window, & partly for Ornament & in Imita of a certain kind of Window Blinds he made a little wooden double fan & putting it in the Hole, found it almost ppetualy in Motion. He then tho't of applyg it to Clocks, he did & it succeeded. This was March 1783. In May 1783 he made his first Clock...He obtained a patent from the Assembly in Jan. 1784." In 1785, Hanks advertised, "Pneumatic Clocks in Mahogany or Cherry-tree cases—Also Church Clocks that will go without winding and perform with Exactness...." Common winds on his 10-inch ventilator would raise a weight of 56 pounds, ample power to drive a small tower clock, but there is no direct evidence that Hanks ever actually made one. From his own description of the invention, the prototype was a house clock with a high tooth count five-wheel time train, a four-wheel strike train, 16-leaf pinions and endless screw connections between the window fan and the winding barrels. Historical accounts of Hanks during the Litchfield period assert that he installed an air-driven tower clock in the Old Dutch Church at the corner of Nassau and Liberty Streets in New York City. Reformed Dutch Church archives have no record of such a tower clock or its maker. The building passed through many hands and was razed years ago. NTCS.

HANKS, JULIUS: b. 1784, Litchfield, Connecticut; d.——. Troy, New York. The third son of Benjamin and Alice (Hovey) Hanks, Julius learned the brass foundry and clock and instrument-making trades from his father. In 1808 he married Olive MacCall of Mansfield, Connecticut. The same year he accompanied his father to the Gibbonsville section of Washington, (later West Troy, now Watervliet) New York, where they established Benjamin Hanks & Son, a brass foundry at 237 Broadway, making bells, cannons, town clocks and instruments. The well-located business prospered, with Julius left in charge of routine operations. Benjamin Hanks died in 1824. The following year Julius moved the business across the Hudson River to Troy, New York, into a two-story building at 28 Fifth Street on the corner of Elbow. It served as both living quarters and workshop, and had a public clock in a gable below the roof line. Julius advertised the sale of brass bells, town clocks, surveyor's instruments, door plates and numbers, and in 1829, "Town Clocks on a superior plan with escapements which operate without friction and require no oil." Julius failed in 1830. His brother Truman and an uncle handled the business until Oscar Hanks, Julius' son, completed his apprenticeship and took over the operation. He made brass bells and assorted metal instruments until about 1852. NTCS.

HARLAND, THOMAS: b. 1735, of Scotch/Irish descent; d. March 31, 1807, Norwich, Connecticut. Harland immigrated to America from the British Isles at age 38, a well-educated, trained goldsmith and clockmaker. He had served a long apprenticeship in England, followed by a tour of Europe as far east as Warsaw, Poland, exercising his skills and learning foreign techniques. Harland and his clockmaking tools arrived in Boston Harbor in 1773 on the brig *Sally*. Finding Boston a disrupted city, Harland departed almost immediately for Norwich, Connecticut, a quieter place north of New London with deep water access to the sea. After a year in this prosperous city of 7,400 inhabitants, Harland was able to thank his friends for their patronage of his establishment, which by 1790 grew to 10 hands in constant employment. He is reported to have made 200 watches and 40 clocks annually, probably representing total sales, including imported movements. Harland married at age 44 to Hannah (Leffingwell) Clark; they had four daughters and three sons. Harland advertised often between 1773 and 1806, but only once upon first arrival in Norwich specifically offered town clocks. Yet it appears he did make at least two, one for Norwich and another for New London. Further, considering his northern England origins, Harland may have introduced in this country the widely used tower clock *chair frame* construction based on his observations of its invention by Henry Hindley (1701-1771) of Yorkshire. Many former apprentices of Harland—including Benjamin Hanks, Daniel Burnap, Seril Dodge, Ezra Dodge, Gurdon Tracy, and William Sloan—advertised themselves as church clock makers, which suggests that Harland was their common source of instruction in the skill. In 1797, the City of Norwich paid Harland for repairs made to an "engine [clock] at Beanhill," an adjacent community. On December 1, 1790, Harland wrote to the First Congregational Church of New London a testy letter bearing the earmarks of a man defending his own craftsmanship: "Being unwell I sent the Bearer to see what was amiss in your clock from whence he has just returned. Had the person who winds it the clock known where to have apply'd a few drops of oyl [sic] the difficulty would have been prevented; from whence you will see the propriety of having the clock wound up by a person who is acquainted with the business...At the same time should any part of the work fail or give way I shall be ever ready to wait upon you at shortest notice." The bearer of Harland's letter was former apprentice Gurdon Tracy, who was to serve as the clock custodian. The New London clock was replaced in 1852 by one made by Sherry & Byram of Sag Harbor, New York, replaced in turn in 1912 by one made by E. Howard & Co. of Boston. The dials are now electrified. NTCS.

HARMONY SOCIETY, THE: 1804-1905, Ambridge, Pennsylvania. A very successful nineteenth century Christian communal society that emigrated to the U.S. from southwestern Germany under the charismatic leadership of George Rapp. They cleared thousands of acres of wilderness in Pennsylvania and Indiana, erecting three self-sufficient towns over a period of 30 years. Town clocks were critical to the timely and profitable pursuit of the society's agricultural/industrial endeavor. (See **1827 • The Harmony Society**, page 72.)

HASHAM, STEPHEN: b. ca. October 21, 1764, Boston, Massachusetts; d. February 3, 1861, Charlestown, New Hampshire. At work in Charlestown from about 1785 to 1852. A master builder and master clockmaker, he made fine tower clocks, nine of which have survived. Hasham was a brilliant, highly productive, but controversial figure whose long colorful life ended in tragedy. (See **1816 • Stephen Hasham**, page 61.)

HASKELL, MOODY: b. 1806 or 1810, Massachusetts; d ——. At work as a clockmaker and watch repairer at various addresses in Burlington, Vermont, between 1842 and 1871. Although habitually living alone in rooming houses, he showed a real estate evaluation of $8,000 in 1860, which increased 10 years later, following his marriage to the 24-year-old Delia, to $20,000. Clocks signed by Haskell are still found in Burlington. According to local old timers, the original clock in Burlington's Unitarian Church was replaced by Haskell (date unknown). The four dials of this clock were once illuminated by means of gas jets, a practice later abandoned as too troublesome. The clock broke down in January of 1895 and was repaired by Chester Hildreth (1823-1902), a Burlington jeweler. NTCS.

HEEBNER, DAVID S.: b. 1810, Worcester Township, Montgomery Co., Pennsylvania; d. 1888, Lansdale, Pennsylvania. Bored with farming and possessing a natural mechanical aptitude, David drifted gradually into the life of a successful clockmaker, cleaning and repairing clocks and watches of his neighbors and later making fine tall case clocks. The business failed due to the influx of cheap Connecticut factory clocks. About 1840, he began inventing, manufacturing and selling labor-saving machinery to meet the needs of neighboring farmers. By 1862, he brought two sons into the expanding business as partners in Heebner & Sons Agricultural Works. Ten years later, they reorganized as Heebner Sons & Co. at Lansdale, Pennsylvania, in a three-story factory that featured a 70-foot tower with four dials.

Heebner's four-dial striking clock mechanism measured 37 inches high by 21 inches wide. Its 17-inch great wheels were of cast-iron, with the remaining brass wheels measuring from six to 10 inches across. All patterns and rough castings were made in the Heebner factory. A bell was hung and the clock set running on January 1, 1884. The 73-year-old Heebner completed the job in 87 days, and served as clock custodian as long as he was physically able. NTCS.

HEISELY, FREDERICK: b. October 17, 1759, Lancaster County, Pennsylvania; d. March 12, 1843, Harrisburg, Pennsylvania. A maker of tall case and tower clocks, surveying instruments, a watch repairer and silversmith, Heisely was apprenticed to John George Hoff of Lancaster, married his daughter, and later joined him briefly as a business partner. At work ca. 1779-1840 in Lancaster, Pennsylvania, Frederick, Maryland, and Harrisburg, Pennsylvania. (See **1791 • Frederick Heisely**, page 28.)

HEISELY, GEORGE J.: b. November 29, 1789, Frederick, Maryland; d. June 27, 1880, Harrisburg, Pennsylvania. While serving as a volunteer in the War of 1812, he is credited with having selected the tune for our National Anthem. He learned clockmaking, instrument making, and silversmithing from his father, Frederick Heisely. At work as his father's partner and alone in Harrisburg from 1811 to 1865. (See **1831 • George J. Heisely**, page 79.)

HEYDORN & IMLAY: ca. 1808-1811, Hartford, Connecticut. C. Heydorn, the senior member of the firm, learned clockmaking in his native Germany before coming to America. He may have worked with Nathan Allyn, a Hartford, Connecticut, watchmaker, before joining up with R. Imlay, who served as Heydorn & Imlay's promoter and business manager. Clock historian Penrose Hoopes claims they "bought Doolittle business." Starting as eight-day mantel and tower clock makers, they soon added gold and silver work, watch repair, and a line of general store goods to the enterprise. Early in 1811 they sold what they described as complete a line of clockmaker's tools as could be found in the country, and left the state for parts unknown. NTCS.

HILL, BENJAMIN MORRIS JR.: b. ———1771; d. December 29, 1848, Richmond Township, Pennsylvania. Tall case clockmaker Benjamin Hill lived with his family on a small farm in Richmond Township near Kutztown, about 12 miles northeast of Reading, Pennsylvania. He was described as being a stout man almost six feet tall. From 1822 to 1826, he is said to have worked with Daniel Oyster, Reading's most prolific tall case clockmaker. Later he made his own moonphase tall clocks, and also installed a town clock in the second Berks County Courthouse (constructed at Reading in 1837-1840). Hill was rumored

to have secured the contract though an influential friend, County Commissioner David Kutz of Kutztown. Newspapers reported the 1841 clock was a good timekeeper for about seven years. Old Benjamin Hill, as he came to be known, died intestate in 1848, leaving a wife, eight children, and a farm of 72 acres. His estate inventory included the following: 1 24-hour "Yenkee clock" @ $3, 1 telescope @ $2, a lot of clock and watchmaking tools @ $50, a turner bench with contents @ $15, and a lot of blacksmith tools @ $20. As for his town clock, a Reading newspaper mourned that after Hill's death it refused to tick any more, that it had "come to a sudden halt in its career. Its tongue is silenced and its hands are paralyzed. But what are we to do for time? Must our city of 16,000 inhabitants be without a chief regulator to direct their movements?" On February 15, 1851, the commissioners contracted with Sylvester Penfield of New York City for a new town clock. It cost $490, with $20 allowed for the old works taken in part payment. The clock installed by Penfield was probably made by Reeve & Co. of New York City with whom Penfield had initiated similar clock installations at other locations. NTCS. (Patrick J. Reynolds) (See **1851 • Reeve & Co.**, page 140.)

HILL, WILLIAM S.: ca. 1867-1873, at work in the Williamsburg section of Brooklyn, New York. Hill is first listed in the 1867-8 Brooklyn Directory as a clock manufacturer on the corner of 1st and South 11th, living at 30 Rush. The following year he was joined at the same business address by Andrew S. Hotchkiss, an experienced tower clock designer with a growing national reputation. The two men set up a "co-partnership agreement" whereby they did business together while maintaining their independent status. Tower clock hardware and services supplied by Hill were billed to Hotchkiss who paid up accordingly. This included everything from screws, cartage, bevel gears, and dial motion work to complete tower clocks ranging in price from a No. 1 timepiece at $100 to a No. 4 Model at $425. An agreement drawn up by Hotchkiss' lawyers in 1869, held Hill liable for "loss in case of fire, etc." of clocks bought from Hill and left in his store. Other transactions included Hotchkiss payments to Hill for putting up church clocks in Lancaster and Titusville, Pennsylvania. All expenses, from cartage and installation hardware to labor at 50¢ an hour, were itemized by Hill on ruled paper with no billhead. These two Pennsylvania installations appeared along with many other early Hotchkiss tower clocks to pad out the list of representative Seth Thomas installations in an 1874 tower clock catalog. Hill normally worked and lived in Brooklyn, but from 1868 to 1871 he abruptly changed his home address from Brooklyn to Birmingham, (redesignated Derby) Connecticut, an industrial hub located about 10 miles north of Bridgeport. This Birmingham connection provided ready access to heavy duty foundries, rolling mills and machine shops appropriate to the fabrication of large tower clock parts, and may explain, in part, Hill's usefulness to a busy entrepreneur like Hotchkiss. In late 1870, Hotchkiss had his lawyer extend the Hill "co-partnership agreement" through 1871. The following year Hotchkiss sold out to Seth Thomas & Co. and became deeply engrossed in helping to establish the new Seth Thomas/A.S. Hotchkiss tower clock division. Apparently, no provision was made in the deal for Hill, who continued to live and work as a clockmaker in Brooklyn until mid-1873, when he dropped out of the city directory. There is no question that during their early association Hill supplied A.S. Hotchkiss with both parts and complete tower clocks, but none are known to have survived signed by Hill as the maker. (See **1867 • Andrew S. Hotchkiss**, page 169.) NTCS.

HOLBROOK, GEORGE: b. April 28, 1767, Wrentham, Massachusetts; d. September 29, 1846, East Medway, Massachusetts. Apprentice to Paul Revere. From 1795 to 1812, he lived at Brookfield, Massachusetts, a clock and watchmaker who also made large church bells and town clocks. The family moved to East Medway in 1815, where it remained in business for four generations. (See **1810 • George Holbrook**, page 49.)

HOLBROOK, GEORGE HANDEL: b. July 21, 1798, Brookfield, Massachusetts; d. March 20, 1875, East Medway, Massachusetts. He learned bell casting and clockmaking from his father, George Holbrook Sr., then worked in East Medway (now Millis) from 1815-1871. Colonel George Handel Holbrook was a skilled musician, bell founder, church clock, and pipe organ maker, and the key figure in a successful family business that spanned 100 years. (See **1832 • George Handel Holbrook**, page 82.)

HOPKINS, HENRY A.: Henry A. was born in 1818, the son of Henry Sr. and Achsah Hopkins of Prattsburg, a small town in central upstate New York about 35 miles northwest of Elmira. It was hilly upland cut by north/south valleys and small streams, the one called Five Mile Creek being the site of several mills established by Harry's father and uncle. With his father's passing, the extensive land, water rights and mill holdings were sold, with Henry acquiring an equal half-share of the assets described later as foundry, tanning and flouring mills. By 1850, the village population had grown to 600; Henry was listed in the census as a 32-year-old millwright, with real estate valued at $1,000, a 21-year-old wife named Betsy, and four children includ-

ing twin boys age six. From the mid-1800s into the early twentieth century, Prattsburg's pride and joy was its enlightened Franklin Academy, a source of education akin to high school that drew students from the surrounding area. According to the local historians, a "large wooden clock made by Henry A Hopkins" was installed in the Academy building in 1845. The clock warped badly after a few years and would not run. In 1852, Hopkins "made a better one with metal wheels and guaranteed it for 20-years." The improved clock ran for 70 years, until lost in a catastrophic fire that burned the Academy building to the ground on February 28, 1923. Henry A. Hopkins had the experience and the manufacturing capability to have produced additional tower clocks on a commercial basis, but no other installations are known. A church, complete with Seth Thomas "factory" clock, was subsequently built on the former Academy site. NTCS. (Russell Oechsle)

HOPKINS, WRIGHT & MILLARD: 1849-1851, DeRuyter, New York. The town of DeRuyter, about 30 miles southeast of Syracuse in upstate New York, was for a brief period the site of a town clock manufactory. A factory of modest proportions was located in the "Quaker Basin" section, taking water power from a branch of the Tioughnioga River. The principals in this enterprise were Daniel Hopkins, a newcomer in town, and two DeRuyter farmers, David Wright and Ira Millard. Hopkins was the clockmaker, 49-year-old Wright the machinist, and Millard financed the operation and also co-signed a Hopkin's promissory note of $400 to buy a house lot. The *New York Census of Manufacturing* sheds some light on the scope of the operation in 1850: the DeRuyter "Town Clock Manufactory" used 30 hundredweight of iron, 200 pounds of brass, and 50 pounds of steel to produce 10 clocks. Judging from the materials used, their clocks were of metal construction, as were the Cazenovia tower clocks produced about the same time on the same road a few miles to the north. Inevitably, the DeRuyter operation encountered financial problems, forcing Millard to mortgage his property for $1,500 on November 11, 1850, to keep the enterprise going. Added funds did not halt the slide as Hopkins, Wright & Millard failed in June 1851. The same month, Hopkins sold his house to pay off the mortgage, and left with his wife for parts unknown. Wright stayed on in Quaker Basin, working variously as a farmer and as a helper at his brother's saw and grist mill. Ira Millard, the financial backer of the enterprise, was the big loser, having to liquidate his 225-acre farm to pay off the creditors. Shortly afterward he and his family moved to the town of Sullivan, settling on a small parcel of land formerly part of the Oneida Reservation. No Quaker Basin tower clocks are known to have survived, but records at Oxford, New York, 25 miles to the southeast, show the installation of one in 1850. In addition, pictures of DeRuyter's Union Church before it was demolished in 1883 show a large single dial with face and hands intact, probably a Quaker Basin clock. In 1835, the Baptist Society built an impressive stone structure known as DeRuyter Academy (Union School). Around 1850, an "oversized clock made in Quaker Basin" with dials facing north, east, and south was installed in the building's huge cupola. The building was demolished in 1907, a team of horses attached by a long cable looped around the top of the structure pulled it crashing to the ground. The clock probably went with it. NTCS. (Russell Oechsle)

HOSTETTER, JACOB: b. May 9, 1754, near York, Pennsylvania; d. June 29, 1831, Columbia County, Ohio. After attending common schools, Hostetter was apprenticed to Richard Chester. He set up in business as a silversmith and watch repairer but was known as the best of all the Hanover, Pennsylvania, eight-day tall case clockmakers. Active as a Democrat in state politics, he was elected to both the General Assembly and Congress of Pennsylvania. In 1825, he went to Lisbon, Ohio, to go in business with his son, Jacob Jr., who had relocated to the area in 1822. It is said Hostetter set up a watchmaking operation in Ohio, and later turned to the design and manufacture of tower clocks. NTCS.

HOTCHKISS, ANDREW S.: b. December 14, 1814, Burlington, Connecticut; d. September 13, 1901, Brooklyn, New York. At work in New York City by 1847, he was a skilled tower clock designer, first associated with H. Sperry & Co. and later in business for himself as A.S. Hotchkiss & Co. He sold out to the Seth Thomas Clock Co. about 1872, contributing substantially to the startup of their tower clock manufacturing business. (See **1867 • Andrew S. Hotchkiss**, page 169.)

HOTCHKISS, A.S. & CO.: Tower clock makers in Williamsburg (Brooklyn) and Manhattan, New York, ca. 1867-1872. The company, first listed in New York Directories in 1871-72 with the American Clock Co. shown as sole agents, produced several clock models signed by Andrew Hotchkiss as early as 1867. In 1872, the company, its installation credentials and the founder himself were absorbed into the Seth Thomas Clock Company, providing a foundation for a new line of factory engineered tower clocks that sold in the thousands. (See **1867 • Andrew S. Hotchkiss**, page 169.)

HOTCHKISS, ELISHA JR.: May 4, 1787, Burlington, Connecticut; d. May 9, 1882, Hartford, Connecticut. A wooden tower clock displayed in the Burlington Congregational Church is said to have been made by Elisha Hotchkiss Jr. in 1820. His wooden shelf clock manufactory, Hotchkiss & Fields, was Burlington's largest industry, employing 30 to 50 men. It went bankrupt in 1847. (See **1820 • Elisha Hotchkiss Jr.**, page 65.)

HOWARD & DAVIS: Boston, 1847-ca. 1860. The principals were Edward Howard and David P. Davis, successors to Stephenson, Howard & Davis. They ran a profitable balance and clockmaking business, later widely diversifying into ventures that did less well. Manufacturing occurred in Roxbury, with sales offices in Boston and New York City. Succeeded to by E. Howard & Company. (See **1847 • Howard & Davis**, page 128.)

HOWARD, EDWARD: b. October 6, 1813, Hingham, Massachusetts; d, March 4, 1904, Dorchester, Massachusetts. A former apprentice to Aaron Willard Jr., Howard was a brilliant mechanic, inventor and entrepreneur. He was a driving force in Stephenson, Howard & Davis 1844-47, Howard & Davis 1847-60, and after 1850 in several corporations associated with his leadership in the mass-production of quality watches. (See **1843 • Edward Howard**, page 111.)

HOWARD, E & CO.: A Boston manufacturer of fine clocks and watches, formed in December 1858 by Edward Howard and his cousin, Albert Howard. The name became a trademark for many Howard products, including a full spectrum of "factory" tower clock models produced in large numbers until 1964. Very many examples survive. TCS Post 1870. (See **1843 • Edward Howard**, page 111.)

HUGHES, JOHN: Taneytown, Maryland. In 1815, Hughes installed a town clock in the County Court House at York, Pennsylvania, where it remained until the building was torn down in 1841. The demolition made room for construction of a new court house with a magnificent clock driving five outside dials. The mechanism was purchased in 1849 for $1,500 from G.W. Carpenter, who had acquired it at the estate sale of Isaiah Lukens of Philadelphia. Hughes' old clock was moved to the Christ Lutheran Church of York, where it continued to serve the public for another 30 years. It became erratic toward the end, eventually striking 169 times non-stop, a problem solved by a parishioner pouring molten pitch over the gear train. The old clock was replaced about 1870. NTCS. (Lee Davis, Donn H. Lathrop)

HUSTON, JAMES: b. —-, Trenton, New Jersey; d. 1822, Montreal, Canada. A journeyman clockmaker employed in the shop of John Probasco at the corner of Warren and State Streets, Trenton, Huston made the first town clock in Trenton. Initially installed in the steeple of the First Presbyterian Church in

1805-06, it was later moved to the city hall. Starting about 1820, Probasco became clock custodian until moving in 1823 to Lebanon, Ohio. Little else is known about Huston or the fate of his town clock. NTCS.

IPSWICH: In 1762, a town clock, probably of English origin but not specifically identified, is described as bought by public subscription and having "landed" at Ipswich, a river town with access to the sea, 10 miles northwest of Gloucester, Massachusetts. An earlier "Town clock," purchased in 1702, appears to have been of the small portable type. The town clock put up in the steeple of the 1st Parish Congregational Church in 1762 had two one-hand dials. Following the addition of a new 135-foot steeple in 1847, the clock was modified to drive three two-hand dials with gilt pewter chapters. The Ipswich meeting house burned in 1965, but clock parts rescued by Max Elser of Ipswich permit a reasonably accurate description of the movement. Its open box frame of 3½" square hardwood beams with mortise-and-tendon corners, measured overall 42⅜" wide by 17½" deep by 36" high. Time and strike trains pivoted in forged iron vertical risers with brass-bushed pivot holes. Well-defined, high tooth-count brass wheels with four shaped spokes were mounted on tapered forged-iron arbors with leaf pinions. The great wheels measured 17½" across and were connected by ratchets to short stocky wooden barrels. Strike control was by a locking plate mounted outside the frame along with a two-blade ratchet-driven fly. The pendulum was rated by a "horned" nut under its 12½" diameter lenticular bob. Surviving dial work, probably dating from the 1847 renovation, included the following: hour and minute hands of an American design for three five-foot diameter outside dials, five-spoke motion work with exceptionally long extensions, a transmission, universal joints and rolled sheet metal leading off rods. The clock's most unusual feature was its escapement: 20 undercut paddle-like radial teeth projected laterally from a 5½" brass escape wheel, engaging an anchor with deadbeat pallets (an English form dating from 1745, suggested by Beeson to predate the French use of the pinwheel escapement in very large clocks).

JAMES, WILLIAM: at work ca. 1714-17, Portsmouth, Rhode Island. In 1714, James offered the Newport City Council a town clock with a four-pound hammer that showed the time in "rain or shine," an improvement over the usual sundial to mark the hour. In 1717, the Freemen of Newport appointed a committee to purchase the clock from James, its destination unknown. NTCS.

JEROME, JEWELL & CO.: Bristol, Connecticut, ca. 1847-1849. Company principals were Noble Jerome,

the inventive brother of Chauncey Jerome, Lyman Jewell and David Matthews, all of whom participated in the manufacturing boom of brass clock movements. Facing acute competition in a crowded marketplace, this venture appears to have been one of several failed attempts to turn a profit by reorganizing and changing the product line. We know from bankruptcy papers filed on January 8, 1849, that they made and dealt in a number of apparently unrelated products. Their main asset at the time was a large inventory of "Electro Mechanical Machines" (stimulation apparatus used by physicians), plus the equipment and materials necessary for their manufacture. They also made door weather stripping, marine compasses, and town clocks. At the time of bankruptcy, their clock manufacturing assets included two pinion lathes @ $17, one wheel engine $65, five chucks for making balance wheels @ $.66, one town clock unfinished $190, two town clock frames @ $1.50, one lot of town clock patterns $1.00, 68 pounds of 10 oz. brass clock wheels, etc., heavy scrap $10.29, plus miscellaneous structural and decorative components probably associated with clock frame construction. NTCS. (Snowden Taylor)

JOCELIN, SIMEON: b. October 22, 1746, East Haven, Connecticut; d. June 5, 1823, New Haven, Connecticut. Possibly apprenticed to Isaac Doolittle (1721-1800) of New Haven. Jocelin set up shop in New Haven by 1771, where he made and repaired clocks and watches of all sorts, including "silent running" house clocks of his own invention and steeple clocks. He was also a publisher, an engraver of bank notes, and a skilled mathematician acclaimed as the most scientific of early American clockmakers. (See **1799 • Simeon Jocelin**, page 31.)

JOHNSON, CHARLES FRED: b. 1804, Stratford, Connecticut; d. July 6, 1882, Dorchester, Massachusetts. A well-educated gentleman farmer and inventor, living in upstate New York near Owego, Johnson thought up a number of ingenious ideas but failed to capitalize on them; included was his invention of a tower clock controlled by the brass works of a common kitchen clock. (See **1846 • Charles Frederick Johnson**, page 122.)

JOHNSON, NELS: b. November 26, 1838, Sjelland, Denmark; d. January 13, 1915, Manistee, Michigan. Born into an impoverished Danish family and with little or no formal education, Johnson was put to work by the age of 7 and at 14 became a blacksmith's apprentice. Traveling as a stowaway, he managed to reach Quebec, then slowly worked his way to Milwaukee where he found work as a blacksmith's helper, eventually becoming a skilled machinist. In 1865, he married Frances Green of Milwaukee, the mother-to-be of his two sons and three daughters. In

August of 1871, he opened his own machine shop in Manistee, Michigan, planning to build and repair machinery for sawmills, the area's major industry. After some reversals, such as the loss of his shop by fire, the need to borrow money and to take on a partner, he managed by 1893 to become sole owner of the Johnson Machine Shop at 523 Water Street in Manistee. Years earlier, Johnson had shown a passing interest in clockmaking. While still in Milwaukee he had experimented with an electrical clock and later in Manistee made tall case regulators for his children. As early as 1876 he installed in his shop tower a public clock that became the town's time standard. A turning point for Nels Johnson came in the mid-1880s when he took his wife (now blind) to Ann Arbor for medical care. While there, he spent his free time in the observatory talking to college professors, which sparked his lifelong interest in astronomy and higher mathematics. He made his own transit and six-inch telescope to determine perfect time from the stars. These studies provided the basis for the high accuracy and success of his Century Tower Clocks, starting about 1886. Johnson kept the clock business completely apart from the machine shop, one he handled entirely by himself. He never took on assistants or apprentices, and even his two machinist sons, August and Nels Jr., never learned clockmaking. It is estimated that Johnson made about 50 clocks in all. They sold mostly in the northern mid-western states, although two ended up in the Orient. In general, his flatbed clocks had the heavy look of factory equipment, made as they were by a machinist more concerned with function than aesthetics. This is not to take away from his workmanship, which was of the highest quality. The wheels and pinions were of gunmetal or close-cast-iron, with all teeth fashioned by Brown & Sharpe involute cutters. Various size models included timepieces, hour-strikers and quarter-strikers, with an option for Graham deadbeat or gravity escapements. The accuracy and price of his clocks was such that he competed on equal terms with E. Howard, Seth Thomas, and Johnson Service, at times winning contracts on which he was the highest bidder. Toward the end of his life Johnson concluded, "For years I tried to build a clock that would keep perfect time, but now I am convinced that only the Creator can do that. The stars in their course through the heavens never vary, but man-made timepieces will ever be fallible. I have made clocks that vary only three or four seconds in a month, but I believe that is the limit." TCS post-1870.

JOHNSON, SIMON: b. 1804, England; d. 1870, Sanborton, New Hampshire. A clockmaker who specialized in regulator movements for the trade, he also made jeweler's regulators, patent timepiece banjos,

and large tower clocks, some selling from $300 to $500. In an era when most clockmaking was a hand operation, his 1830 shop had a penstock to a water wheel which powered his clockmaking machinery. In 1840, Simon Johnson Jr., a Sanbornton clockmaker, purchased eight acres; a second land purchase in 1845 eliminates "Jr." and shows him as a clockmaker with a wife named Nancy. He was succeeded in business by his sons Robert Stuart (1832-1911) and Richard Davis (1845-1919). Simon's favorite hobbies were hunting, fishing, and farming in a small way. NTCS.

JOHNSON, WARREN SEYMOUR: b. 1847, Rutland County, Vermont; d. December 5, 1911 (Bright's disease), Los Angeles, California. H.L. Menken wrote of Warren Johnson, he "is one of the great benefactors of humanity, I wouldn't swap him for a dozen MARCONI'S, a regiment of Bell's or a whole army of Edison's." When Warren Johnson was 2 years old, his family moved from Vermont to Wisconsin, settling in Dunn County, 300 miles northwest of Milwaukee. As a young man he worked as a printer, teacher, surveyor, and superintendent of schools until being appointed a professor at the State Normal School at Whitewater in 1876. A strikingly original teacher, his consuming interest was experimentation with electrochemistry, the glamour science of the day. He focused on remote temperature control, patenting the first room thermostat on July 24, 1883. With patent in hand, "the Professor" as he was always called, got financial backing to establish the Milwaukee Electric Manufacturing Company. In 1883, it was renamed Johnson Electric Service Co., then Johnson Service Co., and finally simply Johnson Controls, a Milwaukee-based international corporation in business today. Although the nominal CEO of these companies until his death in 1911, the Professor occupied himself almost exclusively with experimentation and product development. He set a fast pace, the diversity of his inventions often outstripping the ability of the factory to keep up. Products ranged from springless door locks and puncture-proof automobile tires to wireless communication, pneumatic clocks, and steam-powered trucks. Most of his devices, however, depended on controlling power by air, steam or fluid pressure, in which Warren had confidence surpassing his faith in electricity. None of the Professor's inventions impressed the general public more than his pneumatic tower clocks. They were huge affairs, with dials up to 112 feet in diameter, with hands weighing up to more than a ton, and striking on bells weighing up to 11 tons. Johnson first experimented with wet cell batteries for power, but found compressed air more reliable. Beyond his faith in compressed air as the best solution, he knew that publicity surrounding these huge public clocks helped validate the pneumatic system employed in his profitable temperature controls business. Quite correctly, he wrote, "The conditions under which such a clock must operate...becomes an engineering problem and not a horological problem...In brief, the real clock, the accurate timepiece, serves only to put in motion and to control the tower mechanism, and there is, therefore, no clock at all at the great height of the dials...The whole is based in the fundamental principle of all modern mechanisms, namely the governing and directing of great forces by comparatively feeble ones" (in the case of his clocks, a puff of air). The full details of Johnson's system are described in the *Journal of the Franklin Institute*, Vol. CLI, No. 2, February 1901. At least 10 Johnson pneumatic clocks were put into service between 1895 and 1906. Representative installations included: Colorado Springs, Colorado; Grand Rapids, Michigan; St. Louis, Missouri; and Heightstown, New Jersey. His 1896 Milwaukee City Hall clock struck an 11-ton bell. His 1895 clock for the Minneapolis Court House was made in eight months compared to the years it took to complete the Westminster clock in London, and it boasted larger dials, as did Johnson's Philadelphia City Hall dials which were located 362 feet above the street. Johnson's largest and most widely publicized clock was designed for the St. Louis World's Fair of 1904. The dial of this "Great Floral Clock" was a gentle slope of lawn 112 feet in diameter, with 15-foot high chapters consisting of planted flowers. The hands weighed 2,500 pounds each and the clock struck on a 5,000-pound bell with a 150-pound hammer. Power was transmitted by a 70-foot long rod from a small pavilion that housed the master clock and its pneumatic components; Johnson Service Co. also offered pneumatic carillons striking on eight bells, with all gears and driving parts gold-plated to prevent corrosion. Examples of Johnson clock dials, portions of the pneumatic hardware, pressure tanks and pipe connections, along with water-pressure backup devices, have survived at Colorado Springs and Heightstown, New Jersey. TCS post 1870.

JOHNSTON, ARTHUR: b.——; d. 1846, Hagerstown, Maryland. At work as a clock and watchmaker, silversmith and jeweler in Hagerstown, Maryland, ca. 1785-1846. Of Scottish descent, nothing is known of his origins or where he learned the trade. Elegant tall case clocks surviving from the 1790s were made and signed by Johnston; they are Sheridan-style, eight-day brass works with white enamel dials showing calendar and moon phase. He also made mantel clocks in partnership with a clockmaker named Melhorn from nearby Boonsboro. Over the years, Johnston drifted in and out of a number of partnerships, including those with his brother William, a jeweler and dentist, and one with his brother-in-law, a jeweler in Frederick, Maryland. Johnston's well-known shop provided for cabinet work on the second floor. It was located on the northwest corner of the Hagerstown public square on land he bought in 1812 for £850, a sizable sum for a man with his precarious livelihood. Johnston was highly regarded in Hagerstown, not only for his mechanical skills but because of his active civic life. He was a Mason, a member of the Union Missionary Society, the inspector of fire engines, an incorporator of the Antietam Fire Company, and from 1831 to 1837, a director of the Hagerstown Bank. In 1833, he and his brother were commissioned to supply a town clock for the Hagerstown City Hall. It was to have a large bell and four outside dials. The clock was installed in 1836 at a cost of $1,000, collected by public subscription. In 1889, the tower was heightened and the dials raised about 35 feet to increase their line of sight. The clock continued to give excellent service, but was removed in 1938 prior to demolition of the building to make room for a new city hall. The old clock, stored in a collapsed shed on an old farm, was abandoned to rust and the pigeons until recently, when it was beautifully restored by local volunteers. Except for its rack-and-snail strike control and an adjustable crutch, the Hagerstown clock is identical to a clock made by A. Willard Jr., in 1824, still running hand-wound in Kennebunkport, Maine. In fact, both clocks strike on bells cast at the George H. Holbrook foundry located about 20 miles away from Willard's shop at Boston Neck, Massachusetts. Cartage from New England to Maryland may account in part for the unusually high $1,000 cost of the Hagerstown clock. Johnston probably handled the installation of the clock and bell and their connections, including those to the outside dial hands. He may also have devised the beat-setting adjustable elbow on the escapement crutch, as it does not appear on the earlier Kennebunkport clock. The same year that the clock was installed, the farming community experienced a devastating crop failure. This taken with the financial panic of 1837 all but eliminated the need for a clockmaker in Hagerstown. It spelled disaster for the aging Arthur Johnston. He never really recovered from the depression that followed, losing almost everything he owned, and dying in debt in the autumn of 1846. NTCS.

JONES, GEORGE A. CO.: 1870-1873, a clockmaker/dealer located at 6 Cortlandt Street, New York City. His well-to-do father, George Jones of Bristol, Connecticut, counted among his assets a full city block in New York City. A tower clock timepiece signed "G.A.JONES, NEW YORK" has survived.

Recently converted to household furniture on wheels by Howard Bomar, it has a compounded pendulum and electric rewind. The A-frame and all clockwork, including its 1½-second pendulum and transmission, are identical to timepieces made by Geo. M. Stevens & Co., Boston, in the 1870s. Its jeweled deadbeat escapement and more delicate flatbed on cabriole legs appear to have been added by Jones. Nevertheless, the clock is uniformly painted and decorated overall. Former partner James Wood claimed to have been the successor to the Jones Company, but it was actually taken over in 1873 by R.J. Davies (the former Jones' superintendent) and D.G. Hodgens, doing business as Davies & Hodgens. They continued to deal in tower clocks, regulators, and a general line of American clocks at 5 Cortlandt Street, having a manufactory at 6 Cortlandt. This was the same street address as a sales office occupied in 1872 by Geo. M. Stevens of Boston, who probably enlisted both Jones and Davies & Hodgens as sales agents for Stevens tower clocks.

LAFEUER & BEARY: 1854-1856, New York City town clock makers and machinists at White and Elm Streets. The principals were Augustus LeFeuer and William Beary, both residing at 42 Franklin Street. This company was probably a short-lived spinoff of the successful Reeve & Co., where LaFeuer was employed in 1852-53. NTCS.

LATHROP, WILLIAM: b. 1688; d. 1778. A surveyor of Norwich-town, Connecticut. In 1743 Lathrop was paid £8/10/5 for labor and materials in connection with his installation of a steeple clock in the Norwich-town Meeting House. Lathrop married three times, and in 1751 was dismissed from the church for having joined the Separatist (Congregational) movement. The 1743 clock, thought to have been imported from England, was repaired and its dial repainted in 1770. The clock that replaced it in 1797 was lost in an 1807 church fire. An 1882 Seth Thomas tower clock serves the church today. NTCS.

LEIDGEN, JOHN: ca, 1875-1880, Milwaukee, Wisconsin. First listed at 1331 North Avenue as a saloonkeeper, then as a clock manufacturer; later shown at different addresses as a machinist. On January 25, 1876, he received U.S. Patent No. 172.638 for "Improvements in Clock Escapements." The patent drawing showed a jerry-rigged A-frame with the time train clockwork reduced to a pendulum, escapement, great wheel and a weight-driven winding barrel. The escapement was complex, working on both ends of the pendulum rod. A ratchet and pawl at the suspension end was periodically tripped by the swing of the pendulum, releasing power to an array of counter-balanced levers, stops and a roller working inside a diamond shaped opening at the bob end of the rod. The pendulum was kept in motion by being pulled to one side to trip an escapement pawl. NTCS.

LEROY, ABRAHAM: At work ca. 1750-1764, Lancaster, Pennsylvania. A tower clock thought to be an English import was put up in the Lancaster County Courthouse in 1756. In May 1757, Abraham Leroy, a Swiss emigrant, was paid £1/15s for care of the clock, plus £1 in November of the same year and semi-annually thereafter. After his death in 1764, the authorities "agreed with Rudy Stoner, clockmaker, to take care of ye said clock at £4 yearly from this date [1764]." About five years later, the job was assumed by George Hoff Sr. and the following year taken over by John Eberman Jr., a Stoner apprentice who became clock custodian until its loss by fire on July 9, 1784. (See **1785 • John Eberman Jr.**, page 19.)

LOESCH, JOHANN JACOB: b. June 13, 1760, Bethabara, North Carolina; d. October 8, 1821, Fayetteville, North Carolina. Bethabara was the first settlement in a huge tract of Moravian land called Wachovia that encompassed all and more of what is now Winston-Salem, North Carolina. Johann was the second son of the five children of Jacob and Anna (Blum) Loesch. His father, who pioneered in the move from Bethlehem, Pennsylvania, to Wachovia in 1753, was considered the business manager of the first settlers, and later farm manager of the Bethabara plantation. In 1769, the family returned to Bethlehem and two years later moved a few miles east to Nazareth. Johann had a good Moravian education at home, and was later trained as a gun and locksmith. At the age of 21 he sought to establish himself at Salem, where he lived with the Single Brothers. Unable to find work in his trade due to a lack of seniority, he fell in debt until being taken on as an assistant to Adam Koffler, a clockmaker. The job did not last long as Koffler claimed that the eager Loesch had siphoned off his best customers. Unemployed again, a frustrated Loesch moved in 1789 to Bethania, a small Moravian settlement just north of Salem. A year later he married Susanna Leinbach, the mother of his six children. Active in Bethania community affairs, he found employment teaching school in English and as a clockmaker (reporting the theft of five clocks in 1792). In 1797, Loesch made a small town clock for the steeple of the Bethania community house (*Gemein Haus*). The building was dismantled in 1851, its timbers reused in a later structure, but the fate of the tower clock is unknown. In addition to his other talents, Loesch's skill as a musician stood him in good stead: he sang in the choir, and tuned, played, repaired and finally built pipe organs. At age 56 he moved to Raleigh, North Carolina, where he set up the state capitol's water works. Five years later, while engaged in a similar project for Fayetteville, North Carolina, he fell ill and died at the age of 61. NTCS.

LOGAN, SYDNEY ALGERNON: b. May 17, 1849, Philadelphia, Pennsylvania; d. December 11, 1925, Gushenville, Pennsylvania. A rich Philadelphia Main Line blue blood, Logan was surrounded with luxury, culture and privilege. He attended Yale briefly but was bored and quit. Logan distracted himself with European travel, writing prose and poetry, photography, navigation, animal husbandry, and, eventually, clockmaking in 1912. He erected a fully-equipped machine shop on his gentleman's farm, making several "grandfather" clocks that kept excellent time. Embittered by World War I, he escaped in the construction of what he called his "Peace Tower," a 65-foot high free-standing tower with a single dial and bell. He designed and perfected the clockwork in his own machine shop. The project was completed in June 1920. The clock did not run during winter when ice obstructed the hands, and it was largely abandoned after Logan's death. NTCS.

LOWREY, DAVID: b. July 13, 1740; d. December 7, 1819. A blacksmith and clockmaker of Newington, Connecticut, he initially approved and later maintained a public clock with three faces installed in the Old Wethersfield meeting house in 1791. Probably of English origins as was the Society's bell, he reported the clock as "good, strong and well constructed, and fully equal to that in Farmington Society." (William L. Willard)

LUKENS, ISAIAH: b. April 24, 1779, Horsham Township, Pennsylvania; d. November 12, 1846, Philadelphia. Isaiah moved from the family farm in 1811 to Philadelphia where he achieved great prestige as a clockmaker, tool and instrument maker, and expert in the natural sciences. Many of his tower clocks survive. (See **1812 • Isaiah Lukens**, page 55.)

LUPP (LEUPP, LOOP), HENRY: b. 1760, New Brunswick, New Jersey; d. 1816, ——. Henry was part of a large family of New Jersey silversmiths and clock and watchmakers. He learned the trade from his father, Peter Lupp, a clockmaker, and by 1783 had set up shop as a clock and watch repairer on Albany Street, two doors below the ferry house in Brunswick-Town. The following year he advertised: "HENRY LUPP.—To Be Sold, A Very good Eight Day Town-Clock, neatly finished, has run but about four years, which now stands in Christ's Church in this city...apply to the subscriber, who will warrant it as good as any in the states." Lupp account books indicate that Henry's cousin, William Lupp, had

charge of New Brunswick's town clock for some period between 1801 and 1827. NTCS.

LUSCOMB, SAMUEL: b. ——; d. September 1782, Salem, Massachusetts. Luscomb is reported to have made church clocks for two meeting houses in Old Salem, Massachusetts, both subsequently destroyed by fire. The diary of a Salem resident reads, "1792—June 25...By Caesar I read the Bell in the East Meeting House was put up in October 1772, & the Clock on the 22nd May 1773, made by a Mr. Liscombe [*sic*], belonging to the town...." The *Salem Gazette* dated September 11, 1782, called for claims and payments due on the estate of Samuel Luscomb, late clockmaker of Salem, be made for speedy settlement to Lydia Luscomb, executrix, "or expect to meet with trouble." NTCS.

MARSHALL, JUSTICE: b.1828——; d. 1905, Cazenovia, New York. A talented machinist and tower clockmaker working for, and then succeeding to, Austin Van Riper's manufactory as a co-partner with John Stone in Stone & Marshall. (See **1859 • Stone & Marshall**, page 158.)

M'CABE, JOHN: b. —, Dublin, Ireland; d. July 1778, Baltimore, Maryland. Irish immigrant M'Cabe claimed to have been trained by "the most capital artists in London, Dublin and Liverpool." In March 1774, he opened a shop opposite the coffee house on Market Street, Baltimore, assuring the public that he would execute and furnish "plain, repeating, horizontal, stop or seconds watches: musical clocks, to go either by springs or weights; astronomical, chime, quarter, and plain ditto adjusted with balance, common or compound pendulums; also turret, or steeple clocks, constructed to endure for a long continuance of time...." In addition, he claimed to make electrical apparatus, air pumps, and spring clocks for mariners and also to repair orreries and navigation instruments. Two years later he advertised for workers at a cotton, wool and tow manufactory newly established at his house in Baltimore. In September of 1777, he advertised the sale of "the time of a healthy Servant girl who has 3$\frac{1}{2}$ years to serve...an exceedingly good spinner...." Reported to have joined the Baltimore Artificers Company of Militia, M'Cabe was killed in action during the American Revolution. On July 28, 1778, Phebe M'Cabe, administratrix, called for settlement of his estate. NTCS.

MENEELY, ANDREW: b. 1801, Washington, New York; d. October 1851, West Troy, New York. Meneely was the Protestant son of an Irish immigrant. Following an apprenticeship with Julius Hanks, he established the Meneely foundry in West Troy, New York, manufacturing large bells, surveying instruments and tower clocks. After his death, the business continued as the country's leading bell foundry, run until 1950 by his descendants in the Troy area under various company names. (See **1839 • Andrew Meneely**, page 101.)

MILLER, AARON: b. —; d. 1779, Elizabethtown, New Jersey. A clock and instrument maker with his own brass foundry, Miller had many apprentices, including clockmaker Isaac Brokaw who became his son-in-law and later inherited his tools. On November 16, 1747, he advertised in *The New York Gazette*, "makes and sells all Sorts of Clocks, after the best Manner...likewise makes Compasses and Chains for Surveyors; as also Church Bells of any size, he having a Foundry for that Purpose...." In 1765, Benjamin Franklin wrote from London praising his improvements in the surveyor's compass. Miller is said to have exercised similar ingenuity counterfeiting government coins from dies and molds of his own making. Both the 1759 steeple clock and its bell in the old First Presbyterian Church on Broad Street in Elizabethtown have been attributed to Miller as the only craftsman in town with the necessary skills to do the job. The possibility is enhanced by local history which indicates that the church had a high steeple "with a town clock in it of which a Mr. Miller had the care for many years." The church and all contents — including the clock, bell and records — were put to the torch by British troops in 1780. A year later, Mary Miller, executrix, and Isaac Brokaw, administrator, called for settlement of Miller's estate. NTCS.

MILLINGTON, NORMAN: of Shaftsbury, Vermont by 1852. *Walton's Register* for 1862 lists Millington as living in Shaftsbury, "a maker of church and town clocks." NTCS.

MILNE, ROBERT: 1798-1802, New York City, later of Philadelphia. On June 17, 1800, he advertised his clock manufactory had moved from 212 Water Street to 65 Partition Street, "near the Bear Market where he manufactures and repairs all kinds of Steeple and House Clocks on the shortest notice." Bear Market, the only one on the City's North River side, got its name because the first meat sold there was from a bear killed while swimming from the Bergen, New Jersey, shore. NTCS.

MORRILL, BENJAMIN: b. January 16, 1794, Boscawen, New Hampshire; d. April 21, 1857, Boscawen, New Hampshire. Best known for his New Hampshire mirror clocks, he also made tall case, Massachusetts shelf, banjo and several tower clocks. When the demand for high quality clocks slackened, he turned to the manufacture of scales and musical instruments. (See **1835 • Benjamin Morrill**, page 88.)

MUNROE, DANIEL:b. 1775, —; d. 1859, Boston, Massachusetts. Munroe served a seven-year apprenticeship with Simon Willard, who proclaimed him "one of the best workmen in America." In 1798, he set up his own shop in Concord, Massachusetts, opposite the clothing mill, advertising on November 3 "...every kind of Clock Work, such as large Clocks for Church Towers; Chime Clocks; Spring Clocks; and common House Clocks. Also Time-pieces for Meeting-houses, and common house Time-pieces, of different kinds...." He also repaired all sorts of watches and supplied "Sheet Iron Stoves, with funnels suited to any direction." Between 1800 and 1807 he was joined in Concord by his brother, Nathaniel, following which he moved to Boston, first working with Ezekiel Jones for a couple of years and after 1809 working alone at 51 Newbury Street. Munroe is said to have worked at the bench until he retired at age 83 in 1858. NTCS.

NEISSER, AUGUSTINE: b. 1717, Sehlen, Moravia; d. 1780, Germantown, Pennsylvania. He immigrated to America, landing in Savannah, Georgia, in 1736. On the migration north with the Moravians who established Bethlehem, Pennsylvania, Neisser settled in Germantown (now part of Philadelphia) as a watch repairer and clockmaker for almost 40 years. In 1747, he made and installed at Bethlehem's Central Moravian Church this country's longest running tower clock. (See **1747 • Augustine Neisser**, page 7.)

NORTHWEST TOWER CLOCK CO.: see **Powers (Power), David,** page 204.

O'NEIL, CHARLES: At work in New Haven, Connecticut, ca. 1800-1830. As an apprentice to Simeon Jocelin, he claimed to have helped make Jocelin's tower clock for Yale's Old College Chapel. On his own in 1814 as a clockmaker and watch repairer, by about 1820 he went to work for Merriman & Bradley, jewelers at 58 State Street, New Haven. NTCS.

PARKER, GARDNER: b. March 14, 1772, Hubbardston, Massachusetts; d. February 16, 1816, (suicide) Northborough, Massachusetts. Starting at age 14, he served a full apprenticeship to the Willards of Grafton. From 1790 to 1815, he was at work in Westborough and Northborough as a clockmaker, cabinetmaker and gunsmith. He made tall case clocks and also fine tower clocks patterned after those of Abel Stowell of neighboring Worcester. (See **1806 • Gardner Parker**, page 43.)

PARMELEE (PARMELE), EBENEZER: b. November 22, 1690, Guilford, Connecticut; d. September 17 (or 27), 1777. Clockmaker, cabinetmaker, boatwright. In 1726-27, he made one of Connecticut's first tower clocks for the Meeting House at Guilford, followed in 1742 by a second tower clock for the First Church of Milford. (See **1726 • Ebenezer Parmelee**, page 2.)

PENFIELD, SYLVESTER: at work ca. 1845-1857. Penfield was listed in New York City as a clockmaker at 205 9th Avenue; however, he spent much time in neighboring states peddling tower clocks made in Manhattan. During the late 1840s while an agent for Smith's Clock Establishment (located at 7½ Bowery Street, in lower Manhattan) Penfield installed two tower clocks in Hartford, Connecticut, one at the Center Church, and another at Hartford's State House. Each cost $300. Both of these clocks have been lost, but two other Smith's clocks not sold by Penfield have survived in Canandaigua, New York, and Natchez, Mississippi. They are of the distinctive A-frame type almost identical to town clocks made in New York City by Reeve & Co. and sold by Penfield after 1850 when Smith's ceased doing business in the city. On February 19, 1851, the Berks County Commissioners of Reading, Pennsylvania, awarded S. Penfield of New York a contract to put up a town clock in their new courthouse steeple at a cost of $480, less $20 credit for the old clock it replaced. The new clock was warranted not to vary a minute in a month and guaranteed for five years. Penfield was also authorized by the commissioners to install the new bell, acquired from the Meneely Foundry in Troy, New York. The clock ran four dials on the steeple, plus a wall clock in the main court room. The driving weights consisted of hemlock boxes filled with river stones; limited weight fall of 18 feet necessitated winding the clock three times a week. Although now lost, it seems certain that the Reading clock was acquired by Penfield from Reeve & Co. as it corresponds to similar transactions with surviving clocks from Morristown, New Jersey (1852) and Marietta, Pennsylvania (1853), both signed "S. Penfield, New York" on the setting dials and "Reeve & Co, New York" in the casting of the frame front plate. (See **1851 • Reeve & Co.**, page 140.)

PHILLIPS, JOSEPH: New York City clockmaker at work ca. 1713-1735. Also shown for the same period in New York City is a John Philip, "Brass and bell foundry. Made clock parts." They may be related or the same individual. On February 23, 1716, New York City's Common Council received a gift of £50 from Stephen deLancy (his salary as an assemblyman) toward the purchase of a public clock. In April a committee reported to the council that Joseph Phillips, a clockmaker, would make "a good substantial Town Clock for public use." Its largest wheel would be nine inches in diameter; it would have two dials of red cedar, painted and with gilt numbers. He would provide all the workmen and materials for the clock and its pendulum, putting it in the city hall within six months at a cost of £60, payable upon completion of the work. He also offered to keep the clock in good order for 20 shillings a year, after the first year for which he would charge nothing. Phillips received a part payment from deLancy's gift on May 23, 1716, and the balance on March 20 the following year. Profits from this transaction helped Phillips to finance "a furnace to cast new bells of better mettel than any that comes out of Europe for churches or meeting houses." He did not get the clock maintenance contract; the "winden up & Keeping in Repare ye Publick Clock of ye Siety of new york" was awarded to John Wright, a New York City watchmaker, for £3 annually. Phillip's clock was not mentioned in city records after June 29, 1734. NTCS. (See **Wright, John**, page 216.)

POLLHANS, ADAM EDWARD: b. 1842, St. Louis, Missouri; d. 1878, St. Louis, Missouri. A.E. Pollhans learned tower clockmaking from his father, Phillip Pollhans, worked for him, and succeeded to the family business after the father's death in 1878. He renamed the firm A.E. Pollhans Clock Co., continuing his father's practice of making tower clocks to order. He also sold huge ornately carved "passage clocks," so called for their use in the hallways of large buildings. A number of his tower clocks have survived: R.F. Tschudy, writing in 1964, indicated he knew of at least 10 in small town churches within a 25-mile radius of his home in St. Louis. The A.E. Pollhans catalog offered models made in all sizes driving any number or size of dials, striking the hours, halves, and quarters, or chiming on up to four or more bells. A typical A.E Pollhans cast-iron frame was a curvilinear plate-and-pillar vertical structure on elaborately bowed and painted cabriole legs. Escapements were Graham deadbeat with 30-tooth wheels, with a clutch arrangement to reset the hands without stopping the clock. Strike control was by a flanged count wheel, mounted along with a two-hand setting dial outside the frame. All wheels and Vuillamy-type bushings were bronze, with the arbors and leaf pinions of fine polished steel. His one-second pendulums had 150-pound lenticular bobs and cleared the floor with the frame slightly raised. It was his practice to make clocks in lots of three. It took two men from six to nine months to complete a single clock as the wheel teeth were all cut by hand in prime numbers. The acquisition of a wheel-cutting machine in 1892 was a moment of supreme satisfaction for A.E Pollhans, but brief in duration as he died shortly thereafter of tuberculosis at the age of 36. Several years later his widow married foreman George J. Hoffman, who continued the business under the A.E. Pollhans Clock Co. name until about 1914 when everything was sold

POLLHANS, PHILLIP: at work in St. Louis, Missouri, from 1842 to 1878. Phillip Pollhans was born in Munster, a Rhine Province in Westphalen, Germany. He entered the United States in 1840, a trained clockmaker and mathematician, and was naturalized in March 1851. In the 1840s, St. Louis was a mecca for German Catholics, who represented over a quarter of the city's population of 30,000. First employed as a janitor at St. Louis University, by 1850 he conducted small classes in mathematics along with having a clock and watch repair shop at his home at 1230 North 13th Street. He placed outside his shop a three-foot high cast-iron figure of a fat punchinello with a public clock mounted in his belly. On the roof of the house he built a cupola for a bell "as big as a small bucket," connected by a wire to a clock in his shop to strike the hours. It was all the advertising he needed to draw in business from the crowds of shoppers at the nearby Biddle Market. Phillip Pollhans had only built two small tower clocks before 1845 when he took on the construction of a large clock for the St. Joseph's Catholic Church, newly built for the German-speaking parish at the corner of Biddle and North 11th Streets. It took two years to complete the clock, which struck the hours and the quarters, and drove the hands of four seven-foot dials. The large flatbed with cabriole legs was wound every two days, and ran regularly until the 1950s, when it was electrified. On the frame was printed in German, "All the hours quickly pass. May the last be happy for you." After Phillip's death in 1878, the firm was taken over by his son, Adam Edward, followed some years later by George J. Hoffman who continued in business until about 1914. TCS post 1870.

POWERS (POWER), DAVID G.: b. 1849——; d. 1883, Milwaukee, Wisconsin. Powers was an immigrant real estate agent who turned to tower clock making. His Northwest Tower Clock Co. exhibited a very large, elaborately decorated tower clock at the 1876 Philadelphia Centennial Exposition. The clockwork was mounted in three arched frames measuring 10 feet across, and surmounted by symbolic figurines. The center time module supported a compensated pendulum displaying on its upper end a gilt eagle on an orb engraved "Centennial." Smaller flanking frames supported mechanisms striking the hour and the quarters. A mechanism to the rear provided for playing a full chime of bells. The clock measured overall 10 feet wide by 6 feet deep. First exhibited in Milwaukee, it was to occupy the northwestern tower of the main Philadelphia Centennial Exposition building, and to operate 12 dials, the outer ones being 12 feet in diameter. In 1878, he began a short manufacturing career in a machine shop at 619 Cedar Street in Milwaukee. Little else is known about the man. NTCS.

QUIMBY, PHINEAS PARKHURST: b. February 16, 1802, Lebanon, New Hampshire; d. January 16, 1866. He probably learned clockmaking from his brother William Quimby (1821-1850). Phineas lived most of his life in Belfast, Maine, an inventor, and maker of tall case clocks, Willard-type banjos, and (in partnership with Timothy Chase) the tower clock for the First Church of Belfast. (See **1836 • Chase & Quimby**, page 95.)

REEVE & CO.: New York City machinists and tower clock makers from 1850 to ca. 1860. The principals were Joseph & Thomas Reeves, presumably brothers. Their distinctive A-frame clocks with pinwheel deadbeat escapements and outboard barrels achieved wide distribution. (See **1851 • Reeve & Co.**, page 140.)

RIDGWAY (RIDGEWAY), JAMES: b. 1768, Boston, Massachusetts; d. September 11, 1850. A silversmith and jeweler, he worked successively at Boston, Worcester and Groton, Massachusetts, later at Keene and Nashua, New Hampshire. In 1802, he married the oldest daughter of tower clockmaker Abel Stowell, and in 1809 installed Groton's Town Clock. (See **1809 • James Ridgway**, page 45.)

ROBINSON, S.W.: In 1870-1878, S.W. Robinson, a professor of mechanical engineering at what is now the University of Illinois, taught in six months what took three years to learn under the old apprentice system. He inspired a group of students from the class of 1878, led by Fred Francis, to design and build a much-needed university tower clock using the limited facilities of the engineering shop. It was a one-of-a-kind timepiece, original in its approach to many advanced horological features; however, its design was starkly functional with none of the grace of the best commercial clocks of its day. Its frame consisted of a trough-like iron flatbed on which a time train of six in-line wheels (made by Brown & Sharpe Mfg. Co.) pivoted in removable bearing blocks. Vertical A-frame extensions at opposite ends of the flatbed supported a 1½-second compensated pendulum with a single-leg gravity escapement, and the dial take-off connections to a four-dial bevel gear transmission mounted overhead. Clutch mechanisms permitted the motion work of each dial to be reset independently. If one dial was obstructed, the clock continued to run, displaying the time on the unaffected dials. Installed in the west tower of old University Hall, this unusual timepiece, hand-wound until 1938, helped keep students on schedule. Moved to another building in 1941 and electrified, it continued to serve the campus until being replaced by an electric motor in 1963. After years of neglect, the handiwork of the class of 1878 was restored to original condition by the class of 1989. TCS post 1870.

RODGERS (ROGERS), JAMES: b. 1801, Scotland; d. 1878, New York, New York. Completing his apprenticeship in Scotland, Rodgers immigrated to America, arriving in New York in 1822, when he set up as a watchmaker on Chatham Street. He was later joined by his father, a clockmaker. In 1830, he moved to 410½ Broadway, which provided a shop behind his dwelling place. He purchased the property in 1840, and erected a new building where he lived and worked until 1851. He turned primarily to the manufacture of tall case clocks and regulators of the finer grade. He is said to have made over 50 public clocks for vessels and large buildings, including those for the old Grand Central Depot and Trinity Church in New York's financial district. His awards from the annual American Institute Fair included a silver medal in 1841 for a device to measure the revolutions of a steam engine, and a gold medal in 1846 for his *arrangement, manufacture and finish* of the Trinity clock. Rodgers made some of the first telegraph instruments, being shown in 1852-53 as a clockmaker, supplying "telegraph register's magnets." In 1854, he moved his residence farther uptown, while working at several locations along Broadway near Canal Street. Later he located at the corner of Fulton and Williams, where he remained active until his death. He was succeeded by his son, William H. Rodgers, shown as a tower clock and model maker. None of James Rodger's tower clocks have survived, but data exists on the Trinity Church installation which caused quite a stir. The clock cost $3,600 plus $744 for added work. It was described as the heaviest in America, weighing almost 7,000 pounds. Frame style was unspecified, but it stood nine feet wide by five feet high, providing time, strike, and the quarters, while driving four eight-foot dials. Newspapers described the escapement as "exquisitely finished," its hardened steel anchor fitted with "massive jewels, which will nearly make it indestructible." The great wheels were solid castings 30 inches across and two inches thick, the barrels two feet in diameter. Winding jacks were provided on both barrels, along with maintaining power on the time train. Calculated to run eight days, it took 850 turns of the crank to wind up each of the three weights, a task for two men working over an hour. The 18-foot pendulum had a white pine rod, saturated with hot tallow, and a 200-pound ball oscillating 25 times per minute. James Rodgers serviced the clock until 1874, when the task was given over to the American Clock Co. For all its cost and massive proportions, the Trinity Church clock, along with the Demilt clock in the cupola of city hall, were criticized by the press in 1850 as being unreliable timekeepers. The *New York Journal of Commerce* wrote, "The city has no public timepiece so distinguished for its accuracy as to serve as a standard of time for the regulation of other timepieces, for the departure of Steamboat and Rail Road trains, for the closing of Banks, Public Offices, &c. The importance and value of a uniform standard of time in a city like this is too obvious to require remark." *Scientific American* and other journals joined in the attack. As a consequence, the Demilt clock in city hall was replaced in 1853 by one made by Sherry & Byram of Sag Harbor, New York. Poor timekeeper or not, James Rodgers' clock remained in Trinity Church until 1905, when it was replaced by an E. Howard quarter-striker, the dials now electrified. NTCS.

RODGERS, WILLIAM H.: the son and successor to James Rodgers. For several years starting in 1877 he was in business as a tower clock and model maker at 100 Fulton Street, living at the former home of his father at 154 East 37th, New York City. NTCS. (See **Rodgers, James**, above.)

RUSSELL, GEORGE W.: 1832-1850, at work in Philadelphia, Pennsylvania, a watchmaker and silversmith at 18 North 6th Street. A much-altered three-dial tower clock signed "G.W. RUSSELL, PHILADELPHIA" has survived in a public school in New Holland, about 12 miles east of Lancaster, Pennsylvania. The clock was moved from a previous unknown location to New Holland ca. 1875, when the transaction was financed and a large bell made by Fulton's Sons was installed. The table type cast-iron flatbed frame measures about 45" wide by 21" deep by 43" high. Decorative brass bearing blocks of the old style support the main arbors, but many of the clock's original components have been replaced. Geo. M. Stevens & Co. of Boston rebuilt the trains to include a Stevens deadbeat escapement and strike deep-tooth count wheel, and Seth Thomas & Co. installed glass dials and the associated connections back to the clock mechanism. Its conventional pendulum measures about 64" overall, and the clock runs 14 days on a winding. Traveling pulleys on threaded shafts mounted on the frame below the barrels ensure uniform distribution of the weight line during rewinding. TCS post-1870.

SAXTON, JOSEPH: b. 1799, Huntington, Pennsylvania; d. 1873, —. The second of 11 children, Saxton was put to work at age 12 in his father's nail factory, and later served as an apprentice to a local watchmaker. At 18 he floated down the Susquehanna River on a raft to Harrisburg, then walked overland to Philadelphia, where he continued his training under the renowned Isaiah Lukens. Lukens' busy shop provided the environment to encourage Saxton's ingenious and inquiring mind. In 1824, his tower clock designs for a bi-metal temperature compensated pendulum and a two-pawl escapement that went "without oil" were exhibited at Philadelphia's Franklin Institute. Luken's confidence in his young assistant was such that when away from Philadelphia on his usual six to eight week summer vacations and during an extended leave in England, Saxton was left in charge of the Philadelphia shop. When Lukens returned from England in October 1827, he and Saxton set to work almost immediately on a contract to build a large new clock for Philadelphia's State House (now Independence Hall). Some claim that Saxton's ideas contributed substantially to the clock's design. In 1831, Saxton followed the path cut by Lukens with a trip to England. During his several years abroad, Saxton met physicist Michael Faraday, along with other leading scientists, and in 1833 devised a rudimentary commutator that contributed to the development of a practical electrical generator. Returning to America in 1837, he worked for the U.S. Mint as a skilled instrument and scale maker. In 1843, he joined the U.S. Coastal Survey where he helped to develop weights and measures standards adopted nationwide. (See **1812 • Isaiah Lukens**, page 55.)

SCHWALBACH, MATHIAS: b. December 17, 1834, Prussia; d. February 29, 1920, Milwaukee, Wisconsin. Schwalbach outlived three wives and fathered 23 children, many of whom died young. Trained as a blacksmith and tower clock maker in Germany's Rhine country, he immigrated to America in 1857, working first as a journeyman machinist in Albany, New York, then moving on to similar employment in Syracuse before settling down in Milwaukee, Wisconsin, in 1863. For nine years he worked as a master machinist at Kleinsteuber's Machine Shop, contributing to a team of experts that developed the first sewing machine and workable typewriter. In 1873, Schwalbach established a tower clock manufactory at 1002 Galena Street, Milwaukee, then moved in 1887 to a two-story building complete with a clock tower that he built at 426 Ninth Street. Schwalback's U.S. Patents in 1874, 1880 and 1890 set forth successive tower clock improvements which included a spring-remontoire pinwheel escapement, with deadbeat pallets mounted on the pendulum rod above its suspension. Along with other innovations, Schwalbach clocks had a distinctive appearance. Large spiral-spoked wheels extended well beyond the sides of a truncated A-frame. The frame and stand with out-curving legs were cast-iron, and usually painted with fanciful detail. Different sizes of four models included a timepiece, plus hour and quarter-hour strikers. A Roman Catholic, Schwalbach's best customers were churches of that faith. In an era when tower clock sales were dominated by large corporations, this small independent maker installed over 55 tower clocks in a dozen states, testifying to the high quality output of his Star Tower Clock Works. In 1902, Louis C. and Robert A. Schwalbach joined their father as M. Schwalbach and Sons, Clockmakers. After Mathias' death at age 86, family members who had participated in the business continued making tower clocks until the market collapsed during the Great Depression. Toward the end, Robert A. and Elizabeth Schwalbach operated the Star Tower Clock and Machine Co., and Mathias J. and Felix Schwalbach specialized in tower clock repair as the Acme Machine Repair. Several good examples of Schwalbach's best work survive in operating condition where originally installed. TCS post-1870.

SHARPE, JULIAN: b. March 20, 1830, Providence, Rhode Island; d. October 17, 1899, en route from Europe. The son of Wilkes and Sally (Chaffee) Sharpe, he was well-educated through two years of high school equivalency. In 1848, he was apprenticed to Joseph R. Brown, a leading Providence machinist and clockmaker, Julian's father paying $50 a year for room and board. While proficient as a machinist, Sharpe's forte was business management and administration. Brown saw this as a way to avoid paperwork that he detested, and took on Sharpe as a partner before he completed his apprenticeship! Their first and only known tower clock was installed in Newport's old Colony House in 1853. It was the work of Brown's fine machinist hand, but it carried the new company name of J.R. Brown & Sharpe. Brown's inventiveness and mechanical genius were the company's foundation, but its dramatic corporate growth was due largely to Sharpe's business acumen. Together, they achieved worldwide leadership in the manufacture of precision instruments and machine tools, incorporating as Brown & Sharpe Manufacturing Company in 1868. (See **1849 • Joseph R. Brown**, page 132.)

SHERRY & BYRAM: 1850-1854, Sag Harbor, New York. This partnership of John Sherry, a Sag Harbor entrepreneur, and Ephraim Niles Byram, a mechanical genius, operated the Oakland Works in Sag Harbor. The brass foundry and machine shop facility consisted of three wooden factory buildings and a free-standing tower to test their clocks. Sherry & Byram advertised clocks for churches, public buildings, plus timepieces for astronomical purposes, jewelers, watchmakers, also for vestry and session rooms, banks, offices, railroad stations, etc. They produced innovative tower clocks in five sizes, and also glass-illuminated dials. At least seven tower clocks were sold, including one to New York City Hall. After dissolution of the partnership in 1854, Byram continued on alone as a tower clock maker and Sherry ran foundry operations at the Oakland Works for a few years before moving on to new enterprises. (See **1838 • Ephraim Niles Byram**, page 98.)

SIBLEY & MARBLE: 1801-1807, New Haven, Connecticut. Clark Sibley (b. August 15, 1777) learned clockmaking as an apprentice to Major Josiah Wheelock of Sutton, Massachusetts. He and Simeon Marble first set up business in 1801 on Chapel Street, New Haven, moving two years later to State Street, where Simeon Jocelin, the principal town clockmaker, was well-established. Their rival advertisements often appeared side-by-side in the local newspaper. In 1801, Sibley & Marble offered steeple clocks costing from $200 to $1,000, plus a line of clocks, watches, silverware, and jewelry. In 1803, they added "a number of elegant plated, steel and gilt swords, cutlasses, Fowling pieces, Fifes, Spy Glasses, etc. —a few gold and silver Watches, Watch Chains, Seals and Keys, together with a good assortment of Jewelry. Warranted eight day Steeple and House Clocks,—Clock Engine Lathes...clocks, watches and instruments repaired." The partnership ended with the death of Sibley in 1807; Marble carried on for several years, primarily in the retail jewelry and silverware line. NTCS.

SIMNET, JOHN: b. ca. 1728, Ireland; d. after 1786, New York, New York. Emigrating from London in late 1768, Simnet set up in business at Piscataqua, (now Portsmouth) New Hampshire, claiming 25 years experience as a watchmaker in London, also "Citizen of London, and principle Manufacturer in England and Ireland, Inventor of, and Skeleton Watch-Finisher." Other braggadocio included, "Chief watchmaker in America," "Finisher to Mr. Gray and Mr. Ellicot, Watch-Makers to his late and present Majesty," and "Finisher to Mr. Tompion, Graham, Storey, Toulmin; and every other Maker (of Note), in London." Apart from his only charging two shillings to clean a watch, the man appears to have been mostly hot air. His most noticeable accomplishment was the frequency, length and vituperation of his advertising notices, the preparation of which must have seriously reduced time left over for watch repair. While in Portsmouth he targeted a slanderous attack on Nathaniel Griffith, a competitor, and none too savory a character himself (see **Griffith, Nathaniel,** page 191). After a prolonged duel of words with Griffith, Simnet tried his luck in New York City by 1770, setting up shop "At the new Dial, the low shop beside the Coffee House Bridge." Here, he attacked the credentials of another London immigrant who claimed to have received instruction in England from "the ingenious Mr. Neale" (see **Yeoman, James,** page 216). His final advertisement appeared June 9, 1786, in the *New York Packet*. For the first and only time he offered turret clocks in his litany of goods and services. It is unlikely he ever made any. NTCS.

SIMON, ANDREW: In 1808, the following appeared in *Kline's Carlisle* [Pennsylvania] *Weekly Gazette*, "ANDREW SIMON, clock and watch-maker...carries on the above branches in all their various arts...in the home occupied by Mr. Jacob Weaver, Wagonmaker, in York street, near Mr. Humrick's tavern, in the borough of Carlisle. He further informs, that he is well acquainted with the making of Town Clocks on various construction and moderate terms. Should he be engaged for the making of a Town Clock, he will give approved security for the performance of the work and the performance of the Clock." Little else is known about the man or his work, as there are no further references to him in any Carlisle records. The name is shown in the Pennsylvania Census just once in 1820, but as a resident of distant Washington County. The name of Jacob Weaver, however, does appear in Carlisle records as a clock and watch maker, in 1798 having a small lot with two houses, one suitable for rental. NTCS.

SLOAN, WILLIAM: of Hartford, Connecticut. His advertisement of March 17, 1794, in the *American Mercury* read, "WILLIAM SLOAN, next door west of the Loan-Office, makes House and Church Clocks—Watches; Stocking Looms; Plate and Jewelry, and every article in the Gold and Silversmith's line...particularly the making of new and repairing old Watches. Having served a regular apprenticeship to the above branches, with the celebrated Mr. Harland of Norwich, he flatters himself he shall be able to give satisfaction to his employers. N.B. Wanted one or two active boys, 14 or 15 years of age, as apprentices to the above business." NTCS.

SMITH'S CLOCK ESTABLISHMENT: 1835-1851, New York, New York. Also known as Andrew B. Smith, Smith & Brothers, and Ransom Smith, they were clockmakers located at No. 7½ Bowery, in lower Manhattan. They manufactured and dealt in "Clocks and Time-pieces, Large and Small," including a few tower clocks. (See **1842 • Smith's Clock Establishment**, page 109.)

SMITH, LUTHER: b. November 30, 1766, Walpole, Massachusetts; d. October 21, 1839, Keene, New Hampshire. By 1793 a resident of Keene, New Hampshire, where he lived the rest of his life. Luther Smith married Sarah Eveleth, and they had three daughters. He carried on the "Clock-Making business, in Keene Street, almost opposite the Tavern of Mr. Ralston—where may be had the best kind of Warranted eight day Clocks, cheap for cash, any kind of country produce, or Neat Stock,—He also cleans and repairs Watches. Cash, and the highest price, given for old Copper and Brass." His main output was tall case and banjo clocks. In 1806, he built the north section of the Eagle Hotel Block, and, toward the end of his working days, operated a brass foundry. His estate inventory showed no clockmaking tools. In 1794, shortly after Smith's arrival in Keene, a public subscription was undertaken to pay for a town clock to be placed in the tower of the Fourth Meeting House at the head of Main Street. He agreed to make, warrant, and attend such a tower clock for 10 years for the sum of £36. Local tradition has it that the mechanism was carried into place by two strong men mounting ladders set against the side of the building. The clock's single octagonal dial with two hands faced south. After a while it ran irregularly then stopped altogether, resulting in local pranksters climbing the tower where the silent clock stood "to make the wheels buzz." By about 1817, Stephen Hasham of Charlestown offered Keene a new mechanism at a reduced price because the dial and hands were already in place. Despite the offer, Smith's clock remained in the tower until 1828, when major renovations to the meeting house required its removal. The clock was stored temporarily in the horse sheds, where it again became a plaything for hooligans who scavenged its brass gears. About this time, the Unitarians separated from the congregation, erecting their own church in 1830 at the corner of Main and Church Streets in Keene. In 1839, the new church received the donation of a one-dial clock made by George Handel Holbrook of East Medway, Massachusetts. It served as the town clock for a number of years, until 1868 when it was replaced by a free-pendulum remontoire-driven tower clock made by Geo. M. Stevens & Co. of Boston. NTCS. (David Proper)

SMITH, PHILIP L.,: b. 1804, Lafayette, New York; d. after 1865, ——. Philip was one of seven children of blacksmith Lemuel and Martha (Washington) Smith. When he was nine years old the family moved 35 miles southwest of Syracuse to the town of Otisco. By 1829, he bought property in the nearby hamlet of Amber, where he produced clock cases fitted with Connecticut wooden movements taken in exchange for good cherry timber which he supplied. Later he joined with Jared Arnold Jr. in the manufacture of fine shelf clocks with brass movements. In May 1834, Smith purchased a factory with water rights and a dam on Nine Mile Creek at nearby Marcellus, New York. Starting with a few wooden clocks, ultimate production consisted of distinctive empire-cased clocks with eight-day brass movements. Some clock labels from this later period add the phrase,

"Church and Town Clocks Made to Order." He certainly had the manufacturing capability, but no Philip Smith town clocks are known to have survived. His career ended abruptly with an arrest in April 1846 by Federal Marshals on the charge of manufacturing "spurious coin," transported in clock shipping cases. Smith jumped bail and fled to Philadelphia, but was apprehended and returned to custody the following year. There is no record of a trial or conviction. He last appeared in 1851-1865 Syracuse Directories as a "daguerrean artist" and a producer of piano-fortes. NTCS. (Russell Oechsle)

SMITH, RANSOM: See **1842 • Smith's Clock Establishment**, page 109.

SPEED, JOHN J.: b. 1803, Mecklenburg County, Virginia; d. June 15, 1867, Brooklyn, New York (pulmonary attack.) Speed spent most of his life in and around Ithaca in upstate New York. A man of untiring energy, he lived up to his name, being a merchant, farmer, inventor, accomplished public speaker, entrepreneur, member of the state legislature, and high-ranking officer in the State Militia. He was known as the last to give up and the first to recover. When his collaboration with fellow inventor Charles Johnson, dealing with the "transmission of intelligence by electricity," failed, Speed struck up a working alliance with Ezra Cornell and Professor Samuel Morse who had perfected the telegraph. Speed contributed to the stringing of over 16,000 miles of wire from Portland, Maine, to Omaha, Nebraska. He accumulated a fortune from this and other investments, including the manufacture of train rails in Brooklyn, New York. Early in his career, he helped construct a time and strike church clock invented by his associate Charles Johnson: it used ordinary household clockworks to regulate and advance the dial hands at 2½ minute intervals. (See **1846 • Charles Fred Johnson**, page 122.) Only one clock was sold and it had a short life, severely testing Speed's reputation as a man never discouraged by failure. NTCS. (Russell Oechsle)

SPELLIER, LOUIS: b. January 6, 1841, Germany; d. August 22, 1891, Philadelphia, Pennsylvania. Of French-German ancestry, Spellier claimed to have been tutor to the royal family of Germany before escaping to America to avoid military service. In 1869, he and fellow immigrant Abraham Yeakel established a clock, watch, and jewelry store on the corner of State and Main Streets in Doylestown, Bucks County, Pennsylvania. Subsequently, Yeakel moved to Perkasie, Pennsylvania, leaving Spellier to carry on alone in Doylestown. He was an expert mechanic with an inventive mind. In the course of business, Spellier made three very distinctive public clocks, including two single-dial advertising timepieces and a large four-dial striker for the Bucks County Courthouse. All three clocks featured unusual escape wheels having two concentric rings of pins, and large setting dials showing the hour, minute and second. Frames were of cast-iron plate-and-pillar construction, with the mechanism raised off the floor on posts. This allowed clearance for one-second pendulums having mercury-compensated bobs. Also provided were rack-and-snail strike control and Harrison maintaining power. As with other clockmakers of the period, Spellier became fascinated with the time-telling potential of electricity and telegraphy. While still in Doylestown, he experimented in his spare time with a galvanic battery-driven clock connected by wire to a slave timepiece in a building across the street. Later in Philadelphia, he perfected and patented an "Electromagnetic Escapement" and a "Sparkless Current Breaker" which allowed an almost limitless number of slave dials to be added to a single circuit. He lectured on the system and was awarded the Franklin Institute's highest medal for the achievement. Ironically, his invention had greater use and was more highly acclaimed abroad than in the United States. Spellier, who never married, visited Europe in 1891. Upon his return in August, he contracted pneumonia at the New Jersey seashore; complications led to his death at home in Philadelphia at age 50. Louis Spellier was buried in Doylestown, where his mechanical tower clocks are preserved in the collection of the Mercer Museum. TCS post 1870.

SPERRY, HENRY: b. ca. 1812, Burlington, Connecticut; d. 1859 (will proven May 4), New York, New York. An enterprising, successful dealer in clocks and mirrors in New York City: from 1844-1850 a partner with Sperry & Shaw, major clock dealers and exporters; from 1851-1859 founder and owner of H. Sperry & Co at 388 and 487 Broadway. (See **1851 • H. Sperry & Co.**, page 143.)

SPERRY, H. & CO.: 1851-1859, New York City. Founded by Henry Sperry as the successor to Sperry & Shaw, the company claimed their clock inventory to be the largest and most varied in the United States, challenging the world to compete. They also manufactured and installed large tower clocks designed by A.S. Hotchkiss, a member of the firm. Succeeded to in 1860 by Sperry & Co. (See **1851 • H. Sperry & Co.**, page 143.)

SPERRY & CO.: 1860-1864, New York, New York. Successors to H. Sperry & Co.; succeeded by Alonzo Taylor. At one time or another all three companies had the same address at 487 Broadway in New York City. After Henry Sperry's death early in 1859, a number of loose ends had to be tied up. Included was collection of money due on an H. Sperry & Co. tower clock installed in 1858-59 in New York's Murray Hill Brick Church. In March and July of 1859, W. Sperry received payments of $800, $300, and $400 toward the $1,500 cost. W. Sperry was William Stillman Sperry (1819-1902), a seven-year younger brother of the deceased Henry, who, along with another brother Timothy Shelton Sperry (1825-1895), established Sperry & Co. in 1860. For a while, they managed to capitalize on the national reputation and the clock inventory of their enterprising older brother. A stylish duplex frame tower clock introduced by H. Sperry & Co. in the mid-1850s was also sold by Sperry & Co. and later by Alonzo Taylor. Surviving examples signed Sperry & Co. include tower clocks in Picton, Ontario, Canada, and in Port Austin, Mississippi. The latter cost $500 in 1860. (For a description of the Sperry duplex tower clock, see **1864 • Alonzo Taylor**, page 165.)

STAR TOWER CLOCK & MACHINE CO.: Milwaukee, Wisconsin. (See **Schwalbach, Mathias**, page 206.)

STEPHENSON, HOWARD & DAVIS: 1844-1847, Boston and Roxbury, Massachusetts. Balance and clockmakers at 42 Congress Street (later at 72 Water) with facilities at Hingham, Boston, and later at Roxbury. Examples of their innovative tower clocks survive. (See **1845 • Stephenson Howard & Davis**, page 116.)

STEPHENSON, LUTHER S.: Stephenson, of Hingham, Massachusetts, was an established manufacturer of Dearborn's Patent Balance. In 1844 he joined forces with E. Howard and D.P. Davis as senior partner in Stephenson, Howard & Davis. They made precision balances and a wide range of clocks at Hingham and Boston, later moving to a new factory at Roxbury. Stephenson broke off with his partners in 1847, thereafter doing business as L. Stephenson & Co., balance maker at Hingham and Boston. (See **1845 • Stephenson Howard & Davis**, page 116.)

STEVENS, COLLINS: b. —, Maine; d. December 3, 1873, Boston, Massachusetts. Collins Stevens was at work in Boston as a shoe last manufacturer from about 1835 to 1858. In 1859, he and George A. Walker, agent, joined Moses Crane as partners in the Turret & Marine Clock Co. at 5 and 13 Water Street, Boston. Stevens learned what he knew about tower clocks from young Crane, the inventive machinist son of Aaron D. Crane on whose patents the company operated. About 1860, Stevens brought the oldest of his three sons, George M. Stevens, into the company as clerk/bookkeeper. By late 1861, there was a falling out of the partners which resulted in Moses Crane leaving and taking the Crane patents with him. Walker and Collins Stevens, the surviving partners, operated from 1862 to 1864 as the Turret Clock Co. at the same address. No tower clocks survive from the period, but on March 4, 1862, Collins and George Stevens received U.S. Patent No. 34,599, "Clock." It featured what they called the "Stevens Detached Remontoire," an outright steal of the escapement used by the Turret & Marine Clock Co. and a possible cause of Moses Crane's sudden departure. This was one of three patents taken out by Collins Stevens and his son George, including one in 1873 for a crane-striker fog alarm, an item that contributed substantially to company profits. In 1864, Stevens and his son George reorganized as Geo. M. Stevens & Co., Boston tower clock makers. The company flourished in the prosperity that followed the Civil War, with Collins Stevens supervising field installations until just before his death in 1873. No patents are associated with the Geo. M. Stevens & Co. after Collins' death. (See **1864 • George M. Stevens & Co.**, page 162.)

STEVENS, GEORGE MILTON: b —, 1838, Boston, Massachusetts; d. February 1917, Cambridge, Massachusetts. George worked first as a bookkeeper, then as clerk with the Turret & Marine Clock Co. In 1864, he and his father organized Geo. M. Stevens & Co., a successful tower clock operation where he worked until his retirement in 1905. A shrewd businessman, George Stevens left an estate worth over $270,000. (See **1864 • George M. Stevens & Co.**, page 162.)

STEVENS, GEO. M. & CO.: 1864-1916, Boston, Massachusetts. Successor to the Turret & Marine Clock Co., Stevens manufactured a range of tower and street clocks in direct competition with tower clocks made by E. Howard and Seth Thomas. Stevens also offered Crane's floating hammer, street clocks, patented fog alarms, and telegraphic fire alarm systems. Many tower clocks survive. (See **1864 • George M. Stevens & Co.**, page 162.)

STOKELL, JOHN: b. ———; d. 1857, New York City. A maker of high quality regulators, he was at work in New York City from 1825 until 1858. In 1855 he assembled and installed at the Marble Collegiate Church a large "bedstead" frame tower clock probably imported from England. (See **1855 • John Stokell**, page 149.)

STONE, JOHN: b. 1836—; d. 1882, Cazenovia, New York. A partner in Stone & Marshall, successors to the tower clock business of Austin Van Riper of Cazenovia, New York. (See **1859 • Stone & Marshall**, page 158.)

STONE & MARSHALL: 1859-ca. 1875, the partnership of John Stone and Justice Marshall of Cazenovia, New York. They were first employees, then successors to Austin W. Van Riper's tower clock business, and were later joined by Milton Card and Philo Felter in the American Lock Company. (See **1859 • Stone & Marshall**, page 158.)

STOWELL, ABEL: b. June 12, 1752, Worcester, Massachusetts; d. August 3, 1818, Worcester, Massachusetts. A clock and watchmaker best known for his meeting house tower clocks. He is thought to have introduced in this country the first widely copied wood-beam flatbed tower clock with a pinwheel escapement, invented after 1740 by the French as *horloge horizontale*. (See **1799 • Abel Stowell**, page 34.)

STOWELL, A. & SON: 1815-1860, Worcester and Charlestown, Massachusetts. This father and son business establishment, adjacent to the Worcester Town Green, offered stoves, small machinery of brass and iron, and tower clocks made to order. After his father's death in 1818, Abel Jr. and his brother John established a clock, watch, and jewelry store in Charlestown (now part of Boston), making use of the same Worcester name. (See **1845 • Abel Stowell Jr.**, page 119.)

STOWELL, ABEL JR.: b. February 14, 1789, Worcester, Massachusetts; d. ——— 1861, Baltimore, Maryland. The second son of Abel Stowell, from whom he learned clockmaking and with whom he was a business partner in Worcester from 1815 to 1818. After his father's death, Abel Jr. moved to Charlestown, Massachusetts, where he joined his younger brother, John, in an upscale jewelry store business. (See **1845 • Abel Stowell Jr.**, page 119.)

STRETCH, PETER: b. October 14, 1670, Tatton, Cheshire, England; d. 1746, Philadelphia, Pennsylvania. Peter learned clock and watchmaking in Leek, England, from Samuel Stretche, said to have been his uncle or an older brother. In 1702, at the age of 32, Stretch emigrated from the English Midlands to America with his wife, Margery (Hall) and four children, including sons Daniel, Thomas and William. As a Quaker, he met with immediate acceptance in Philadelphia, known as "Quaker City." His business and personal qualities soon made him a social and political factor in the town, where he served on the common council from October 6, 1708, until his death in 1746. He made high-quality lantern clocks, tall case clocks and scales, instructing his sons in the trade. In 1717, Peter Stretch was paid £8/18/10 for repairs made to the Philadelphia Town Clock, not otherwise specified as to type or location. His establishment at the junction of Front and Chestnut Streets came to be known as "Peter Stretch's Corner at the Sign of the Dial." NTCS.

STRETCH, THOMAS: b. ——. England; d. 1765, Philadelphia, Pennsylvania. Emigrating from England to Philadelphia in 1702, he learned clockmaking in his father's shop at the corner of Chestnut and Front Streets. After his father's death in 1746, Thomas sold the shop and opened his own establishment farther uptown at the corner of Second and Chestnut Streets. He made and repaired watches, tall case clocks and tower clocks. An active Quaker, he helped found the Philadelphia Hospital. About 1753, city leaders directed that a large time and strike clock with suitable dials showing the minutes and the hours be constructed for public convenience. The influential Robert Morris wrote, "We expect it will prove better than any from England, as when they put it out of their hands they are done with it, but here the workman would feel very mean if he did not exert his utmost skill as we do not stint him in the price of his labor." Thomas Stretch got the commission in 1759, and was paid in old tenor money the equivalent of $2,500, a fortune in those days. The clock mechanism was located directly under the roof of the old State House (now Independence Hall), and was connected by long rods which extended to the gable ends of the building. Dials on the exterior walls were framed by ornamental relief brickwork to the ground, simulating tall case clocks of the period. Thomas Stretch was clock custodian until 1762, followed successively by Jacob Gotshalk, Griffith Owen, Robert Leslie, and Isaiah Lukens. It was said that by Lukens' tour of duty he was the very good keeper of a very bad clock. In 1828, Lukens contracted to make a new State House clock with four illuminated dials at a cost of $2,000. Stretch's old clock was sold to the Church of St. Augustine on North 4th Street in Philadelphia, later destroyed by fire during the anti-Catholic riots of May 1844. In 1876, Lukens' clock was moved to the Town Hall of Germantown, replaced in Independence Hall by one made by Seth Thomas & Co. in connection with the 1876 Centennial Exposition. NTCS.

TAYLOR, ALONZO: Origins and training unknown. Taylor was shown as a machinist at work in New York City ca. 1855-1869. Initially, he was deeply engaged in the manufacture of sewing machines, but about 1865 he took on the tower clock business of Sperry & Co., the successor to H. Sperry & Co. Two separate tower clock models signed by Alonzo Taylor survive. (See **1864 • Alonzo Taylor**, page 165.)

TERRY, ELI: b. April 13, 1772, East Windsor, (now South Windsor) Connecticut; d. February 24, 1852, Terryville, Connecticut. An apprentice to fellow townsman Daniel Burnap. Working first at Plymouth and later at Terryville, Eli pioneered in the mass-production of low-cost 30-hour wooden clock movements. In later years, he "engaged in making now and then a church clock...." (See **1833 • Eli Terry**, page 85.)

TERRY, SAMUEL (JR.): b. January 24, 1774, East Windsor, (now South Windsor) Connecticut; d. May 4, 1853, Bristol, Connecticut. Samuel (and sons) worked for his famous older brother, Eli, before establishing in Bristol, Connecticut, a successful wooden shelf clock business catering to the trade. Starting as early as 1811, Samuel became the most prolific maker of wooden tower clocks in the first half of the nineteenth century. (See **1811 • Samuel Terry**, page 51.)

THOMAS, SETH CLOCK CO.: 1853-1942, Plymouth Hollow (Thomaston after 1865), Connecticut. Chauncey Jerome wrote, "It was never Mr. Thomas' practice to get up anything new...His great success was in money making." The Seth Thomas' story (1785-1859) is beyond the scope of this work, except to say that he built a large and profitable business by hard work, honest dealing, and, particularly, by minimizing risk. He rarely committed himself to the manufacture of clock models unproven in the marketplace. Seth Thomas Clock Co., a joint stock company with a corporate structure, was established in 1853 to support the expanding business of its founder. After old Seth's death in 1859, his sons took over the company, with Aaron Thomas serving as president from 1859 until 1892. The sons were more adventurous than their father, launching several new clock models. At the same time they continued old Seth's conservative approach, expanding the line by acquisition of proven properties. In January 1865 they took over and reorganized the American Clock Co., which had been established in 1850 as a New York City sales outlet for major Connecticut clock manufacturers. The takeover principals were Ethel C. Hine and Seth E. Thomas. This acquisition provided the vehicle by which Seth Thomas & Co. established itself in the tower clock business, then entering a post-war boom period dominated by E. Howard & Co. In 1871, the American Clock Co. added to its roster A.S. Hotchkiss & Co., a successful tower clock manufacturer located just a few doors removed on Cortlandt Street. Seth Thomas & Co., which was also represented by the American Clock Co., acquired A.S. Hotchkiss & Co., lock-stock-and-barrel in 1872. The same year, manufacturing was shifted to the Seth Thomas movement shop at Thomaston, Connecticut, with the first Seth Thomas/A.S.Hotchkiss clocks appearing by mid-1872. Shrewdly, Seth Thomas traded in every possible way on the established Hotchkiss national reputation before cutting loose in 1878 with a viable reputation of its own. Their first tower clock catalog in 1874 padded its list of representative installations with many tower clocks actually made and installed by A.S. Hotchkiss years before the takeover. In addition, the early Seth Thomas tower clocks were signed by both Thomas and Hotchkiss, while retaining many distinctive Hotchkiss features in spite of a general shift in frame style to flatbeds surmounted by A-frames. Seth Thomas & Co. was quick to develop its own reputation for excellence with its magnificent clock for Philadelphia's Independence Hall in 1876, followed by many other prestigious installations. Over the years they developed a substantial range of clock models, the largest being an electrically-driven time/strike/and quarter-striker weighing 7,000 pounds, and measuring (in feet) 12 wide by 4.3 deep by 11 high. During the decades of greatest demand for mechanical tower clocks, Seth Thomas & Co. competed head-to-head with E. Howard & Co., in spite of the latter's 30-year head start in the business. As with most "factory" tower clocks, they depended on the best of standardized horological solutions (mostly invented by the English), superior factory engineering, and aggressive marketing, rather than on the varied innovative craftsmanship of an earlier day. Officially, the last Seth Thomas tower clock, No. 3,232, was put up in 1942 at Lebanon, Connecticut, but some estimate over 3,700 tower clocks were shipped to 38 different countries. Very many examples survive. In 1930, Seth Thomas & Co. became part of General Time Instruments Co., renamed General Time Corporation in 1949. TCS post 1870.

THOMPSON, JOHN: Maryland clockmaker, silversmith and jeweler of Boonsboro in 1830-33 and Williamsport in 1834. In 1830, Thompson advertised his qualifications to make a town clock proposed for Hagerstown, Maryland, located a few miles to the northwest. The contract was awarded to local clockmaker Arthur Johnston who was rumored to have had better political connections. NTCS.

THWING, ALMON: b. July 4, 1808, Uxbridge, Massachusetts; d. November 6, 1892, Milford, Massachusetts. Thwing lived at Uxbridge, Medway, and Grafton before settling down in Hopedale, all Massachusetts towns in a 30-mile radius southwest of Boston. He participated in the Hopedale experiment, begun in 1842 as a struggling Christian non-resistance commune on a run-down farm and emerging as a company town which ranked as one of America's most successful examples of pre-Marxian socialism. On March 29, 1851, Thwing signed the following agreement: "Whereas a clock has been made and put up by me in the meeting house of the First Parish [Unitarian] in Weyland, I hereby warrant the same to run well and keep good time; and further I agree to keep said clock in repair for the term of one year, saving all accidents which occur from causes disconnected with any part of my work

thereon." Over 200 people subscribed $600 to pay for the clock, the care of which was taken over by the town selectmen after 1858. It had three large dials with gilt hands and numbers, and struck on an 1814 bell signed Revere & Son. Unfortunately, nothing is known about the clock mechanism, now missing. It was replaced by a Howard "round top" in 1910, subsequently electrified. There is no evidence that Thwing ever made another clock of any kind. In this effort, he may have been inspired by the work of other tower clock makers working in the area as the hands of his dials, for example, are very similar to those used by George H. Holbrook of nearby East Medway (now Millis). His employment in Hopedale was as an inventor, manufacturer and surveyor who held a number of city offices. He is said to have died of grief a few months after the death of Sarah Ann, his wife of 60 years. NTCS. (Bruce Kingsbury)

TRACY, GURDON: b. 1767———; d. 1792, New London, Connecticut. Thomas Harland, being unwell, sent an apprentice, Gurdon Tracey, as his troubleshooting emissary to add "a few drops of oyl" to the New London Town Clock after they reported a difficulty. In 1787, Tracy opened a clock shop in New London, Connecticut, where, on Harland's recommendation, he served as custodian of the town clock for 40 shillings a year. After Tracy's untimely death in 1792, his shop, its stock, and a complete set of tools were taken over by Trott & Cleveland, also of New London. NTCS.

TURRET CLOCK CO.: 1862-1863, 5 Water Street, Boston, Massachusetts. This transition company was set up by Collins Stevens and George F. Walker following the dissolution of the Turret & Marine Clock Co. In 1862, Collins and George Stevens patented the "Stevens Detached Remontoire," a variation of the escapement used on Turret & Marine clocks. No Turret Clock Co. products are known to have survived from this interim period before the establishment of Geo. M. Stevens & Co. in 1864. NTCS.

TURRET & MARINE CLOCK CO.: 1858-1862, Boston, Massachusetts. A short-lived but successful company at 5 and 13 Water Street. They made and installed over 50 tower clocks of revolutionary design, based largely on the patents of Aaron Dodd Crane. Company principals were Aaron Crane's son, Moses Crane, Collins Stevens, and George A. Walker, agent. (See **1858 • Turret & Marine Clock Co.**, page 155.)

URLETIG (ULRICH, ULRICK, UHRELEDIG), VALENTINE: b. 1724, ——— ; d. 1783, Reading, Pennsylvania. The 30-year-old Urletig arrived in Philadelphia by the ship *Brothers* on September 30, 1754. He is believed to have settled in Reading by

1758 and was shown as a clockmaker in the first tax list of 1773, then again in 1775 and 1781. Urletig was Berks County's earliest tall case clock maker, well-known for the excellence of his work. He also installed Reading's first town clock, put up in 1767 in the steeple of the Berks County Court House on Penn Square. The clock had four outside dials, those to the east and west showing the time and the other two being sham dials. The 30-hour clock's three-pound hammer struck on a 300-pound bell made in 1763 for the Berks County Court House by Thomas Bagley of Bridgewater, England. Critical clock parts were probably also imported. On August 2, 1767, the Berks County Commissioners supplied Urletig with the tools, supplies, and raw materials necessary to put up the clock. Twelve days later, the same officials loaned him, "One Clock Frame, Eight Brass Wheels, Two Rools [barrels] to wind up the Clock...." It was hardly a complete inventory of clock parts, but helps to substantiate that Urletig probably assembled critical supplied parts rather than making the clock from scratch. Undoubtedly, he set up and installed the mechanism and bell in the steeple, made its weights, the dials and the hands, and made the necessary connections and adjustments. In any case, Urletig's clock was a good one as it remained in service for 78 years, replaced in 1841 by a new clock made for the second Berks County Court House by Benjamin Hill Jr. Valentine Urletig died in 1783. His estate inventory showed debts to almost 40 people, plus a variety of blacksmith, engraving and clockmaking hand tools, along with clothing, household goods, books, a large Bible, gardening tools and three sheep. NTCS (Patrick J. Reynolds)

VAN HOOK, ISAAC: ca. 1745-52, New York City. An otherwise unidentified steeple clock belonging to the city's New Dutch Church was under his care. (See **Barwell, Bartholomew,** page 182.)

VAN RIPER, AUSTIN W.: b. 1825, Cazenovia, New York; d. September 19, 1859, Cazenovia, New York. A blacksmith, foundryman and clockmaker, Van Riper was successor to the tower clock business of Jehiel Clark Jr. and was succeeded by Stone & Marshall. In only nine years of a very short life, Van Riper produced an amazing array of models of increasing beauty and sophistication which sold as far away as Tennessee and Michigan. (See **1850 • Austin W. Van Riper**, page 135.)

VERDIN COMPANY, THE: This Cincinnati-based company, founded in 1842, has been run by four generations of direct descendants of Francois de Sales Verdin and his brother Michael, who came here in 1835 from Alsace, France. Today, the company continues in business as a major producer of bells, car-

illons and public clocks run by electricity. (See **1842 • The Verdin Company**, page 108.)

WARD, MACOCK: b. July 17, 1702, Wallingford, Connecticut; d. 1783, Wallingford, Connecticut. The son of William and Lettice (Beach) Ward, Macock represented the fourth generation of a Connecticut family going back to Andrew Ward who arrived at Wethersfield in 1638. Hoopes writes that Ward was an apprentice to Ebenezer Parmelee of Guilford; it is not otherwise substantiated except by their close physical proximity. Ward set up as a clockmaker in Wallingford in 1724 at the age of 22, and married Hannah Tyler the same year. In addition to clockmaking, watch repair and working a small farm, he was a versatile mechanic, a button maker, and a skilled wood joiner who built his own clock cases. Wallingford's Third Meeting House was built in 1718-20, with a steeple and belfry added by January 1728. On December 5, 1738, it was voted that "The town gives liberty to Mecock [*sic*] Ward to sett a clok in ye steeple, and if any damage, hee will pay it and taik away ye clok." No other reference is made to Ward's installation, and the meeting house was taken down in 1824 to make room for a Fourth Meeting House. No clocks made by Ward are known to have survived, and the possibility exists that he did not make many, considering his wide-ranging activity. He also practiced law, probably learned from his brother Zenus or his father-in-law John Tyler, both members of the profession. In 1855, he invented and attached to his chaise a mileage counter that rang a bell for each completed mile. Before the American Revolution, he was very active politically, serving six years as a justice of the peace, and being elected to the Connecticut General Assembly in 1743 and again between 1766 and 1774. He also had an excellent military record, serving as a lieutenant in the local Trainband (militia) in 1738, a captain in 1742, and a company commander in 1755 at the age of 53, marching against Crown Point during the French and Indian War. In spite of this impressive military record, Macock Ward remained in Wallingford during the American Revolution, an unrepentant Tory loyal to the Church of England who refused to sign the oath of fidelity to Connecticut. He left an estate valued at £435, including 30 acres of land and a set of clockmaking tools. NTCS. (William L. Willard)

WASHBURN, ASA: b. February 15, 1803, Vermont; d, ——. Of Broome County, New York, in 1815, by about 1819 Washburn moved to Charlestown, Indiana, where he began a seven-year clockmaking and silversmith apprenticeship with George Streepey, both moving to nearby Salem in 1824. Apprenticeship complete, Washburn set up business for himself 35 miles southeast of Salem in Louisville, Kentucky,

213

where he made and installed in the steeple of the Presbyterian Church, Louisville's first town clock. Several years later both church and clock were destroyed by fire. By the end of 1830 he moved to Vincennes, Indiana, where he was employed by the firm of Hone & Leroy and is known to have constructed a number of tall case clocks. On June 14, 1832, he married another newcomer to Vincennes, Lucretia Purley, a native of New York State. The couple was childless. NTCS.

WEISS, JEDEDIAH: b. February 2, 1795, Bethlehem, Pennsylvania; d. September 3, 1873, Bethlehem, Pennsylvania. About 1815, Weiss took over the tall case clockmaking shop of his former master, L. Krause, remaining in the business for 45 years. During this period he was professionally involved with at least two tower clocks in the Bethlehem area. About 1820, he took over as a daily winding custodian of Augustine Neisser's quarter-striker, located in the Bell House of the Bethlehem Moravian community. Four years later he moved the mechanism to a new church building, adding four large dials and the necessary transmission and motion work connections to drive beautiful, pierced metal hour and minute hands. About 1840, Weiss performed a similar transformation for the Moravian congregation at nearby Nazareth, Pennsylvania: he moved a one-hand clock made by John Eberman Jr., of Lancaster, to a new church building, adding minute hands and the appropriate fittings "to furnish a running mate to the lonely old hour hand."

WESTERN TOWER CLOCK MANUFACTORY: 1890-1905, Iowa City, Iowa. (See **Barborka, Joseph,** page 181.) TCS post 1870.

WHITEAR, JOHN: probably of Boston, but at work in Fairfield, Connecticut, by 1736: d. July 1762, Fairfield, Connecticut. Fully trained as a bell founder and clockmaker on his arrival at Fairfield, his tall clock work established the Fairfield school of clock makers, with their distinctive "country style" brass movements. In 1738, he advertised in the *Boston Gazette*, "JOHN WHITEAR of Fairfield (Connecticut.), Bell-Founder, makes and sells all sorts of bells from the lowest to Two-Thousand Weight." He cast a number of large bells for local churches, including one in 1744 for Christ Church of neighboring Stratford, Connecticut. A steeple clock, with a single diamond-shaped dial board, was installed in the same church in 1748-49 and has been attributed to Whitear. While living in Fairfield, he fathered seven children, and was highly respected as a church warden and an active participant in civic affairs. He died intestate and was succeeded in the clock making business by his son John Jr. NTCS. (Winthrop Warren)

WHITEHEAD, JOHN: b. 1791, probably England; d. 1875,———. Whitehead, a maker of tall case clocks with brass movements, is said to have arrived in America in 1821, and taken over the shop of Job Hollinshead in Haddonfield, New Jersey. About 1830, the Cumberland Nail & Iron Co. of Bridgeton, New Jersey, had him construct a clock mechanism that drove the hands of two dials located on opposing sides of the same wall. One dial was located in a tall case frame molded to the inside wall of the company office, and the other was mounted outside the building, serving as Bridgeton's first public clock. The arrangement is not unique as other clockmakers, including Stephen Hasham of New Hampshire, fashioned clockworks with two dials displaying the time on opposite sides of a common wall. NTCS.

WILLARD, AARON JR.: b. June 29, 1783, Roxbury, Massachusetts; d. May 2, 1864. First apprentice then journeyman, and finally successor to the prosperous business of his father, Aaron Willard Sr. Aaron Jr. also prospered, establishing a factory at Boston Neck that employed up to 30 craftsmen over the years. He is said to have invented the lyre timepiece. Included in his product line were high-quality tall case, shelf, wall, and tower clocks. (See **1824 • Aaron Willard Jr.**, page 69.)

WILLARD, ALEXANDER TARBELL: b. November 4, 1774, Ashburnham, Massachusetts; d. December 4, 1850, Ashby, Massachusetts. A distant relative of the Willards of Grafton, Alexander was at work with his brother Philander J. making clocks in Ashburnham as early as 1796. He removed to Ashby in 1800, where he married Tila Oakes of Cohasset; they had six children. Alexander made tall case, musical, timepiece, wooden, and church or turret clocks to the order. In 1805, he and town associates laid out a roadway called the Ashby Turnpike which failed, causing great loss to its backers. He was Ashby's Postmaster from 1812 to 1836. A versatile, innovative mechanic much in demand, he also repaired watches and made surveyor's instruments, odometers, seraphines, and rifles. Few examples of his work survive. NTCS.

WILLARD, BENJAMIN (JR.): b. March 19, 1743, Grafton, Massachusetts; d. September 16, 1803, Baltimore, Maryland. Benjamin Jr. was the son of Benjamin and Sarah (Brooks) Willard and the first of the famous Willard clockmaking brothers. As the oldest son in a farming family, one-half of the family homestead and barn and 92 acres of farmland was conveyed to Benjamin upon reaching his majority. It is uncertain exactly where he learned clockmaking, but he has been associated by some with the Cheneys of East Hartford, with an itinerant English clockmaker named Morris, and later with Nathaniel

Mulliken of Lexington. Benjamin was a rolling stone, with Grafton the home base to which he often returned. Frequent, lengthy advertisements document his career path. The first in 1764 placed him in East Hartford as a "Last-Maker, from Boston, in business at the house of Benjamin Cheny [sic]." In 1768, he advertised himself as a Grafton clockmaker who had moved to Lexington, Massachusetts, where, in taking over the shop of Nathaniel Mulliken, deceased, he had acquired the services of a workman from London. In 1775, he showed up as a watch repairer, first at Roxbury, then at Brookline, Massachusetts. In 1874, after an eight-year absence from Worcester County, Massachusetts, (with "the best approved clock and watch-makers on the continent"), he returned to his farm workshop at Grafton, where in addition to clockmaking he offered the improved roasting jack invented by his brother Simon. Over a period of 23 years he claimed to have manufactured 359 clocks, mostly of the tall case type sold in Massachusetts. In 1789, he moved from Grafton to nearby Worcester where he proposed to carry on the "Clock and Watchmaking Businesses in all their great Variety." Benjamin's shop was located a short distance from Worcester's Old South Church, the proposed site of a town clock. In a pitch directed at this target he advertised, "particularly, he makes Large Clocks suitable for Meeting Houses and Churches, upon a New Plan, and at Half the Expense such cost formerly...." He did not get the Worcester job, nor did his brother Simon, who made a similar advertising pitch for the Worcester installation in 1798. The commission went to Abel Stowell, a native of Worcester whose clock, also designed upon a new plan, was installed in the Meeting House tower in 1800. Little is known about Benjamin's personal life. He was married to Margaret (Peggy) Moore; they had five children, their only son dying at age 13. Toward the end of his life and probably before, Benjamin ran afoul of the law. In 1800, he spent three months in the Worcester County jail for failure to pay his debts. In 1802, a warrant for his arrest charged him with being "Drunk and Brawly," causing injury to a Leominster man. The following year, the last of his life, the ever-resilient Benjamin announced himself as a clockmaker from Boston, Massachusetts, in business on Prine Street in Baltimore, Maryland, associated with Peter Meem of Georgetown. On May 20, 1803, he advertised in the *Republican*, or, *Anti-Democrat* that he was "establishing a manufactory of large Clocks, suitable for churches and other public buildings in the city of Baltimore or Washington." In addition he offered to supply clockmakers with superior dials, and also with "castings for large steeple clocks and a model for making them on an approved plan thought by judges to be the best ever practiced upon...." Ben-

jamin was denied this final dream, dying four months later with no record of his body being returned to Grafton for burial in the Willard family plot. NTCS.

WILLARD, BENJAMIN FRANKLIN: b. November 2, 1803, Roxbury, Massachusetts; d. March 11, 1847, Roxbury, Massachusetts. The fifth son of Simon and his second wife Mary (Bird) Willard, he married Emeline Maine in 1837; their only child, Ada Louise, died at the age of nine. B.F. Willard had limited schooling, but was, like his father who trained him from an early age, a born mechanic, inventor and perfectionist. In addition he was a talented artist both with the pen and the brush. Among the mechanical accomplishments of his comparatively short life were a United States Patent in 1839 for signal lights placed at the entrance of Boston Harbor for which he was paid $230, and an extraordinarily fine jeweled astronomical regulator made in his brother's shop in 1844 that received a Massachusetts Charitable Mechanics Association Gold Medal. A tower clock installed in the First Congregational Church of Falmouth, Massachusetts, was signed "B.F.Willard, 1840," his sole effort in this direction as far as is known. NTCS.

WILLARD, SIMON: b. April 3, 1753, Grafton, Massachusetts; d. August 30, 1848, Boston, Massachusetts. Simon Willard moved to Roxbury by about 1780. A tireless worker and perfectionist, he turned out a wide range of top quality clocks of all types and sizes. He also invented and made the best-selling "Improved Wall Timepiece" (the Banjo), and an improved clockwork roasting jack. In the later years of a long, productive life, he specialized in making custom wall timepieces, large gallery clocks and tower clocks. (See **1802 • Simon Willard**, page 39.)

WITT, DR. CHRISTOPHER: b. 1675, Wiltshire, England; d. January 1765, Germantown, Pennsylvania. Dr. Witt was an English-trained physician who came to Philadelphia in 1704. A follower of the Pietist mystic Johann Kelpius, he settled in Germantown, a physician and naturalist with many skills who made his own telescope and pipe organ, as well as wall, tall case, and tower clocks. (See **1735 • Christopher Witt**, page 5.)

WOOLSON, THOMAS JR.: b. 1777, Danvers, Massachusetts; d. July 3, 1837, Claremont, New Hampshire. At work in Amherst and Claremont, New Hampshire, ca. 1797-1837. Clockmaker, entrepreneur, successful businessman and politician, he made at least two tower clocks, but was best known for the manufacture of cast-iron stoves. (See **1815 • Thomas Woolson Jr.**, page 58.)

WRIGHT, JOHN: 1720-1768. A New York City watchmaker and an importer of English watches, located first on Duke Street and later on Bayard, he was employed by the New York City Council to keep in "Good and Sufficient Repair and Order" the town clock made and installed in city hall in 1717 by Joseph Phillips, also of the city. Phillips had offered to maintain the clock for only 20 shillings a year, but Wright got the job at the substantial increase of £3 annually, raised in later years to £10, plus separately itemized repairs. Clearly, his city hall connections were better than the spelling on his surviving invoices. One read, "ye Sitey of new York Dr to Jno Wright for Windeng & keep-ing in ordar ye poblick Clock Won yeares Selery from may ye 8 1730 to may Last 1731 teen pouend Liquise I tooke Douen part of ye Work with ye Steepels & polis for ye Carpinders to mend ye terit houes & flore I was three Dayes at Work & poot new Wires cams Won poun 11-0-0." Wright serviced the clock for 16 years until June 19, 1734, after which city records no longer mention this installation. Between 1739 and 1754, he advertised in the *New-York Gazette* several times, offering a range of items from very good "Cheshire-cheese" to handsome new silver watches imported from England. Wright died by September 1768, with his lot of ground in the Commons near Princes-street offered for sale at public venue. NTCS. (See **Phillips, Joseph,** page 203.)

YEOMAN, JAMES: b. —— , England; d. May 1773, New York, New York. Yeoman and John Collins emigrated in 1769 from London, England. They set up shop on Hanover Square in lower Manhattan where they cleaned and repaired watches, clocks and guns "as neat as in England." Collins departed after a year, but Yeoman remained to advertise in the August 27, 1770, *New York Gazette*, "...N.B. The above James Yeoman, will, should he meet with Encouragement, undertake to make Clocks for Churches, or Gentlemens Turrets, on an entire new Plan, practiced by very few in ENGLAND, and those esteemed the best Mechanicks in Europe." Yeoman's new plan was most likely the *horloge horizontale*, a horizontal flatbed tower clock with a pinwheel escapement devised by master French clockmakers after 1740. The English ignored the new frame design until after 1850, but Yankee tower clock makers embraced an Americanized version of the French plan, including its deadbeat pinwheel escapement, as early as 1799. Yeoman's 1770 advertisement suggests one way the technology transfer to this country may have come about. Both Yeoman's father, a Fellow of the Royal Society, and "the ingenious Mr. Neale," with whom Yeoman served an English apprenticeship, were sophisticated master horologists. It is reasonable to assume that their knowledge of French tower clock innovations would have been passed on to their young charge, James Yeoman, and his word-of-mouth communication helped plant the seed of the new idea in this country. A slanderous English-born New York competitor of Yeoman's named Simnet (see **Simnet, John**, page 207) attempted to discredit Neale, calling him an ass, a writer of "Hocus Pocus...that miracle monger puts forth a new one every year: by reading them we can get a watch as small as an O, or a turret clock as large as the moon...." Yeoman was a good natured, humorous sort of chap who never responded in print to Simnet's attack. Very likely he never made a turret clock on the new plan either, as he died of a "Bilious Disorder" in May of 1773. Yeoman's passing was mourned by his many chums and admirers who attended the interment in Trinity Church yard in lower Manhattan. NTCS.

addendum The upper end of a wheel tooth beyond the pitch circle.

A-frame An A-shaped plate-and-pillar construction supporting clockwork components. An A-shaped tower clock stands alone, but most A-frames are secondary support units attached to a flatbed frame (q.v.).

arbor (also **shaft**) A rotating axle that usually carries wheels (q.v.) and pinions. The turned down ends of the arbor are called pivots.

barrel (also **drum**) A wood or metal cylinder around which the clock weight line (q.v.) is wound.

bearing block (also **pillow block**) A drilled and reamed block supporting a pivot and usually attached to the frame by screws. It may be plain or decorative in design and made of brass, bronze, brass-bushed cast iron, or wood.

beat The tick-tock sound of the escape wheel teeth or pins contacting the pallets. When "in beat" the time interval between the tick and the tock is equal. When "out of beat" the interval is irregular (short-long or long-short), which can stop the clock.

beat setting Assuming correct escapement geometry, the beat is made equal by adjusting the midway horizontal position of the crutch end to the left or right with respect to the pendulum rod. Being "in beat" is better determined by ear than by eye.

bell-crank lever The pivoted right-angled lever of the hammer. One arm, connected to movement strike control, lifts the hammer end to fall by gravity on the bell during strike.

bevel gear One of a set of matched gears having angled teeth cut on beveled edges; commonly used to transmit motion to arbors at right angles to each other. Bevel gear pairs having a 1:1 ratio and at right angles to each other are also known as miter gears.

bob (also **ball**) The heavy mass at the bottom end of a pendulum rod. Principal shapes in tower clocks are lenticular (lens-shaped), cylindrical, and spherical (cannon ball).

bushing (also **plain or sleeve bearing**) A sleeve of low friction material, such as brass, force-fitted into a clock frame to support a pivot. A Vuillamy bushing (attributed to Benjamin Vuillamy, 1780-1855) is an oversized removable bushing held in the clock frame by screws, allowing removal of a single component without major disassembly.

cam Usually a disk having all or part of the rim at varying distances from its center, as in a snail (q.v.); while revolving it transmits a measured motion to a follower. Also a stationary irregular form with a traveling follower.

catch box A sturdy box filled with broken rocks, placed below the weight chute (q.v.) to reduce the impact of a clock weight should its line fail.

cock A bracket supported at one end (as compared to a bridge with two supports). Often used to suspend the pendulum and support its fine rating adjustment.

compensated pendulum A pendulum employing a device, or so constructed, to maintain the same effective length, automatically counteracting the expansion or contraction of the pendulum rod due to changes in ambient temperature.

compounding Weight line runs through various combinations of pulleys (q.v.) to achieve an eight-day winding schedule in towers with a limited weight drop. Compounding reduces the vertical drop required, but increases the weight needed to do the same work.

contrate wheel (also **crown wheel**) A gear with teeth at right angles to the plane of the wheel; it usually meshes with a regular pinion or wheel to transmit motion at right angles.

counterpoise (also **counterweight**) A balancing weight; typically, a rod extension added inside or outside the tower dials to counterbalance the weight of long heavy hands.

count wheel (also **locking plate**) A disk or flanged wheel with radial notches or pins spaced at increasing intervals to control the number of blows in a strike sequence. A deep-tooth count wheel is a brass friction-mounted 78-tooth wheel (78 bell strikes in a 12-hour period) with deep slots appropriately spaced between the teeth to end the strike sequences.

crank A tower clock winding tool analogous to the key in house clocks. Some cranks incorporate an integral pinion that turns the large reduction gear of a winding jack (q.v.).

crutch A rod or lever linking the escapement pallet arbor to the pendulum. It usually engages the pendulum rod with a fork or a crutch pin.

dial port A covered hole in a tower dial allowing access outside the dial to its hands.

escapement A device at the top end of the time train that checks and releases the clock's driving force at regular intervals while also impulsing the pendulum. The most common escapements in early American tower clocks are recoil, deadbeat, and pinwheel.

fall Any weight line (q.v.) from which the driving weight is suspended. A weight line attached directly to the barrel on one end and the weight on the other is called a single fall. Compounding (q.v.) requires at least one pulley at the weight, resulting in two-lines at the weight called 2-fall compounding; three-lines appearing at the weight is called 3-fall compounding; and so on.

fly (also **fan**, **fan-fly**, **air governor**, **wind-vanes**) The last component of the strike train, consisting of ratchet or friction-driven blades or vanes; they are usually adjustable and sometimes heavily weighted. While rotating they slow the speed of the strike train, hence the interval between blows on the bell in a strike sequence. A fly is also used to cushion the otherwise violent action of some escapements.

frame The wooden, forged-iron or cast-iron structure supporting the clockwork components. Early American tower clock frames include:

1. **cage frame** (also **bird cage, lantern, bedpost**). A box-like open frame of forged-iron bars held together by wedges, bolts, or rivets.

2. **chair frame** (also **double frame, extended barrel, upright piano**). A lower frame extended to support long winding barrels, surmounted at one end by a tall shallow frame to accommodate the balance of the clockwork on short sturdy arbors.

3. **duplex frame** Tower clocks with the time and strike mechanisms mounted in separate frames having a strike-triggering connection.

4. **flatbed frame** A wood beam or cast-iron flat horizontal table to which independent bearing blocks and/or A-frames are attached.

5. **plate-and-pillar frame** Cast-iron or wooden front and back plates, spaced apart and secured as a unit by sturdy posts. The plates are of various shapes and usually skeletonized.

freewheeling A very common early technique to set the dial hands ahead. Disengagement of the pallets from the escape wheel allows fast-forwarding of the time train, while using one's hand as a brake on a train arbor. (See **pivot hole cap.**) The procedure is risky, particularly when reengaging the escapement. To set the hands back, the pendulum is stopped for the period necessary to make the time correction. Later tower clocks feature various clutch arrangements which allow setting the outside dial hands either ahead or back, while the mechanism continues to keep time in a normal fashion.

gathering pallet The one, two, or three-tooth pinion that winds back the rack (q.v.) during a clock strike sequence.

great wheel (also **barrel wheel, main wheel**) A clock train's first and largest wheel, usually mounted on the barrel arbor. Wheels of a clock train are customarily numbered, starting with the great wheel as #1.

gunmetal An alloy, sometimes used for wheels or bearing blocks, consisting of 90% copper and 10% tin. Bell metal is 75% copper and 25% tin.

intermediate wheel The #3 wheel in a four-wheel time train, located between the minute and escape wheels.

knife-edge suspension A derivative of the knife-edge pivot used in seventeenth century verge escapements. A type of pendulum suspension consisting of twin knife-edges pivoting in twin V-bed cocks to minimize friction.

lantern pinion A pinion consisting of round or leaf-shaped trundles anchored to the arbor by shrouds at both ends. In an open lantern pinion, the trundles are anchored in a single shroud at one end.

leading-off rods Long rods of wood or iron, or sheet metal tubes, transmitting minute-hand motion from the mechanism transmission to the outside dial motion work, or to a remote transmission above or below the mechanism and then to the dial motion work. Leading-off rods usually require a slip joint plus universal joints (q.v.) at each end; some require roller bearing support.

locking plate See **count wheel**.

maintaining power An auxiliary driving force on the time train to maintain timekeeping when the main driving force is interrupted during winding. Principal types include:

1. **gravity bar maintaining** (also **modified bolt and shutter**). A bar weighted at one end, with a flexible finger on the other which is manually engaged in the tooth of a time train wheel. During winding, the levered weight of the bar continues to drive the time train for several minutes, then automatically disengages from the wheel.

2. **Harrison maintaining** A curved, straight, or spiral steel spring brought to bear during winding, usually on the time great wheel, by means of a large secondary ratchet working in opposition to the barrel winding ratchet.

minute wheel (also **center wheel**) In tower clocks, usually the #2 wheel of the time train making one revolution in 60 minutes. The wheel's arbor can also drive the transmission, trip the strike, run the setting dial, and advance the snail in a rack-and-snail strike control system.

motion work (also **dial work**) 12-to-1 reduction gearing mounted behind an outside dial which converts the hourly rotation of the minute hand shaft to the 12-hour rotation of the hour hand.

movement (also **mechanism, clock-work, works, engine**) The frame and all moving parts in the tower clock driving mechanism. Not included are the outside dial motion work and hands, the bell hammer, the weights or all of their connections to the movement.

operator interfaces Features requiring access by the custodian to control clock operation. Examples include the winding squares, the setting dial and hand-setting system, strike control components, maintaining power, plus rating and beat adjustments to the pendulum. An optimal design puts most operator interfaces on the winding square side (considered the front of the clock).

pallets Escapement parts on which the escape wheel teeth or pins work to impulse the pendulum. Made of hardened steel or jewel stone and highly polished, they are subject to wear and often provide for easy replacement.

pendulum An oscillating device consisting of a knife-edge or flat-spring suspension, a long wood or metal rod, and a heavy mass at its bottom end. Most tower clocks beat at 1, 1½ or 2-second intervals driven by and imposing a constant rate on the escapement (q.v.). (See **knife-edge suspension**.)

pillars (also **spacers**) The posts, sometimes decoratively turned, which hold the plates of a clock frame together while also fixing the space between them.

pinwheel A wheel with evenly spaced pins projecting at right angles around its rim. Time trains can incorporate a pinwheel in their deadbeat escapement. In strike trains, the #1 or #2 wheel is a pinwheel with evenly-spaced axial studs (sometimes fitted with rollers) that lift or depress the bell lever tail to cock and release the bell hammer during a strike sequence.

pivot-hole cap A movable stop over a pivot hole permitting temporary axial disengagement of the pallet arbor from the escape wheel, to set the dial hands ahead by freewheeling (q.v.).

pulley (also **sheave**) A wood, cast-iron, or steel wheel with a grooved rim, mounted in a frame, used to guide or change the direction of a rope or cable. Guide pulleys provide no compounding (q.v.), but serve to realign the weight fall off the barrel or to redirect the weight line around the tower to the top of the weight channels (q.v.). A floor roller or self-aligning fleeting pulley helps ensure tight uniform turns of the line on the barrel during winding.

rack-and-snail In tower clock strike control systems, the rack consists of a segment of a circle or a straight bar with ratchet teeth cut along one or both edges. Its associated rack tail determines the extent of rack drop by contact with the snail, a stepped cam making one rotation in 12 hours. A rack hook engages the rack teeth to prevent the rack from falling back on the snail while it is being returned to a neutral position by the **gathering pallet** (q.v.).

remontoire A device enabling the main driving power to rewind a small spring or lift a small weight periodically, thus providing constant force to a critical mechanism such as the escapement.

rubble box A sturdy wooden box filled with sand, gravel, fieldstone, or scrap cast iron, frequently used as an alternative to solid blocks of granite, soapstone, cast iron, or lead as tower clock driving weights.

setting dial (also **pilot dial, index dial, set-hands dial**) A small dial located on the clock mechanism, which is synchronized with the outside dials and used for visual reference when resetting the outside dial hands. Setting dials vary from simple 60-minute discs rotating under a fixed pointer to fancy two-hand indicators with an engraved, silvered dial plate and a decorative bezel. Frequently, the name and address of the clockmaker appear on the dial plate.

strike lever a straight or U-shaped lever, pivoted on the frame and acted upon by the strike-train pin-wheel to retract the bell hammer during a strike sequence.

stud A short post or pin on which a wheel or lever turns, or to which a spring is attached.

timepiece A tower clock giving the time only, as distinguished from striking or quarter-chiming clocks.

train A combination of wheels and pinions interconnected to perform a specific tower clock function. A single-train clock is a timepiece (q.v.), two-train clocks tell the time and strike the hour, and three-train clocks, tell the time, and strike both the hour and the quarters.

transmission (also **distribution gearing, leading-off work**) A nest of gears (usually beveled), located on the clock frame or in a remote tower location, serving to distribute power to the motion work of two or more outside dials.

universal joint (also **U-joint**) A flexible joint used with leading-off rods (q.v.) allowing limited angular and/or linear displacement between the movement and the outside dials due to misalignment, building shifts, and thermal excursions. Also used to connect angled sections of rod transmitting power around the bell or tower structure to reach remote outside dials. Typical U-joint types include the fork, single pin, and yoke (or stirrup).

Vuillamy bushing See **bushing** (q.v.).

warning The initial release of the strike train just moments prior to strike; it sets the strike count system and cocks the bell hammer, assuring that the first blow of the strike sequence will occur on the instant of the changing hour. The first blow of the hammer on the bell is the best criterion that the tower clock is "on time," as minor discrepancies in outside dial hand position due to inclement weather or other causes are common.

weight chutes Wooden channels in which the clock driving weights run. They are sized to accept the weight, and frequently extend from high in the tower to the basement of the building.

weight line (also **rope, cable**) The line attached to the clock-driving weight and wound around the barrel. It is sometimes compounded (q.v.) and can be natural or synthetic fiber rope, steel wire rope, or iron link chain (on a sprocket).

wheel A gear of 16 or more teeth, as compared to a pinion which has fewer than 16 leaves. In a mated pair of toothed gears, the smaller is the pinion and the larger is the wheel. In clockwork, the wheel usually drives the pinion, exceptions being the dial motion work and the winding jack (q.v.).

winding jack (also **rewinding gear train**) Auxiliary reduction gearing mounted integral to the winding square (q.v.), used in particular on the strike side, to aid in rewinding very heavy tower clock weights.

winding square The square or squared end of the barrel arbor or the integral winding jack (q.v.) on which the crank is fitted to wind-up the driving weights. Considered the front of the clock.

worm gear Toothed wheel gearing where the axis of a screw of several turns is tangential to a matched worm wheel, transmitting motion at right angles to each other.

BIBLIOGRAPHY

General Reference

Becket, Edmund, Lord Grimthorpe, *A Rudimentary Treatise on Clocks, Watches & Bells for Public Purposes*. London: Crosby Lockwood and Son, 1903.

Beeson, C.F.C., *English Church Clocks 1280-1850*. Kent, England: Brant Wright Associates LTD, 1977.

Boorstin, Daniel J., *The Discoverers*. New York: Vantage Books, 1985.

Benson, James W., *Time and Time-Tellers*. London: Robert Hardwicke, 1875.

Dohrn-Van Rossum, Gerhard, *History of the Hour*. Chicago: University of Chicago Press, 1996.

Mayr and Stephens, *American Clocks, Highlights from the Collection*. Smithsonian Institution, 1990.

McKay, Chris, Editor, *A Guide to Turret Clock Research*. East Sussex, England: The Turret Clock Group Monograph No. 1, Antiquarian Horological Society, 1991.

McKay, Chris, *Stands The Church Clock*. England: Leisure Services, 1989.

Millham, Willis I., *Time and Timekeepers*. The Macmillan Co., 1923.

Peters, Samuel, *A General History of Connecticut*. London: First Edition, 1781.

Porter, Noah, *The New England Meeting House*. Yale University Press, 1933.

Reid, Thomas, *A Treatise on Clock and Watch Making*. London: Blackie & Son, Second Edition, 1826.

Ungerer, Alfred, *Les Horloges d'Edifice, Leur Construction, leur Montage, leur Entretien*. Paris: Gauther-Villars & Cie, 1926.

Frequently Referenced (FR)

FR-1 Crossman, Charles T. "A Complete History of Watch and Clockmaking in America." *The Jewelers' Circular and Horological Review* (1889-1891).

FR-2 Drost, William, *Clocks and Watches of New Jersey*. Elizabeth, NJ: Engineering Publishers, 1966.

FR-3 Gibbs, James W. *Pennsylvania Clocks and Watches*. State College, PA: Pennsylvania State University Press, 1984.

FR-4 Harris, J. Carter. *The Clock & Watch Advertiser*. Unpublished ms, 1984.

FR-5 Hoopes, Penrose. *Connecticut Clockmakers of the Eighteenth Century*. Hartford, CT: E.V. Mitchell, 1930.

FR-6 New York City Business Directories, 1825-1880. Publishers include: Carroll, Doggett, Rode, Trow, and Wilson.

FR-7 Palmer, Brooks. *The Book of American Clocks*. New York: Macmillan, 1950.

FR-8 Parsons, Charles S. *New Hampshire Clocks and Clockmakers*. Exeter, NH: Adams Brown Co., 1976.

FR-9 Records of the United States Patent Office, 1800-1875.

FR-10 Shelley, Frederick. *Aaron Dodd Crane An American Original*. NAWCC BULLETIN Supplement 16, 1987.

FR-11 Small, Percy Livingston (by Gerrit Nijssen). "The Watches of E. Howard & Co." NAWCC BULLETIN No. 292. (October 1994).

FR-12 Stokes, Isaac N.P. *Iconography of Manhattan Island 1496-1909*. Vol. 5. New York: R. H. Dodd, 1915-1928.

FR-13 Watts, Dr. Henry F.R. "Tower Clocks." Boston Clock Club papers, December 7, 1935. NAWCC BULLETIN No. 33 (April 1950).

FR-14 Whisker, James B. *Pennsylvania Clocks, Watchmakers, and Allied Crafts*. Cranbury, NJ: Adams Brown Co., 1990.

FR-15 James B. Whisker, Daniel D. Hartzler, & Steve Petrucelli. *Maryland Clockmakers*. Cranbury, NJ: Adams Brown Co. Inc., 1996.

FR-16 Willard, John Ware. *Simon Willard And His Clocks*. New York: Dover Publications, 1968.

Reference by Maker

Adams, Elmer W.:
Deed and mortgage records of Seneca County, New York.
"In Times Long Ago," Seneca Falls Historical Society, February 1, 1969.
Letter: Daniel Grigg to David Grigg Jr., Waterford, New York, April 15, 1838. Hirschfeld Collection.

Allen, Alexander:
Correspondence with Nick LoVerde, Town Historian, Mount Morris, New York, 1997.
Mount Morris Union [New York], October 11, 1862.
Saltsburg Press [Pennsylvania], September 17, 1886.
1860 Rochester Directory advertisement. FR-14 p. 2.

Allen, William:
FR-4 advertisement #1065

American Clock Co.:
FR-6 1850-1880. FR-7 p. 136-7.

Anderson, David M.:
Eppihimer, Margaret, *The Honey Brook Presbyterian Church 1835-1985*. Church Centennial brochure.
Eppihimer, Margaret, "Honey Brook Church has vintage clock." *Tri-County News*, Chester Co. Historical Society, West Chester, PA. 1976.
Scrapbook newspaper clippings from *The Daily Village Record* and *Tri-County News*, Chester County Historical Society, West Chester, Pennsylvania.

Ansonia Clock Co.:
Dale F. Nofziger, Ansonia Clock Co.: printed account of company history.
Lloyd Larish: *Local Landmark Restored to Beauty*, J.B. Lundstrom and H.F. Smith, ca. 1988.
FR-7 p. 137-8.

Bagnall, Benjamin:
"Benjamin Bagnall," Boston Clock Club papers, Dec. 1, 1934, pp. 22-25.
Crom, T.R. "Bagnall Family of Boston," NAWCC BULLETIN, Dec. 1996.
FR-1 March 1890, p. 73. FR-4 advertisements #48-52, 59-62. FR-7 p. 141.

Balzer, The Family:
Correspondence with Linda Balzer, February 29, 1996.

Bailey, Thomas I.:
Correspondence with Lloyd Larish and Russell Oechsle.
Letter: Thos. I. Bailey to Meneely's, July 1, 1859.
Nashville, TN, court records and newspaper ad.

Balch, Daniel:
Antiques Journal, February 1951. FR-1 July 1890, p. 79. FR-7 p. 142.

Baldwin, Asa:
Hesse, W., "A History Commemorating the 200th Anniversary of the Old Stone Church Building in East Haven, Connecticut," brochure, East Haven, CT, 1974.
FR-1 July 1890, p. 62. FR-7 p. 142 (Olmstead).

Barborka, Joseph:
Conversations with Lloyd Larish, Faribault, Minnesota.
Herriman, Carl L., "Carson City's Tower Clock," NAWCC BULLETIN No. 236, (June 1985), p. 319 ff.
Robinson, Floyd E., "Joseph Barborka, Iowa Clockmaker," NAWCC BULLETIN No. 154, (October 1971), p. 1472 ff.

Barwell, Bartholomew:
FR-4 advertisement #97-100. FR-7 p. 145. FR-12 Vol. 5.

Basset, Nehemiah:
Source in text.

Beals, J.J. Clock Establishment:
Boston Business Directory, 1859-60, p.15. FR-7 p. 147.

Bisbee, J.:
FR-1 July 1890, p. 76. FR-7 p. 150.

Blakeslee, Ziba:
FR-5 p. 53. FR-7 p. 152.

Boston, Early Clocks of:
FR-5 p. 4-5.

Brown, David and Joseph R.:
Hanna, W.F. and C.E. Crowley, "Just Yesterday." A pictorial history of Taunton, Mass, 1989, 350th Anniv. Comm..
Johnson, E.J. *David Brown, the Clock and Watchmaker.* Pawtucket, RI: Spaulding House Research Library ms, 1995.
Newport Historical Society, Newport, Rhode Island.
Representative Men and Old Families of Rhode Island, Vol. 2. Chicago: J.H. Beers & Co., 1908.
Rhode Island Historical Society, Providence, Rhode Island.
Sharpe, Henry Dexter. "Joseph R. Brown, *Mechanic*, and the *Beginnings* of Brown & Sharpe," Providence, RI: The Newcomen Society, 1949.
The Chronicle. Editorial, "Town Clock." Pawtucket, Rhode Island, October 18, 1828.
FR-1 August 1890, p. 62.

Brown, Gawen:
Hanson, Capt. David. "Gawen Brown, Soldier and Clockmaker." Boston Clock Club papers, November 6, 1937.
Husher, Richard W. and Walter W. Welch, *A Study of Simon Willard's Clocks.* Nahant, MA, published by the authors, 1980.
Proper, David. "Two Historic Boston Clocks." NAWCC BULLETIN No. 106, (October 1963), p. 990 ff.

FR-1 July 1890, p. 76. FR-4 advertisements #207-217. FR-7 p. 160. FR-13 p. 95-6.

Burnap, Daniel:
Bissell, Charles S. "The Suffield Tower Clockworks." *Connecticut Historical Society Bulletin*, Vol. 27, No. 2, (April 1962).
Correspondence with William L. Willard.
"Daniel Burnap, Esq.," unsigned undated ms.
Hoopes, Penrose. *The Shop Records of Daniel Burnap.* Hartford, CT: Connecticut Historical Society, 1958, p. 3 ff.
FR-1 August 1890, p. 62. FR-5 p. 11, 37, 55 ff.

Byram, Ephraim Niles:
Shelley, Frederick. "Ephraim Niles Byram, Long Island's Only Tower Clockmaker." NAWCC BULLETIN No. 303 (August 1996).

Chase & Quimby:
"First Church Clock 159 Years Old," *Republican Journal*, Belfast, Maine, July 10, 1986.
Correspondence with Henry Stover, Belfast, Maine.
Stover, Henry. "Stover's Jewelry was a Clock Shop 144 Years Ago." *Republican Journal*, Belfast, Maine.
Williamson, Joseph. *The History of Belfast Maine.* Portland, ME, 1877. Vol. I, p. 146, 419. Vol. II, p. 522-524.
FR-1 July 1890, p. 76. FR-7 p. 167, 263.

Claggett, William:
Champlin, Richard L. *William Claggett and his Clockmaking Friends.* NAWCC BULLETIN Supplement 11 (Summer 1976) p. 5 ff.
FR-1 March 1980, p. 74. FR-7 p. 169.

Clark, Jehiel and Jehiel Jr.:
Bailey, Chris and Dana Blackwell. *Heman Clark & the "Salem Bridge" Shelf Clocks.* NAWCC BULLETIN Supplement 13 (1980).
Bryant, G. Clarke. *Deacon George Clark of Milford, Connecticut, and Sons of his Descendants.* Ansonia, CT: 1949.
Cutten, G. B. "The Silversmiths of Central New York." New York State Historical Association speech at Colgate University, September 1937.
History of Otsego County (New York), 1878. Pub. Everts & Fariss.
Madison County deeds, AA 395, BB 127.
New York State Census.
Records of Delphi Falls, New York, United Church.

Clifford, Alfred D.:
Clifford, Maurice. "My Grandfather's Clock." *The Congregational Church of Phillipston MA, 1785-1985*, Commemorative history by L.O. Chandler, pp. 50-53.

Converse & Crane:
Credit in text.

Crane, Aaron Dodd:
Shelley, Frederick. "Aaron Dodd Crane Revisited: 1991 Update." NAWCC BULLETIN No. 273 (August 1991) p. 401 ff.
FR-10 p. 1 ff.

Crane, Moses G.:
FR-10 p. 8 ff.

Currier, Edmund (Jr.):
Proper, David. "Edmund Currier, Clockmaker." NAWCC BULLETIN No. 124 (October 1966) p. 494 ff.
FR-7 p. 175.

Curtis, Joel:
Deed records, Greene County, New York.

Francillon, Ward. "Joel Curtis 30-hour Pull-up." *Cog-Counters Journal*, No. 18 (January 1982).

French, J.H. *Gazetteer of the State of New York*. Syracuse, New York: R. Peasall Smith, Pub.

Gath, F.A. *Dear Old Greene County*. Catskill, New York: 1915.

History of Greene County, New York. New York: J.B. Beers & Co., 1860.

Custer, Jacob:

Athans, Marego. "Helping the Hands of Time." *The Philadelphia Inquirer METRO*, October 27, 1991, p. 5 f.

Barrington, S.H. "Custer and His Clocks." NAWCC BULLETIN No. 30 (October 1949).

Conversations with Charles Haines, Bristol, Pennsylvania.

Forman, Bruce R. "Directory of Montgomery County Clockmakers." *Bulletin of the Historical Society of Montgomery County*, Vol. XXVI, No 3 (Fall 1988).

Norris. "Norristown's First Town Clock Had a Curious Record." Scrapbook clipping, September 19, 1955.

Ringer, Bob. "Collins Building Serves as the First Town Hall." *The Record Herald*, Waynesboro, Pennsylvania, April 28, 1993.

"Sexton Ill; the Town Clock Stops." *The Plain Dealer*, Williamstown, New Jersey, December 27, 1929.

U.S. Lighthouse Commission records, 1855-1859.

FR-1 August 1886, p. 218. FR-7 p. 177. FR-14 p. 29-30.

Davies, J.H.:

Davies & Hodgens advertisement, *The Watchmaker and Jeweler*, August 1873.

Heffner, Paul. "George A. Jones Clock Company." NAWCC BULLETIN No. 245 (December 1986) p. 469 ff.

Shelley, Frederick. "New York, G.A. Jones Tower Clock." NAWCC BULLETIN No. 293 (December 1994).

FR-7 p. 178.

Davis, John:

"The Church of England In Stratford, Christ Episcopal Church." *History of Stratford*, p. 459.

FR-7 p. 307.

Davison (Davidson), Barzillai:

Lambert, Edward R. *The History of New Haven Colony*. New Haven, CT: Hitchcock & Stafford, 1838, p. 106.

FR-7 p. 178. FR-13 p. 95.

Demilt, Samuel and Benjamin:

Frank Leslie's Illustrated Newspaper. New York, New York, September 1858.

"Queens College Project New York City Inventories" and "Miscellaneous Documents." NAWCC BULLETIN No. 220 (October 1982) p. 564-565.

Shelley, Frederick "Ephraim Niles Byram, Long Island's Only Tower Clockmaker." NAWCC BULLETIN No. 303 (August 1996) p. 439.

FR-1 December 1889, p. 89. FR-8 p. 179. FR-12 Vol. V, 1826-1832.

Dennison, A.L.:

Boston Almanac Boston: Thos. Groom & Co., 1842.

Correspondence with William H. Knode, Shepherdstown, West Virginia.

Priestley, P.T. *Watch Case Makers of England*. NAWCC BULLETIN Supplement 20, Spring 1994, p. 69 f.

Priestley, P.T. "Aaron Lufkin Dennison—Early Family Papers," NAWCC BULLETIN No. 296 (June 1995) p. 321 ff.

FR-1 Sept. 1890, p. 76. FR-7 p. 179. FR-11 p. 567, 571.

Dewey, Hiram Todd:

Correspondence with D.H. Lathrop.

West, James T. "Vermont Clockmaker Jeremiah Dewey." NAWCC BULLETIN No. 295 (April 1995) p. 219.

Dueble, George Michael:

Correspondence with W.J. Weber, July 13, 1994, McKinley Ramsayer Research Library, Canton, Ohio.

Gibbs, James W. *The Dueber-Hampton Story*. NAWCC BULLETIN Supplement, February 1954.

Hartman, R.R. "Great Names in Canton History, No. 14, George M. Dueble." newspaper article.

FR-15 Patent No. 11,302, 1854.

Dodge, Ezra:

FR-4 advertisements #464-475. FR-7 p. 181.

Dodge, Seril:

FR-4 advertisements #478-480. FR-7 p. 181.

Douglass, John:

Atwater, Edward E. *The History of the Colony of New Haven to the Present Time*. New York: W.W. Munsell & Co., 1887.

Connecticut Census, July 1850.

New Haven City Directories, 1825-1855.

FR-1 August 1890, p. 62. FR-7 p. 182

Dow, William:

FR-15, 1996.

Dudley, Benjamin:

Clock subscription list, March 15, 1785, Newport Historical Society, Newport, Rhode Island.

FR-1 August 1890, p. 62. FR-4 advertisement #538-539. FR-7 p. 183.

Duffield, Edward:

FR-1 September 1890, p. 54 and November 1890, p. 70. FR-7 p. 183-4.

Dungan, Elmer Ellsworth:

Terwilliger, Charles. *Elmer Ellsworth Dungan & the Dickory Dickory Dock Clock*. NAWCC BULLETIN Supplement 4 (Summer 1966) p. 4-5.

FR-7 p.184.

Dunster (Dempster), Charles:

Sloan, Harold F. "A Tale of Two Ohio Tower Clocks." NAWCC BULLETIN No. 239 (December 1985) p. 672 ff.

Conversations with Harold Sloan, North Canton, Ohio, and W.J. Weber, Ramsayer Research Library, Canton, Ohio.

Eberhardt , Johann:

Albright, Frank P. *Johann Ludwig Eberhardt*. Chapel Hill, North Carolina: 1978.

Albright, Frank P. *The Home Moravian Church*. Winston Salem, North Carolina: Winston Printing Co. 1983.

Correspondence with Jonathan Betts, National Maritime Museum, Greenwich, England, 1994.

Lloyd, Allen and Pauline. *History of the Town of Hillsborough 1754-1991*, Hillsborough, NC.

McBride, Sarah. "Clock and Winder Go Way Back." *The Hillsborough Herald*, August 14, 1994.

Eberman, John (Jr.):

Moore, Jack. "Courthouse's 1784 Clock To Be Restored." *Lancaster New Era*, July 16, 1970.

Woodbridge, Cas and Stacy B.C. Wood. "Tower Clocks of John Eberman, Jr., of Lancaster, Pennsylvania." NAWCC BULLETIN No. 283 (April 1993) p. 146.

FR-1 December 1890, p. 65. FR-4 advertisement #556. FR-7 p. 185-6.

Elliot, Luther:

See Woolson, Thomas Jr. FR-7 p. 188.

Emrich, Edward:
Hagans, Orville. *Hobbies Magazine*. (October 1969).

Essex, Joseph:
FR-4 advertisements #589-591. FR-5 p. 17. FR-7 p. 189.

Evans, David:
FR-4 advertisements #600-610. FR-7 p. 190. FR-15.

Fasoldt, Charles:
Correspondence with Donald Saff, Ernest Martt, and James Starrow.

Fasoldt's chronometer list notebook, 1861-1872. Albany, NY.

Gohl, H. Anthony. "Fasoldt's 1876 Centennial Tower Clock," NAWCC Bulletin No. 243 (August 1986) p. 296 ff.

Sleeman, G. Martin "Charles Fasoldt, Watch, Clockmaker and Inventor." *Annals and Recollections* #24. Rome [New York] Historical Society, April 1982.

The Industries of Albany. Albany, New York: Elstner Publishing Co., 1888.

FR-1 January 1889, p. 57. FR-7 p. 191.

FR-15 Pats. 137, 603 Clock Escapements, and 165,991 Tower Clocks.

Fenton, Gamaliel:
FR-4 advertisement #637.

Floyd, Thomas:
FR-4 advertisements #668-669. FR-7 p. 193.

Fournier, Stanislaus:
Correspondence with J.M. Kinabrew Jr., September 1994.

Dufour, Pie. "Group Will Honor Early Clockmaker." *The Times Picayune*, New Orleans, March 28, 1971.

Kinabrew, John Jr. "Stanislaus Fournier, New Orleans Clock and Watch Maker." NAWCC Bulletin No. 307 (April 1997) p. 189 ff.

FR-7 p. 195.

Foster, Nathaniel:
FR-7 p. 195.

Frary, Obadiah:
Archive papers, Pocumtuck Valley Memorial Association Library, Old Deerfield, Massachusetts.

Conversations with David Proper. FR-7 p. 196.

Frary, Margaret and Ann Frary Lepak. *The Frary Family in America 1637-1980.* Hampton, NH: The Frary Family Association, 1981.

Geiring, Floria:
Myers, Elizabeth. "The Old Town Clock 1746." *Bethlehem-Globe Times* [Pennsylvania], January 19, 1955, and NAWCC Bulletin No. 60 (October 1955) p. 573.

See Neisser, Augustine.

Griffith, Nathaniel Sheaff:
FR-4 advertisements #840-860.

Hamlen, Nathaniel:
FR-1 July 1890, p. 76. FR-7 p. 206.

Hanks, Benjamin and Julius:
"Chronology of Mansfield, Connecticut 1702-1972." History Workshop of the Mansfield, Connecticut, Historical Society.

Cole, C.R. *History of Tolland County, Connecticut.* New York: W.W. Preston & Co., 1888.

Correspondence with Winthrop Warren and Russell Oechsle.

Correspondence with Rita Hollenga, Archivist, The Collegiate Reformed Protestant Dutch Church of the City of New York.

FR-7 p. 207.

Hanks, Benjamin. "Description of a Pneumatic Clock." Beneke Rare Book and Ms. Library, Yale University, New Haven, Connecticut.

Miscellaneous Hanks documentation, the Litchfield Historical Society, Litchfield, Connecticut.

Stiles, Ezra. *The Literary Diary of Ezra Stiles.* Vol. III. New York: Scribners, 1901.

Warren, Winthrop. "Bell Founders of New York and Beyond." AC&WM *Timepiece Journal*, Vol. 5, No. 6 (Winter 1995).

1829 Troy, New York, Directory (advertisement).

FR-4 advertisements #885-892. FR-5 p. 79 ff.

Harland, Thomas:
Anderson, George P. "Thomas Harland (1735-1807)." The Boston Clock Club papers, November 5, 1938.

Blake, Rev. S.L., *Later History of the First Church of New London, Connecticut.* New London, CT, 1900, p. 219.

Harland papers, Leffingwell House Museum, Norwich, CT.

Willard, William L. "Thomas Harland, Clockmaker, Watchmaker, and Entrepreneur." NAWCC Bulletin No. 295 (April 1995) p. 185.

FR-4 advertisements #900-911. FR-5 p. 83 ff.

Harmony Society, The:
Arndt, J.R. *Economy on the Ohio.* Harmony Society Press, 1984.

Conversations with Raymond V. Shepherd Jr., Lynne Wohleber, and Joseph Millie.

Old Economy Village. A brochure, 1992.

Hasham, Stephen:
Lathrop, Donn Haven and Frederick Shelley, "The Amazing Stephen Hasham." NAWCC Bulletin No. 293 (December 1994).

FR-7 p. 207.

Haskell, Moody:
Carlisle, L.B. *Vermont Clock and Watch Makers, Silversmiths and Jewelers 1778-1878.* Lunenburg, NH: Stinehour Press, 1970, p.162.

Heebner, David S.:
Eckhardt, George H. *Pennsylvania Clocks and Clockmakers.* Bonanza Books, Devin-Adair Co.: New York, p. 14.

FR-3 p. 135

Heisely, Frederick and George J.:
Correspondence with Greene County (Pennsylvania) Historical Society, 1995-1996.

Ellis, Franklin and Samuel Evans. *The History of Lancaster County*, Philadelphia, PA, 1883.

LaFond, E.F. "Frederick Heisely Strikes Again..." NAWCC Bulletin No. 133 (April 1968) p.227 ff.

Lang, Martha C., "The Heisely Family." Unpublished ms., Fairfax, Virginia.

Smart, Charles E. "The Heisely Family," NAWCC Bulletin No. 132 (February 1968) p. 153.

FR-4 advertisements #925-929, 995. FR-7 p. 210. FR-15 p. 41-42.

Heydorn & Imlay:
FR-5 p. 45 ff. FR-7 p. 211.

Hill, Benjamin Morris Jr.:
Correspondence with Patrick J. Reynolds, Curator, Historical Society of Berks County.

Machmer, Richard and Rosemary. *Berks County Tall Case Clocks.* Reading Historical Society Press of Berks County, PA 1995.

Steinmetz, Mary. "Early Clockmakers of Berks County," *Historical Review of Berks County,* Berks Co., PA, 1935.

"The 3 Town Clocks," scrapbook newspaper clipping, Reading, Pennsylvania, July 2, 1903.

FR-3 p. 150. FR-7 p. 211.

Hill, William S.:

Brooklyn (New York) Business Directories, 1867-1873.

Conversations with Ian Roome.

A.S. Hotchkiss/William Hill documents, Connecticut State Library archives, Hartford, Connecticut.

Seth Thomas/ A.S. Hotchkiss Tower Clock Catalog, 1874.

Holbrook, George and George Handel:

Shelley, Frederick. "The Holbrook Dynasty." NAWCC BULLETIN No. 300 (February 1996).

Hopkins, Henry A.:

Census of New York State.

Deed records of Stueben County, New York.

French, J.H. *Gazetteer of the State of New York.* Syracuse, New York: R. Pearsall Smith, Pub., 1860.

History of the Presbyterian Church, Prattsburg, New York, 1988.

Hopkins, Wright & Millard:

Breed, Henry C. *History of Quaker Basin from 1800 to 1900.* DeRuyter, New York: The Gleaner, 1931.

Census of New York State.

Deed and mortgage records, Madison County, New York.

Millard, Ira vs. Daniel Hopkins, New York State Supreme Court Judgement, October 20, 1849.

Oechsle, Russell and Richard Babel. "Tower Clock Makers of Madison County." *Madison County Heritage,* No. 11, Madison County Historical Society, Oneida, New York, January 1982.

Wood, Walter R. *History of DeRuyter and Vicinity,* DeRuyter, New York, 1964.

Hostetter, Jacob:

Biographical Directory of the American Congress, 1774-1927.

FR-3 p. 198. FR-7 p. 215.

Hotchkiss, A.S.:

deMagnin, Paul R. "The Old Town Clock at Tarrytown New York." NAWCC BULLETIN No. 100 (October 1962).

Frank Leslie's Illustrated Newspaper. New York, NY, June 3, 1857, September 11, 1858.

Hill/A.S. Hotchkiss business papers, Connecticut State Library archives, Hartford, Connecticut.

Historical Society of Burlington, Connecticut, Leonard Alderman, historian.

St. Georges' and Rutgers Presbyterian Church records. New York City: 1850-1856.

Tweet, Roald. *The Rock Island Clock Tower, From Ordnance to Engineers.* Rock Island, Illinois: U.S. Army Corps of Engineers, May 1977, p. 17-21.

FR-6 Manhattan and Brooklyn, New York Business Directories.

Hotchkiss, Elisha:

Burlington Ecclesiastical Society and Methodist Episcopal Church records.

Burlington Historical Society files, correspondence with Leonard Alderman.

Hotchkiss family records compiled by Lois Humphry.

Peck, Epaphroditus. *Burlington, Connecticut Centennial Celebration.* Bristol Press, June 16, 1906.

Taylor, Snowden. "The Elisha Hotchkiss Tower Clock in Burlington CT." NAWCC BULLETIN, No. 301 (April 1996) p. 221-2.

Howard: Stephenson, Howard & Davis; Howard & Davis; E. Howard & Co.:

Boston City Directories, 1840-1868.

Correspondence with Henry A. Mattson, Bucksport, Maine, May 29, 1995.

"Death of Edward Howard." *The Jewelers' Circular-Weekly,* Vol. 48, No. 6 (March 9, 1904).

Howard, Edward. "American Watches and Clocks." *1795-1895, 100 Years of American Commerce.* Chauncey Depew, 1895.

Nijssen, Gerrit. "The Watches of E. Howard & Company." NAWCC BULLETIN No. 292 (October 1994) p. 563-575.

FR-7 p. 216, 284. FR-13 p. 97.

Hughes, John:

Rica, Shuto. "A Man You Should Know." NAWCC BULLETIN No. 52 (February 1954) p. 89 ff.

York, Pennsylvania, Courthouse tower clock acquisition papers.

FR-15 p. 46.

Huston, James:

FR-2 p. 133. FR-7 p. 218.

Ipswich, Massachusetts:

Conversations and conference with Max Elser.

Waters, T.F. *Ipswich in the Massachusetts Bay Colony.* Ipswich Historical Society, 1917, Vol. II pp. 6, 410, 440, 441, 449.

James, William:

Newport Historical Society, Newport, Rhode Island, misc. records. FR-7 p. 221.

Jerome, Jewel & Co.:

Correspondence with Snowden Taylor.

Taylor, Snowden. "Bankruptcy of Jerome, Jewel & Co." Research Activities and News, NAWCC BULLETIN No. 224 (June 1983).

Jocelin, Simeon:

New Haven Colony Historical Society Library, Assorted Papers, New Haven, Connecticut.

Parsons, Charles S. "Eli Terry's Equation Clock," NAWCC BULLETIN No. 202 (October 1979) p. 530.

Rice, Foster Wild. "Nathaniel Jocelyn 1796-1881." *The Connecticut Historical Society Bulletin,* Vol. 31, No. 4. (October 1966).

Rice, Foster Wild. "The Jocelyn Engravers." *Essay Proof Journal* (July/October 1948).

FR-1 August 1890, p. 62. FR-4 adv. #1075-1084. FR-5 p. 9, 93 ff. FR-7 p. 223-4.

Johnson, Charles Fred:

Kingman, LeRoy W. "Early Owego." *Owego Gazette,* Owego, New York, 1907, p. 338-340, 620-623.

Kingman, LeRoy W. *Our County and its People,* Elmira, NY: W.A. Ferguson, 1897, p. 457.

New York Telegrapher, New York City, June 24, 1867, obituary.

FR-7 p. 224. FR-9 Patent No. 4.662, July 28, 1846.

Johnson, Nels:

Blackwell, Dana. "Nels Johnson and His Tower Clocks." NAWCC BULLETIN No. 108 (February 1964) p. 82 ff.

Manistee Museum Log, Vol.V, No. 2, November 1977. Manistee County Historical Museum.

FR-7 p. 224. FR-13 p. 98.

222-226Johnson, Simon:
FR-1 July 1880, p. 76. FR-8 p. 321-322.

Johnson, Warren S.:
Correspondence with Col. Robert Rupp and Carl Mattson, Colorado Springs, Colorado.

Harpster, Richard. "Centenary Grads Out To Save Clock." Hacketstown, New Jersey.

Johnson Controls, Right For The Time, 100th Anniversary commemorative booklet, 1985.

Johnson, Warren S. "The Philadelphia City Hall Clock." *Journal of the Franklin Institute*, Vol. CLI, No. 2 (February 1901).

Tschudy, Robert F. "The Clock Struck 73." NAWCC BULLETIN No. 65 (October 1956) p. 291 ff.

Johnston, Arthur:
Mish, Mary V. "A. Johnston, The Man and His Clocks." Hagerstown Historical Society, Hagerstown, Maryland, p. 154-161.

Spangler, L.S. "On Time—A Grandfather's Clock With Historical Background." *Hobbies* (July 1947).

FR-7 p. 224. FR-15 p. 47-48.

Jones, George A. Co.:
Shelley, Frederick. "New York, G.A. Jones Tower Clock." NAWCC BULLETIN, No. 293 (December 1994).

LaFeuer & Beary:
FR-6 1854-1856. FR-7 p. 229.

Lathrop, William:
Kelly, J. Frederick. *Early Connecticut Meeting Houses.* New York: Columbia University Press, 1948.

Leidgen, John:
Baier, Dr. Joseph G. "The Role of Wisconsin Residents in the Early American Clock Industry." NAWCC BULLETIN No. 156 (February 1972) p. 115.

FR-9 Patent 172,638 Clock Escapement.

LeRoy, Abraham:
See Eberman, John Jr. FR-7 p. 232.

Loesch, Johann Jacob:
Mosley, Laura M. *Loesch, Losch, Liesch, Lash.* Bethania, [North Carolina] Historical Association.

Correspondence with Louise B. Kapp, Bethania Church Historian, July 23, 1995.

Logan, Sidney Algernon:
Gibbs, James W. "Quaker Clockmakers, Part 2." NAWCC BULLETIN No. 199 (April 1979) p. 164.

James, Arthur E. *Chester County Clocks And Their Makers.* Exton, Pennsylvania: Shiffer Publishing Ltd., 1947.

FR-7 p. 234.

Lowrey, David:
FR-5, p. 39.

Conversation with Wm. L. Willard.

Lukens, Isaiah:
Eckhardt, G.H. "Isaiah Lukens, Town Clock Maker and Machinist." *Antiques*, Vol. 25 (February 1934).

Ferguson, E.S. *Early Engineering Reminiscences (1815-40) of George Escol Sellers.* Smithsonian, 1949.

Foreman, Bruce. "Isaiah Lukens—An American in England." *Antiquarian*-748.

Lamberton, James R. "Lukens Tower Clock." NAWCC BULLETIN No. 272 (June 1991) p.256.

Luken's obituary. *Journal of the Franklin Institute.* Vol. 41-42 (1846) p. 423 ff.

Rubin, David. "A Relic of Time Rediscovered in Tower." *Philadelphia Inquirer, Suburban Metro,* October 11, 1993.

Wister, C.J. Jr. *A Memoir of Charles J.Wister.* Germantown, Pennsylvania, 1886.

Newspaper scrapbooks, Chester County Historical Society, West Chester, Pennsylvania.

FR-1 Sept 1890, p. 54. FR-7 p. 235.

Lupp (Leupp, Loop), Henry:
FR-2 p. 156. FR-4 advertisements #1283-1285. FR-7 p. 235.

Luscomb, Samuel:
FR-4 advertisement #1286. FR-7 p. 235.

M'Cabe, John:
FR-4 advertisements #1293-1295. FR-7 p. 236. FR-15 p. 64.

Meneely, Andrew:
Correspondence with R.C. Johnson, Winthrop Warren, and Russell Oechsle.

Eaton and Trumansburg, New York, village records.

Meneely advertisements and handbills.

New York State Archives: Meneely installations, letters, litigation, etc.

Warren, Winthrop D. "Bell Founders of New York and Beyond." AC&WM *Timepiece Journal*, Vol. 5, No. 6 (Winter 1995).

Miller, Aaron:
Murray, Nicholas. *Notes, Historical And Biographical Concerning Elizabeth-Town, Its Eminent Men, Churches, and Ministers.* 1844, p.163-179.

FR-2 p. 163-179. FR-4 advs. #1365-1367. FR-7 p. 242.

Millington, Norman:
Carlisle, L.B. *Vermont Clock and Watch Makers, Silversmiths and Jewelers 1778-1875.* Lunenburg, Vermont: Stinehour Press, 1970.

Milne, Robert:
Watson, John F. *Historic Tales...of New York City And State.* New York: Collins & Hannay, 1832, p. 101.

FR-4 advertisement #1373. FR-7 p. 243.

Morrill, Benjamin:
Dover Town Records, 1844-1940: receipts and expenditures.

Harvey, Rev. E.O. "History of the Orford [New Hampshire] Church."

Packard, D.K. Boston Clock Club papers, March 2, 1935.

The Only Henniker on Earth. Henniker History Committee. Canaan, NH: Phoenix Publishing Co., 1980.

Wadleigh, George. *Notable Events in the History of Dover.* Dover, New Hampshire: Tufts College Press, 1913.

150th Anniversary of the Settlement of Boscawen and Webster. Merrimack Co., NH, July 1890, p. 76.

FR-1 June 1890, p. 70. FR-7 p. 245. FR-8 p. 151, 152, 324.

Munroe, Daniel:
FR-1 July 1890, p. 79. FR-4 advertisement #1414. FR-7 p. 247.

Neisser, Augustine:
Bethlehem Globe. Bethlehem, Pennsylvania: April 5, 1946, p. 1.

Cammerhoff, Bishop John C.F. Letter to Count Zinzendorf, March 1747.

Jordan, John W. *Pennsylvania Magazine,* Vol. 8 (1884) p. 429.

Ledger of the Diaconate at Bethlehem. Bethlehem, Pennsylvania, December 1, 1744-December 31, 1748, p. 71.

Levering, Bishop John M. *A History of Bethlehem, Pennsylvania 1741-1892.* Bethlehem: 1903, p. 35.

Minutes of the College of Overseers. Vol. 3, p. 205. Translated by Vernon Nelson, archivist, Bethlehem, Pennsylvania.

The Independent Gazette for Germantown Edition. Philadelphia: October 14, 1926, p.1.

O'Neal, Charles:
FR-1 August 1890, p. 62. FR-7 p. 252.

Parker, Gardner:
Allen, Kristina N. *On the Beaten Path.* Westborough, Mass., 1984.
Proceedings of the Fitchburg [Massachusetts] Historical Society, Vol. V, 1914.
Reed, Dr. C.H. "The Old Town Clock." Ms. Westborough, Massachusetts Public Library.
Westchester County probate and deed records.
FR-7 p. 254.

Parmelee, Ebenezer:
Steiner, B.C. *The History of Guilford, Connecticut.* 1897 Edition, p. 276.
Walters, Jim. *The Family Parmelee.* Unpublished ms, Guilford [Connecticut] Public Library.
FR-5 p. 6 ff., 101 ff. FR-7 p. 255.

Penfield, Sylvester:
Brainard, Newton C. *The Hartford State House of 1796.* The Connecticut Historical Society, Hartford, Connecticut, 1964, p. 44.
New York City Business Census, 1855.
"The 3 Town Clocks." Scrapbook newspaper clipping, Reading, Pennsylvania (July 2, 1903).
FR-6 1840-1860. FR-7 p. 257.

Phillips, Joseph:
FR7 p. 258. FR-12 April 26, 1716-1717.
See Wright, John.

Pollhans, Phillip:
Catalog: *A.E. Pollhans Clock Co.,* St. Louis, Missouri.
FR-7 p. 259.
Faherty, Rev. William. "The Saving of a Shrine." Missouri Historical Society, St. Louis, Missouri.
Tschudy, Robert F. "A.E. Pollhans Clock Co.," NAWCC Bulletin No. 113 (December 1964) p. 570 ff.

Power, David:
Baier, Dr. Joseph G. "Again Wisconsin and Time, An Historical Record." NAWCC Bulletin No. 175 (April 1975) p. 192.
Baier, Dr. Joseph G. "The Role of Wisconsin Residents in the Early American Clock Industry." NAWCC Bulletin No. 156 (February 1972).

Ridgway, James:
Flynt & Fales. *The Heritage Foundation Collection of Silver 1625-1825.* Old Deerfield, Massachusetts, 1968.
Groton, Massachusetts, town and First Parish Church records.
Nutt, Charles. *The History of Worcester and its People.* Lewis Hist. Pub. Co., 1919, pp. 237-239.
Ridgway, George C. *Descent of the Ridgway-Ridgeway Family,* Second ed. Evansville, Indiana, 1926.
Vital records, *The New Hampshire Sentinel.* City directories of Boston and Worcester, Mass. Green, Samuel, MD. *Groton Historical Series,* Vol. 1, Groton, Massachusetts (1887) p. 23,24.

Robinson, Prof. S
Conversations with Donn Haven Lathrop.
Dornech and Hannon. "The Authentic Restoration of an 1878 Tower Clock." NAWCC Bulletin No. 281 (December 1992.) p. 694.

Rodgers, James:
Archival records of Trinity Church, New York City.

Trinity Church Clock." *Salem* [Massachusetts] *Register*, May 11, 1876.
"Trinity's Clock." *Edison Monthly* (December 1925) p. 280-281.
FR-1 Jan 1891, p. 65. FR-6 1836-1877. FR-7 p. 269.

Saxton, Joseph:
Drawings from Saxton's notebook.
Ferguson, E.S., Editor: *Early Engineering Reminiscences 1815-40) of George Escol Sellers.* Smithsonian, Washington, D.C., 1965, p. 52-53.
Frazier, Arthur H., Madison, Wisconsin: correspondence with the Philadelphia Department of Public Property, reference Lukens clock, 1965-1966.
FR-7, p. 272.

Schwalbach, Mathias:
Baier, Dr. Joseph G. "Mathias Schwalbach, His Church and Tower Clocks." NAWCC Bulletin No. 165 (August 1973).
Baier, Dr. Joseph G. "The Role of Wisconsin Residents in the Early American Clock Industry." NAWCC Bulletin No. 156 (February 1972) p. 115 ff.
Manistee Museum Log. Vol. V, No. 2 (November 1977).
"Mathias Schwalbach Time Machine." *Wisconsin Academy Review,* Vol. 20, No. 4 (Fall 1974).
FR-7 p. 273. FR-9 Pats. No. 156, 677; 232,079; 421, 622 — Clock Escapements.

Sharpe, Julian:
See Brown, Joseph R.

Sherry & Byram:
See Byram, Ephraim Niles.

Sibley & Marble:
The Connecticut Journal. New Haven, Connecticut, April 29, May 3 and 5, 1801; May 9, 1803.
FR-7 p. 276.

Simnet, John:
FR-4 advertisements #1755-1786. FR-7 p. 277.

Simon, Andrew:
Cumberland County Historical Society, Carlisle, Pennsylvania. Correspondence, July 1997.
FR-14 p. 115.

Sloan, William:
FR-4 advtisement #1802.

Smith's Clock Establishment:
Brainard, Newton C. *The Hartford State House of 1796.* The Connecticut Historical Society, Hartford, Connecticut, 1964, p. 44-45.
Smith clock advertising and labels.
American Antiques Journal. October 1949.
FR-6 1835-1852. FR-7 p. 277.

Smith, Luther:
Proper, David. *History of the First Congregational Church.* Keene, New Hampshire: Sentinel Printing Co., 1973.
Correspondence with David Proper, February 7, 1996.
FR-7 p. 279. FR-8 p. 330.

Smith, Phillip:
Babel, Richard. *Onondaga County Clock Makers.* Unpublished ms., 1989.
Census records of New York State.
Deed records of Onondaga County, New York.
French, J.H. *Gazetteer of the State of New York.* Syracuse, New York, 1860.

Smith, Ransom:
See Smith's Clock Establishment.

Correspondence with Charles Adams, Natchez, Mississippi, 1994, 1996.

The Weekly Courier-Journal. Natchez, Mississippi (January 1) 1842, p. 1.

FR-6 1835-1852. FR-7 p. 279.

Speed, John J.:

DeWitt Historical Society, Ithaca, New York.

Kingman, L.W. "Early Owego." *Owego Gazette* (1907) p. 620-623.

New York Telegrapher and *The Brooklyn News* obituaries, June 24, 1867.

Spellier, Louis:

Clark, Sarah M. "Farewell To An Era." *Bucks County Magazine* (December/January 1960-61).

Fretz, Mrs. Annie M., "Louis Spellier and His Electric Clocks." Bucks County Historical Society, Doylestown Meeting, May 2, 1936.

Spellier, Louis. "A New System of Electric Clocks." *Journal of the Franklin Institute* (August 1882).

Trauch, W. Lester. "Memories Of The Old Courthouse Bell Are Still Ringing." *The Intelligencer Record* (August 20, 1989) p. A-20.

FR-7 p. 281.

Sperry, H. & Co.:

Frank Leslie's Illustrated Newspaper. June 3, 1857, September 11, 1858.

Miscellaneous records, American Clock & Watch Museum, Bristol, Connecticut.

New York City Industrial Census, 1855.

Rutgers Street Church, 1841-1862, archive records; St. George's Episcopal Church, 1856-1857, January-May 1863; Murray Hill Brick Church, March 18, 1859—all New York City.

FR-6 1851-1859. FR-7 p. 282.

Sperry & Co.:

Fraser, O.W. "The Hand on the Old Church Steeple." NAWCC BULLETIN No. 155 (December 1971).

Murray Hill Brick Church NYC records, Presbyterian Archives, Philadelphia, Pennsylvania.

See Sperry, H. & Co.

Stevens, George M.:

Shelley, Frederick. "The Tower Clocks of Geo. M. Stevens & Co." NAWCC BULLETIN No. 289 (April 1994).

FR-7 p. 284.

Stokell, John:

Berger, Meyer. "About New York." *The New York Times* (December 27, 1957).

FR-1 January 1891, p. 65. FR-6 1825-1860. FR-7 p. 285.

Stone & Marshall:

Babel, Richard B. "The Clockmakers of Cazenovia." NAWCC BULLETIN No. 168 (February 1974) p. 155.

Cazenovia Republican, May 19, 1858; March 25, 30 and September 21, 1859; and November 5 and 12, 1862.

Coleman, J.E. "Stone and Marshall—Marshall and Card." *The American Horologist and Jeweler* (May 1952).

Haley, Don. "American Lock Co." Unpublished ms, Cazenovia, New York.

Smith's, *Madison County* [New York] *History*.

Stowell, Abel:

Cutler, Waldo. *Jottings from Worcester History.* 1932, pp. 17-18.

Lincoln, William & C. Hersey. *The History of Worcester County, Massachusetts.* Worcester: C. Hersey, 1862.

Moore, D.G.E. "An Adjustable Tall Case Clock." NAWCC BULLETIN No. 143 (December 1969).

Nutt, Charles. *The History of Worcester and Its People.* Lewis Hist. Pub. Co., 1919.

Shelley, Frederick. "Early Advertisements A Key To Technology Transfer?" NAWCC BULLETIN No. 287 (December 1993) p. 720 ff.

The National Aegis. Worcester, Massachusetts. June 30, 1802; March 20, 1803.

Ungerer, Alfred. *Les Horologes d'Edifice.* Paris: Gauthier-Villars & Cie, 1926.

Worcester County [Massachusetts] probate and land records. FR-4 advertisements #1875-1880. FR-7 p. 285.

Stowell, Abel Jr.:

See Stowell, Abel. Last will and probate records.

Boston Business Directory, 1859-1860, p. 14.

FR-1 August 1890, p. 61. FR-7 p. 285. FR-13 p. 98. FR-15 p. 37.

Stretch, Peter and Thomas:

Erlandson, Robert A. "A Peter Stretch Lantern Clock." NAWCC BULLETIN #308 (June 1997).

FR-1 September 1890, p.54. FR-4 advertisements #1882-1886 FR-7 p. 286.

Taylor, Alonzo:

New York City Industrial Census, 1855.

FR-6 1855-1880.

Terry, Eli:

Barr, Lockwood. "Connecticut Tower Clocks by Eli and Samuel Terry." *Antiques* (1957).

Parsons, Charles S. "Eli Terry's Equation Clock." NAWCC BULLETIN No. 202 (October 1979) p. 522.

Reeves, Joseph L. "The Vanishing Footprints of the Old Plymouth Clockmakers."

Roberts, Ken and Snowden Taylor. *Eli Terry and the Connecticut Shelf Clock.* Second edition. Fitzwilliam, New Hampshire, 1994.

Shelley, Frederick. "The Tower Clocks of Windsor, Connecticut." NAWCC BULLETIN No. 299 (December 1995).

Terry, Henry. "A Review of Dr. Alcott's History of Clockmaking." *Waterbury American* (June 10, 1853).

FR-5 p. 112 ff. FR-7 p. 289-291.

Terry, Samuel:

Barr, Lockwood. "Terry Clock Book." Unpublished ms. at NAWCC Library.

Barr, Lockwood. "Tower Clocks by the Brothers Terry." NAWCC BULLETIN No. 34 (June 1950) p. 155.

Connecticut church and ecclesiastical society records, Connecticut State Library archives, Hartford.

Stiles, Henry R. *The History of Ancient Windsor, Connecticut 1635-1891.*

Samuel Terry business records, American Clock & Watch Museum archives.

Shelley, Frederick. "The Tower Clocks of Windsor Connecticut." NAWCC BULLETIN No. 299 (December 1995) p. 773.

FR-7 p. 292.

Thomas, Seth & Co.:

Bailey, Chris H. "Seth Thomas The Conservative Clockmaking Yankee." *Illustrated Catalog of Seth Thomas Clocks* (January 1973).

Catalog of A.S. Hotchkiss Tower Clocks, manufactured by Seth Thomas & Co., 1874.

Sangster, J.R. "Seth Thomas A Yankee Clockmaker 1784-1859, Part 3." NAWCC BULLETIN No. 136 (October 1968).

Seth Thomas/American Clock co-partnership agreements. Connecticut State Library archives, Hartford.
FR-1 April 1891, p. 37, 41. FR-7 p. 293.

Thompson, John:
Mish, Mary V. "A. Johnston, The Man and His Clocks," Washington County [Pennsylvania] Historical Society, p. 157.
FR-15 p. 91.

Thwing, Almon:
Correspondence with Bruce Kingsbury, Weyland, Massachusetts.
Hopper, Gordon E. "Almond Thwing, Hopedale Inventor." *Milford Daily News* (February 9, 1991) p. 14.

Tracy, Gurdon:
See Harland, Thomas.
American Collector, June 1947.

Turret Clock Co.:
See Stevens, Geo. M.

Turret & Marine Clock Co.:
See FR-10 p. 36-30, 88-100.

Urletig, Valentine and Hill, Benjamin Jr.:
Machmer, Richard and Rosemary. *Berks County Tall Case Clocks 1750-1850.* Historical Society Press of Berks County, Pennsylvania, 1995.
Steinmetz, Mary Owen. "Early Clockmakers of Berks County." *Historical Review of Berks County.* (October 1935).
FR-3 p. 153. FR-7 p. 298.

Van Riper, Austin W.:
Advertisements and notices, *The Cazenovia Republican*, May 1858, March and September 1859, and November 1862.
Correspondence with Russell Oechsle.
Coleman, J.E. "Stone and Marshall—Marshall and Card." *American Horologist and Jeweler* (May 1952).
Deeds and surrogate records, Madison County, New York.
History of Otsego County, New York, with Illustrations and Biographical Sketches. Pub. Everts & Faris, 1878.
Oechsle, Russell and Richard Babel. "The Clockmakers of Madison County." Madison County Heritage, No. 11, January 1982, Madison County Historical Society, Oneida, New York.

Verdin, The Company:
Celebrating Over 150 Years. Verdin commemorative booklet, Cincinnati, Ohio, 1992.
Communications with Verdin Public Relations, 1994.

Ward, Macock:
Correspondence with William L. Willard.
FR-5 p. 7-8, 38-39. 119 ff. FR-7 p. 302.

Washburn, Asa:
Correspondence from Donn Haven Lathrop.
Redfearn, Jerome. *Indiana Silversmiths, Clockmakers and Watchmakers, 1779-1900.* 1984.

Weiss, Jedediah:
FR-7 p. 304. See Neisser, Augustine and Eberman, John Jr.

Whitear, John:
Warren, Winthrop and Christopher B. Nevins. "Clocks and Clockmakers of Colonial Fairfield, Circa 1736-1813, Part 1." NAWCC BULLETIN No. 286 (October 1993).
FR-5 p. 40. FR-7 p. 307.

Whitehead, John:
FR-2 p. 232-234. FR-7 p. 307.

Willard, Aaron Jr.:
Communication with Don Craig, Hagerstown, Maryland.
Husher, Richard W. and Walter W. Welch. *A Study of Simon Willard's Clocks.* Nahant, MA, pub. by the authors, 1980.
Newton [Massachusetts] Historical Society correspondence.
Stephens, John. "The Portraits of Willard House." NAWCC BULLETIN No. 288 (February 1994).
William L. Willard correspondence.
FR-7 p. 309. FR-11 p.565. FR-13 p. 99, 101-102. FR-16 p. 94-97.

Willard, Alexander Tarbell:
FR-7 p. 309. FR-16 p. 120-128.

Willard, Benjamin:
Brown, Joseph E. "The Willard Clockmakers—An Essay." NAWCC BULLETIN No. 291 (August 1994).
Communications with William L. Willard.
FR-4 advs. #2033-2042. FR-7 p. 309-310. FR-15 p. 100. FR-16 p. 79-84.

Willard, Benjamin Franklin:
FR-7 p. 310. FR-13 p. 99. FR-16 p. 74-78.

Willard, Simon:
Brown, Joseph E. "Some Notes on Simon Willard and His Trapezoids." NAWCC BULLETIN No. 285 (August 1993).
Dyer, Walter A. "The Willards And Their Clocks." *Country Life in America.*
History of St. George's Church, New York, New York, p. 93-94.
Husher, Richard and Walter W. Welch. *A Study of Simon Willard's Clocks.* Nahant, Massachusetts, 1880.
Thwing, W.E. *History of the First Church in Roxbury* [Massachusetts].
FR-4 advertisements #2043-2049. FR-7 p. 310-311. FR-13 p. 99-101. FR-16 p. 1-37, 129-133.

Witt, Dr. Christopher:
Ephrata Cloister Library, Ephrata, Pennsylvania.
Gibbs, James W. "Religious Sect Clockmakers." NAWCC BULLETIN No. 171 (August 1974).
Sachse, J.F. *The German Pietists of Provincial Pennsylvania.* 1895.
FR-7 p. 313.

Woolson, Thomas Jr., and Elliott Luther:
Correspondence with Donn Haven Lathrop, June 27, 1974.
Secomb, Daniel F. *History of Amherst, Hillsborough County, New Hampshire.* Concord, New Hampshire: Evans, Sleeper & Woodbury, 1883, p. 444-446.
Waite, F.R. *History of the Town of Claremont New Hampshire 1763-1894.* Manchester, New Hampshire: J.B. Clark Co., 1895.
FR-7 p. 188, 314. FR-8 p. 33.

Wright, John:
"Miscellaneous Documents: Maintaining The City's Clocks." NAWCC BULLETIN No. 220 (October 1982) p. 564-565.
FR-4 advertisements #2121-2126.

Yeoman, James:
Britten's Old Clocks And Watches And Their Makers. "Former Clock and Watch Makers." 7th Edition. Bonanza Books, New York, 1956.
Shelley, Frederick. "Early Advertisements a Key to Technology Transfer?" NAWCC BULLETIN No. 287 (December 1993) p.720 ff.
FR-4 advertisements #2139-2145. FR-7 p. 315.

INDEX